The Bedside Dickens

an anthology for pleasure

The Bedside Dickens

an anthology for pleasure

Compiled by J.W. Garrod
Illustrated by Bill Geldart

Spring Books
London/New York
Sydney/Toronto

First published 1954 by Souvenir Press Ltd

This edition published 1969 by
The Hamlyn Publishing Group Ltd
London/New York/Sydney/Toronto
Hamlyn House, Feltham, Middlesex, England

Printed in the United Kingdom by
C. Tinling and Co., Ltd, Prescot and London

CONTENTS

INTRODUCTION

SOMEONE once said that we cannot have too much Dickens—certainly there are many among us who never tire of this great English exponent of the art of novel writing and are always 'coming up for more'. With this view in mind I conceived the idea of this anthology, a collection of excerpts from Dickens's books, letters and speeches to remind us of the true greatness of the man and to lead us back yet again to the manifestation of his genius in his books.

There must be many readers, especially the younger ones, who have not as yet embarked upon the rich experience of a Dickens novel. For them too, I hope that this volume will serve as an introduction and an appetizer; they will find that the message of Dickens is just as alive and vibrant today as ever it was.

I have tried to present the series so as to give ample scope for 'dipping', that pleasant browse to fill in the odd moment. Yet I hope that there will be found here opportunity for longer and more sustained readings, either personally or to an audience of friends or the family circle.

The selections are purely personal and are necessarily so, for to please everyone would surely be a superhuman feat in this instance!

I would like to record here my deep gratitude for the assistance and encouragement I have received from two people who share my enthusiasm for Charles Dickens and his books: my wife Sylvia and my very true friend Ronald Payne. Their work has made my labour of love light indeed and has illumined with the glow of truth the sub-title: An Anthology for Pleasure.

JOHN W. GARROD

A Christmas Garland

CHRISTMAS time! That man must be a misanthrope indeed in whose breast something like a jovial feeling is not roused—in whose mind some pleasant associations are not awakened—by the recurrence of Christmas. There are people who will tell you that Christmas is not to them what it used to be; that each succeeding Christmas has found some cherished hope, or happy prospect of the year before, dimmed or passed away; that the present only serves to remind them of reduced circumstances and straitened incomes—of the feasts they once bestowed on hollow friends, and of the cold looks that meet them now, in adversity and misfortune. Never heed such dismal reminiscences. There are few men who have lived long enough in the world, who cannot call up such thoughts any day in the year. Then do not select the merriest of the three hundred and sixty-five for your doleful recollections, but draw your chair nearer the blazing fire—fill the glass and send round the song—and if your room be smaller than it was a dozen years ago, or if your glasses be filled with reeking punch, instead of sparkling wine, put a good face on the matter, and empty it off-hand, and fill another, and troll off the old ditty you used to sing, and thank God it's no worse. Look on the merry faces of your children (if you have any) as they sit round the fire. One little seat may be empty; one slight form that gladdened the father's heart, and roused the mother's pride to look upon, may not be there. Dwell not upon the past; think not that one short year ago, the fair child now resolving into dust, sat before you, with the bloom of health upon its cheek, and the gaiety of infancy in its joyous eye. Reflect upon your present blessings—of which every man has many—not on your past misfortunes, of which all men have some. Fill your glass again, with a merry face and contented heart. Our life on it, but your Christmas shall be merry, and your new year a happy one!

Who can be insensible to the outpourings of good feeling, and the honest interchange of affectionate attachment, which abound at this season of the year? A Christmas family party! We know nothing in nature more delightful! There seems a magic in the very name of Christmas. Petty jealousies and discords are forgotten; social feelings are awakened in bosoms to which they have long been strangers; father and son, or brother and sister, who have met and passed with averted gaze, or a look of cold recognition, for months before, proffer and return the cordial embrace, and bury their past animosities in their present happiness. Kindly hearts that have yearned towards each other, but have been withheld by false notions of pride and self-dignity, are again reunited, and all is kindness and benevolence! Would that Christmas lasted the whole year through (as it ought), and that the prejudices and passions which deform our better nature were never called into action among those to whom they should ever be strangers!

A Christmas Dinner

THEY have rumbled through the streets, and jolted over the stones, and at length reach the wide and open country. The wheels skim over the hard and frosty ground: and the horses, bursting into a canter at a smart crack of the whip, step along the road as if the load behind them: coach, passengers, cod-fish, oyster barrels, and all: were but a feather at their heels. They have descended a gentle slope, and enter upon a level, as compact and dry as a solid block of marble, two miles long. Another crack of the whip, and on they speed, at a smart gallop: the horses tossing their heads and rattling the harness, as if in exhilaration at the rapidity of the motion: while the coachman, holding whip and reins in one hand, takes off his hat with the other, and resting it on his knees, pulls out his handkerchief, and wipes his forehead: partly because he has a habit of doing it, and partly because it's as well to show the passengers how cool he is, and what an easy thing it is to drive four-in-hand, when you have had as much practice as he has. Having done this very leisurely (otherwise the effect would be materially impaired), he replaces his handkerchief, pulls on his hat, adjusts his gloves, squares his elbows, cracks the whip again, and on they speed, more merrily than before.

A few small houses, scattered on either side of the road, betoken the entrance to some town or village. The lively notes of the guard's key-bugle vibrate in the clear cold air, and wake up the old gentleman inside, who, carefully letting down the window-sash half-way, and standing sentry over the air, takes a short peep out, and then carefully pulling it up again, informs the other inside that they're going to change directly; on which the other inside wakes himself up, and determines to postpone his next nap until after the stoppage. Again the bugle sounds lustily forth, and rouses the cottager's wife and children, who peep out at the house-door, and watch the coach till it turns the corner, when they once more crouch round the blazing fire, and throw on another log of wood against father comes home; while father himself, a full mile off, has just exchanged a friendly nod with the coachman, and turned round to take a good long stare at the vehicle as it whirls away.

And now the bugle plays a lively air as the coach rattles through the ill-paved streets of a country town; and the coachman undoing the buckle which keeps his ribands together, prepares to throw them off the moment he stops. Mr Pickwick emerges from his coat collar, and looks about him with great curiosity; perceiving which, the coachman informs Mr Pickwick of the name of the town, and tells him it was market-day yesterday, both of which pieces of information Mr Pickwick retails to his fellow-passengers; whereupon they emerge from their coat collars too, and look about them also. Mr Winkle, who sits at the extreme edge, with one leg dangling in the air, is nearly precipitated into the street, as the coach twists round the sharp corner by the cheesemonger's shop, and turns into the market-place; and before Mr Snodgrass, who sits next to him, has recovered from his alarm, they pull up at the inn yard, where the fresh horses, with cloths on, are already waiting. The coachman throws down the reins and gets down himself, and the other outside passengers drop down also: except those who have no great confidence in their ability to get up again: and they remain where they are, and stamp their feet against the coach to warm them—looking, with longing eyes and red noses, at the bright fire in the inn bar, and the sprigs of holly with red berries which ornament the window.

But the guard has delivered at the corn-dealer's shop the brown paper packet he took out of the little pouch which hangs over his shoulder by a leathern strap; and has seen the horses carefully put to; and has thrown on the pavement the saddle which was brought from London on the coach-roof; and has assisted in the conference between the coachman and the hostler about the grey mare that hurt her off-fore-leg last Tuesday; and he and Mr Weller are all right behind, and the coachman is all right in front, and the old gentleman inside, who has kept the window down full two inches all this time, has pulled it up again, and the cloths are off, and they are all ready for starting, except the "two stout gentlemen," whom the coachman inquires after with some impatience. Hereupon the coachman, and the guard, and Sam Weller, and Mr Winkle, and Mr

Snodgrass, and all the hostlers, and every one of the idlers, who are more in number than all the others put together, shout for the missing gentlemen as loud as they can bawl. A distant response is heard from the yard, and Mr Pickwick and Mr Tupman come running down it, quite out of breath, for they have been having a glass of ale a-piece, and Mr Pickwick's fingers are so cold that he has been full five minutes before he could find the sixpence to pay for it. The coachman shouts an admonitory "Now then, gen'lm'n!" the guard re-echoes it; the old gentleman inside thinks it a very extraordinary thing that people *will* get down when they know there isn't time for it; Mr Pickwick struggles up on one side, Mr Tupman on the other; Mr Winkle cries "All right;" and off they start. Shawls are pulled up, coat collars are re-adjusted, the pavement ceases, the houses disappear, and they are once again dashing along the open road, with the fresh clear air blowing in their faces, and gladdening their very hearts within them.

Pickwick Papers

BUT I am sure I have always thought of Christmas time, when it has come round—apart from the veneration due to its sacred name and origin, if anything belonging to it can be apart from that—as a good time; a kind, forgiving, charitable, pleasant time; the only time I know of in the long calendar of the year, when men and women seem by one consent to open their shut-up hearts freely, and to think of people below them as if they really were fellow-passengers to the grave, and not another race of creatures bound on other journeys.

A Christmas Carol

THE Grocers'! oh, the Grocers'! nearly closed, with perhaps two shutters down, or one; but through those gaps such glimpses! It was not alone that the scales descending on the counter made a merry sound, or that the twine and roller parted company so briskly, or that the canisters were rattled up and down like juggling tricks, or even that the blended scents of tea and coffee were so grateful to the nose, or even that the raisins were so plentiful and rare, the almonds so extremely white, the sticks of cinnamon so long and straight, the other spices so delicious, the candied fruits so caked and spotted with molten sugar as to make the coldest lookers-on feel faint, and subsequently bilious. Nor was it that the figs were moist and pulpy, or that the French plums blushed in modest tartness from their highly-decorated boxes, or that everything was good to eat and in its Christmas dress; but the customers were all so hurried and so eager in the hopeful promise of the day, that they tumbled up against each other at the door, crashing their wicker baskets wildly, and left their purchases upon the counter, and came running back to fetch them, and committed hundreds of the like mistakes, in the best humour possible; while the Grocer and his people were so frank and fresh, that the polished hearts with which they fastened their aprons behind might have been their own, worn outside for general inspection, and for Christmas daws to peck at if they chose.

A Christmas Carol

THE moment Scrooge's hand was on the lock, a strange voice called him by his name, and bade him enter. He obeyed.

It was his own room. There was no doubt about that. But it had undergone a surprising transformation. The walls and ceiling were so hung with living green, that it looked a perfect grove; from every part of which bright gleaming berries glistened. The crisp leaves of holly, mistletoe, and ivy reflected back the light, as if so many little mirrors had been scattered there; and such a mighty blaze went roaring up the chimney as that dull petrifaction of a hearth had never known in Scrooge's time, or Marley's, or for many and many a winter season gone. Heaped up on the floor, to form a kind of throne, were turkeys, geese, game, poultry, brawn, great joints of meat, sucking-pigs, long wreaths of sausages, mince-pies, plum-puddings, barrels of oysters, red-hot chestnuts, cherry-cheeked apples, juicy oranges, luscious pears, immense twelfth-cakes, and seething bowls of punch, that made the chamber dim with their delicious steam. In easy state upon this couch there sat a jolly Giant, glorious to see; who bore a glowing torch, in shape not unlike Plenty's horn, and held it up, high up, to shed its light on Scrooge as he came peeping round the door.

"Come in!" exclaimed the Ghost. "Come in! and know me better, man!"

Scrooge entered timidly, and hung his head before this Spirit. He was not the dogged Scrooge he had been; and, though the Spirit's eyes were clear and kind, he did not like to meet them.

"I am the Ghost of Christmas Present," said the Spirit. "Look upon me!"

Scrooge reverently did so. It was clothed in one simple deep green robe, or mantle, bordered with white fur. This garment hung so loosely on the figure, that its capacious breast was bare, as if disdaining to be warded or concealed by any artifice. Its feet, observable beneath the ample folds of the garment, were also bare; and on its head it wore no other covering than a holly wreath, set here and there with shining icicles. Its dark brown curls were long and free; free as its genial face, its sparkling eye, its open hand, its cheery voice, its unconstrained demeanour, and its joyful air. Girded round its middle was an antique scabbard; but no sword was in it, and the ancient sheath was eaten up with rust.

A Christmas Carol

SUCH a bustle ensued that you might have thought a goose the rarest of all birds; a feathered phenomenon, to which a black swan was a matter of course—and in truth, it was something very like it in that house. Mrs Cratchit made the gravy (ready beforehand in a little saucepan) hissing hot; Master Peter mashed the potatoes with incredible vigour; Miss Belinda sweetened up the apple sauce; Martha dusted the hot plates; Bob took Tiny Tim beside him in a tiny corner at the table; the two young Cratchits set chairs for everybody, not forgetting themselves, and, mounting guard upon their posts, crammed spoons into their mouths, lest they should shriek for goose before their turn came to be helped. At last the dishes were set on, and grace was said. It was succeeded by a breathless pause, as Mrs Cratchit, looking slowly all along the carving-knife, prepared to plunge it in the breast; but when she did, and when the long-expected gush of stuffing issued forth, one murmur of delight arose all round the board, and even Tiny Tim, excited by the two young Cratchits, beat on the table with the handle of his knife, and feebly cried Hurrah!

There never was such a goose. Bob said he didn't believe there ever was such a goose cooked. Its tenderness and flavour, size and cheapness, were the themes of universal admiration. Eked out by apple sauce and mashed potatoes, it was a sufficient dinner for the whole family; indeed, as Mrs Cratchit said with great delight (surveying one small atom of a bone upon the dish), they hadn't ate it all at last! Yet every one had had enough, and the youngest Cratchits, in particular, were steeped in sage and onion to the eyebrows! But now, the plates being changed by Miss Belinda, Mrs Cratchit left the room alone—too nervous to bear witnesses—to take the pudding up, and bring it in.

Suppose it should not be done enough! Suppose it should break in turning out! Suppose somebody should have got over the wall of the back-yard and stolen it, while they were merry with the goose—a supposition at which the two young Cratchits became livid! All sorts of horrors were supposed.

Hallo! A great deal of steam! The pudding was out of the copper. A smell like a washing-day! That was the cloth. A smell like an eating-house and a pastrycook's next door to each other, with a laundress's next door to that! That was the pudding! In half a minute Mrs Cratchit entered—flushed, but smiling proudly—with the pudding, like a speckled cannon-ball, so hard and firm, blazing in half of a half-a-quartern of ignited brandy, and bedight with Christmas holly stuck into the top.

Oh, a wonderful pudding! Bob Cratchit said, and calmly too, that he regarded it as the greatest success achieved by Mrs Cratchit since their marriage. Mrs Cratchit said that, now the weight was off her mind, she would confess she had her doubts about the quantity of flour. Everybody had something to say about it, but nobody said or thought it was at all a small pudding for a large family. It would have been flat heresy to do so. Any Cratchit would have blushed to hint at such a thing.

At last the dinner was all done, the cloth was cleared, the hearth swept, and the fire made up. The compound in the jug being tasted, and considered perfect, apples and oranges were put upon the table, and a shovel full of chestnuts on the fire. Then all the Cratchit family drew round the hearth in what Bob Cratchit called a circle, meaning half a one; and at Bob Cratchit's elbow stood the family display of glass. Two tumblers and a custard cup without a handle.

These held the hot stuff from the jug, however, as well as golden goblets would have done; and Bob served it out with beaming looks, while the chestnuts on the fire sputtered and cracked noisily. Then Bob proposed:

"A merry Christmas to us all, my dears. God bless us!"

Which all the family re-echoed.

"God bless us every one!" said Tiny Tim, the last of all.

A Christmas Carol

THE best sitting room at Manor Farm was a good, long, dark-panelled room with a high chimney-piece, and a capacious chimney, up which you could have driven one of the new patent cabs, wheels and all. At the upper end of the room, seated in a shady bower of holly and evergreens, were the two best fiddlers, and the only harp, in all Muggleton. In all sorts of recesses, and on all kinds of brackets, stood massive old silver candlesticks with four branches each. The carpet was up, the candles burnt bright, the fire blazed and crackled on the hearth, and merry voices and light-hearted laughter rang through the room. If any of the old English yeomen had turned into fairies when they died, it was just the place in which they would have held their revels.

If anything could have added to the interest of this agreeable scene, it would have been the remarkable fact of Mr Pickwick's appearing without his gaiters, for the first time within the memory of his oldest friends.

"You mean to dance?" said Wardle.

"Of course I do," replied Mr Pickwick. "Don't you see I am dressed for the purpose?" Mr Pickwick called attention to his speckled silk stockings, and smartly tied pumps.

"*You* in silk stockings!" exclaimed Mr Tupman jocosely.

"And why not, sir—why not?" said Mr Pickwick, turning warmly upon him.

"Of, of course there is no reason why you shouldn't wear them," responded Mr Tupman.

"I imagine not sir, I imagine not," said Mr Pickwick in a very peremptory tone.

Mr Tupman had contemplated a laugh, but he found it was a serious matter; so he looked grave, and said they were a pretty pattern.

"I hope they are," said Mr Pickwick fixing his eyes upon his friend. "You see nothing extraordinary in the stockings, *as* stockings, I trust sir?"

"Certainly not. Oh certainly not," replied Mr Tupman. He walked away; and Mr Pickwick's countenance resumed its customary benign expression.

"We are all ready, I believe," said Mr Pickwick, who was stationed with the old lady at the top of the dance, and had already made four false starts, in his excessive anxiety to commence.

"Then begin at once," said Wardle. "Now!"

Up struck the two fiddles and the one harp, and off went Mr Pickwick into hands across, when there was a general clapping of hands, and a cry of "Stop, stop!"

"What's the matter!" said Mr Pickwick, who was only brought to by the fiddles and harp desisting, and could have been stopped by no other earthly power, if the house had been on fire.

"Where's Arabella Allen?" cried a dozen voices.

"And Winkle?" added Mr Tupman.

"Here we are!" exclaimed that gentleman, emerging with his pretty companion from the corner; as he did so, it would have been hard to tell which was the redder in the face, he or the young lady with the black eyes.

"What an extraordinary thing it is, Winkle," said Mr Pickwick, rather pettishly, "that you couldn't have taken your place before."

"Not at all extraordinary," said Mr Winkle.

"Well," said Mr Pickwick, with a very expressive smile, as his eyes rested on Arabella, "well I don't know that it *was* extraordinary, either, after all."

However, there was no time to think more about the matter, for the fiddles and harp began in real earnest. Away went Mr Pickwick—hands across—down the middle to the very end of the room, and half-way up the chimney, back again to the door—poussette everywhere—loud stamp on the ground—ready for the next couple—off again—all the figure over once more—another stamp to beat out the time—next couple, and the next, and the next again—never was such going! At last, after they had reached the bottom of the dance, and full fourteen couple after the old lady had retired in an exhausted state, and the clergyman's wife had been substituted in her stead, did that gentleman, when there was no demand whatever on his exertions, keep perpetually dancing in his place, to keep time to the music: smiling on his partner all the while with a blandness of demeanour which baffles all description.

From the centre of the ceiling of this kitchen, old Wardle had just suspended, with his own hands, a huge branch of mistletoe, and this same branch of mistletoe instantaneously gave rise to a scene of general and most delightful struggling and confusion; in the midst of which, Mr Pickwick, with a gallantry that would have done honour to a descendant of Lady Tollimglower herself, took the old lady by the hand, led her beneath the mystic branch, and saluted her in all courtesy and decorum. The old lady submitted to this piece of practical politeness with all the dignity which befitted so important and serious a solemnity, but the younger ladies, not being so thoroughly imbued with a superstitious veneration for the custom: or imagining that the value of a salute is very much enhanced if it cost a little trouble to obtain it: screamed and struggled, and ran into corners, and threatened and remonstrated, and did everything but leave the room until some of the less adventurous gentlemen were on the point of desisting, when they all at once found it useless to resist any longer, and submitted to be kissed with a good grace, Mr Winkle kissed the young lady with the black eyes, and Mr Snodgrass kissed Emily, and Mr Weller, not being particular about the form of being under the mistletoe, kissed Emma and the other female servants, just as he caught them. As to the poor relations, they kissed everybody, not even excepting the plainer portions of the young-lady visitors, who, in their excessive confusion, ran right under the mistletoe, as soon as it was hung up without knowing it! Wardle stood with his back to the fire, surveying the whole scene, with the utmost satisfaction; and the fat boy took the opportunity of appropriating to his own use, and summarily devouring, a particularly fine mince-pie, that had been carefully put by, for somebody else.

Now, the screaming had subsided and faces were in a glow, and curls in a tangle, and Mr Pickwick, after kissing the old lady as before mentioned, was standing under the mistletoe, looking with a very pleased countenance on all that was passing around him, when the young lady with the black eyes, after a little whispering with the other young ladies, made a sudden dart forward, and, putting her arm round Mr Pickwick's neck saluted him affectionately on the left cheek; and before Mr

Pickwick distinctly knew what was the matter, he was surrounded by the whole body, and kissed by every one of them.

It was a pleasant thing to see Mr Pickwick in the centre of the group, now pulled this way, and then that, and first kissed on the chin, and then on the nose, and then on the spectacles: and to hear the peals of laughter which were raised on every side; but it was a still more pleasant thing to see Mr Pickwick, blinded shortly afterwards with a silk handkerchief, falling up against the wall, and scrambling into corners, and going through all the mysteries of blind-man's buff, with the utmost relish for the game, until at last he caught one of the poor relations, and then had to evade the blind-man himself, which he did with a nimbleness and agility that elicited the admiration and applause of all beholders. The poor relations caught the people who they thought would like it, and, when the game flagged, got caught themselves. When they were all tired of blind-man's buff, there was a great game at snap-dragon, and when fingers enough were burned with that, and all the raisins were gone, they sat down by the huge fire of blazing logs to a substantial supper, and a mighty bowl of wassail, something smaller than an ordinary wash-house copper, in which the hot apples were hissing and bubbling with a rich look, and a jolly sound, that were perfectly irresistible.

"This," said Mr Pickwick, looking round him, "this is, indeed, comfort."

"Our invariable custom," replied Mr Wardle. "Everybody sits down with us on Christmas eve, as you see them now—servants and all; and here we wait, until the clock strikes twelve, to usher Christmas in, and beguile the time with forfeits and old stories. Trundle, my boy, rake up the fire."

Up flew the bright sparks in myriads as the logs were stirred. The deep red blaze sent forth a rich glow, that penetrated into the furthest corner of the room, and cast its cheerful tint on every face.

Pickwick Papers

AND numerous indeed are the hearts to which Christmas brings a brief season of happiness and enjoyment. How many families, whose members have been dispersed and scattered far and wide, in the restless struggles of life, are then reunited, and meet once again in that happy state of companionship and mutual good-will, which is a source of such pure and unalloyed delight, and one so incompatible with the cares and sorrows of the world, that the religious belief of the most civilized nations, and the rude traditions of the roughest savages, alike number it among the first joys of a future condition of existence, provided for the blest and happy! How many old recollections, and how many dormant sympathies, does Christmas time awaken!

Pickwick Papers

"SIT fast here, genelmen," said the guard as he clambered up.

"All right behind there, Dick?" cried the coachman.

"All right," was the reply. "Off she goes!" And off she did go—if coaches be feminine—amidst a loud flourish from the guard's horn, and the calm approval of all the judges of coaches and coach-horses congregated at the Peacock, but more especially of the helpers, who stood, with the cloths over their arms, watching the coach till it disappeared, and then lounged admiringly stable-wards, bestowing various gruff encomiums on the beauty of the turn-out.

When the guard (who was a stout old Yorkshireman) had blown himself quite out of breath, he put the horn into a little tunnel of a basket fastened to the coach-side for the purpose, and giving himself a plentiful shower of blows on the chest and shoulders, observed it was uncommon cold; after which, he demanded of every person separately whether he was going right through, and if not where he *was* going. Satisfactory replies being made to these queries, he surmised that the roads were pretty heavy arter that fall last night, and took the liberty of asking whether any of them gentlemen carried a snuff-box. It happening that nobody did, he remarked with a mysterious air that he had heard a medical gentleman as went down to Grantham last week, say how that snuff-taking was bad for the eyes; but for his part he had never found it so, and what he said was, that everybody should speak as they found. Nobody attempting to controvert this position, he took a small brown-paper parcel out of his hat, and putting on a pair of horn spectacles (the writing being crabbed) read the direction half a dozen times over; having done which, he consigned the parcel to its old place, put up his spectacles again, and stared at everybody in turn. After this, he took another blow at the horn by way of refreshment; and, having now exhausted his usual topics of conversation, folded his arms as well as he could in so many coats, and falling into a solemn silence, looked carelessly at the familiar objects which met his eye on every side as the coach rolled on; the only things he seemed to care for being horses and droves of cattle, which he scrutinized with a critical air as they were passed upon the road.

Nicholas Nickleby

"NOW," said Wardle, after a substantial lunch, with the agreeable items of strong-beer and cherry-brandy, had been done ample justice to; "what say you to an hour on the ice? We shall have plenty of time."

"Capital!" said Mr Benjamin Allen.

"Prime!" ejaculated Mr Bob Sawyer.

"You skate, of course, Winkle?" said Wardle.

"Ye-yes; oh, yes," replied Mr Winkle. "I—I—am *rather* out of practice."

"Oh, *do* skate, Mr Winkle," said Arabella. "I like to see it so much."

"Oh, it is *so* graceful," said another young lady.

A third young lady said it was elegant, and a fourth expressed her opinion that it was "swan-like."

"I should be very happy, I'm sure," said Mr Winkle, reddening; "but I have no skates."

This objection was at once overruled. Trundle had a couple of pair, and the fat boy announced that there were half a dozen more downstairs: whereat Mr Winkle expressed exquisite delight, and looked exquisitely uncomfortable.

Old Wardle led the way to a pretty large sheet of ice; and the fat boy and Mr Weller, having shovelled and swept away the snow which had fallen on it during the night, Mr Bob Sawyer adjusted his skates with a dexterity which to Mr Winkle was perfectly marvellous, and described circles with his left leg, and cut figures of eight, and inscribed upon the ice, without once stopping for breath, a great many other pleasant and astonishing devices, to the excessive satisfaction of Mr Pickwick, Mr Tupman, and the ladies: which reached a pitch of positive enthusiasm, when old Wardle and Benjamin Allen, assisted by the aforesaid Bob Sawyer, performed some mystic evolutions which they called a reel.

All this time, Mr Winkle, with his face and hands blue with the cold, had been forcing a gimlet into the soles of his feet, and putting his skates on, with the points behind, and getting the straps into a very complicated and entangled state, with the assistance of Mr Snodgrass, who knew rather less about skates than a Hindoo. At length, however, with the assistance of Mr Weller, the unfortunate skates were firmly screwed and buckled on, and Mr Winkle was raised to his feet.

"Now, then, sir," said Sam, in an encouraging tone; "off vith you, and show 'em how to do it."

"Stop, Sam, stop!" said Mr Winkle, trembling violently, and clutching hold of Sam's arms with the grasp of a drowning man. "How slippery it is, Sam!"

"Not an uncommon thing upon ice, sir," replied Mr Weller. "Hold up, sir!"

This last observation of Mr Weller's bore reference to a demonstration Mr Winkle made at the instant, of a frantic desire to throw his feet in the air, and dash the back of his head on the ice.

"These—these—are very awkward skates; ain't they, Sam?" inquired Mr Winkle, staggering.

"I'm afeerd there's a orkard gen'l'm'n in 'em, sir," replied Sam.

"Now, Winkle," cried Mr Pickwick, quite unconscious that there was anything the matter. "Come; the ladies are all anxiety."

"Yes, yes," replied Mr Winkle, with a ghastly smile. "I'm coming."

"Just a goin' to begin," said Sam, endeavouring to disengage himself. "Now, sir, start off!"

"Stop an instant, Sam," gasped Mr Winkle, clinging most affectionately to Mr Weller. "I find I've got a couple of coats at home that I don't want, Sam. You may have them, Sam."

"Thank'ee, sir," replied Mr Weller.

"Never mind touching your hat, Sam," said Mr Winkle, hastily. "You needn't take your hand away to do that. I meant to have given you five shillings this morning for a Christmas-box, Sam. I'll give it you this afternoon, Sam."

"You're wery good, sir," replied Mr Weller.

"Just hold me at first, Sam; will you?" said Mr Winkle. "There—that's right. I shall soon get in the way of it, Sam. Not too fast, Sam; not too fast."

Mr Winkle stooping forward, with his body half doubled up, was being assisted over the ice by Mr Weller, in a very singular and un-swan-like manner, when Mr Pickwick most innocently shouted from the opposite bank:

"Sam!"

"Sir?"

"Here. I want you."

"Let go, sir," said Sam. "Don't you hear the governor a callin'? Let go, sir."

With a violent effort, Mr Weller disengaged himself from the grasp of the agonized Pickwickian, and, in so doing, administered a considerable impetus to the unhappy Mr Winkle. With an accuracy which no degree of dexterity or practice could have insured, that unfortunate gentleman bore swiftly down into the centre of the reel, at the very moment when Mr Bob Sawyer was performing a flourish of unparalleled beauty. Mr Winkle struck wildly against him, and with a loud crash they both fell heavily down. Mr Pickwick ran to the spot. Bob Sawyer had risen to his feet, but Mr Winkle was far too wise to do anything of the kind, in skates. He was seated on the ice, making spasmodic efforts to smile; but anguish was depicted on every lineament of his countenance.

"Are you hurt?" inquired Mr Benjamin Allen, with great anxiety.

"Not much," said Mr Winkle, rubbing his back very hard.

"I wish you'd let me bleed you," said Mr Benjamin, with great eagerness.

"No, thank you," replied Mr Winkle hurriedly.

"I really think you had better," said Allen.

"Thank you," replied Mr Winkle; "I'd rather not."

"What do *you* think, Mr Pickwick?" inquired Bob Sawyer.

Mr Pickwick was excited and indignant. He beckoned to Mr Weller, and said in a stern voice, "Take his skates off."

"No; but really I had scarcely begun," remonstrated Mr Winkle.

"Take his skates off," repeated Mr Pickwick firmly.

The command was not to be resisted. Mr Winkle allowed Sam to obey it in silence.

"Lift him up," said Mr Pickwick. Sam assisted him to rise.

Mr Pickwick retired a few paces apart from the bystanders; and, beckoning his friend to approach, fixed a searching look upon him, and uttered in a low, but distinct and emphatic tone, these remarkable words:

"You're a humbug, sir."

"A what?" said Mr Winkle, starting.

"A humbug, sir. I will speak plainer, if you wish it. An imposter, sir."

With those words, Mr Pickwick turned slowly on his heel, and rejoined his friends.

While Mr Pickwick was delivering himself of the sentiment just recorded, Mr Weller and the fat boy, having by their joint endeavours cut out a slide, were exercising themselves thereupon, in a very masterly and brilliant manner. Sam Weller, in particular, was displaying that beautiful feat of fancy-sliding which is currently denominated "knocking at the cobbler's door," and which is achieved by skimming over the ice on one foot, and occasionally giving a postman's knock upon it with the other. It was a good long slide, and there was something in the motion which Mr Pickwick, who was very cold with standing still, could not help envying.

"It looks a nice warm exercise that, doesn't it?" he inquired of Wardle, when that gentleman was thoroughly out of breath, by reason of the indefatigable manner in which he had converted his legs into a pair of compasses, and drawn complicated problems on the ice.

"Ah, it does indeed," replied Wardle. "Do you slide?"

"I used to do so, on the gutters, when I was a boy," replied Mr Pickwick.

"Try it now," said Wardle.

"Oh do please, Mr Pickwick!" cried all the ladies.

"I should be very happy to afford you any amusement," replied Mr Pickwick, "but I haven't done such a thing these thirty years."

"Pooh! pooh! Nonsense!" said Wardle, dragging off his skates with the impetuosity which characterised all his proceedings. "Here; I'll keep you company; come along!" And away went the good tempered old fellow down the slide, with a rapidity which came very close upon Mr Weller, and beat the fat boy all to nothing.

Mr Pickwick paused, considered, pulled off his gloves and put them in his hat: took two or three short runs, baulked himself as often, and at last took another run, and went slowly and gravely down the slide, with his feet about a yard and a quarter apart, amidst the gratified shouts of all the spectators.

"Keep the pot a bilin', sir!" said Sam; and down went Wardle again, and then Mr Pickwick, and then Sam, and then Mr Winkle, and then Mr Bob Sawyer, and then the fat boy, and then Mr Snodgrass, following closely upon each other's heels, and running after each other with as much eagerness as if all their future prospects in life depended on their expedition.

It was the most intensely interesting thing, to observe the manner in which Mr Pickwick performed his share in the ceremony; to watch the torture of anxiety with which he viewed the person behind, gaining upon him at the imminent hazard of tripping him up; to see him gradually expend the painful force he had put on at first and turn slowly round on the slide, with his face towards the point from which he had started; to contemplate the playful smile which mantled on his face when he had accomplished the distance, and the eagerness with which he turned round when he had done so, and ran after his predecessor: his black gaiters tripping pleasantly through the snow, and his eyes beaming cheerfulness and gladness through his spectacles. And when he was knocked down (which happened upon the average every third round), it was the most invigorating sight that can possibly be imagined, to behold him gather up his hat, gloves, and handkerchief, with a glowing countenance, and resume his station in the rank, with an ardour and enthusiasm that nothing could abate.

The sport was at its height, the sliding was at the quickest, the laughter was at the loudest, when a sharp smart crack was heard. There was a quick rush towards the bank, a wild scream from the ladies, and a shout from Mr Tupman. A large mass of ice disappeared; the water bubbled up over it; Mr Pickwick's hat, gloves and handkerchief were floating on the surface; and this was all of Mr Pickwick that anybody could see.

Dismay and anguish were depicted on every countenance, the males turned pale, and the females fainted, Mr Snodgrass and Mr Winkle grasped each other by the hand, and gazed at the spot where their leader had gone down, with frenzied eagerness: while Mr Tupman, by way of rendering the promptest assistance, and at the same time conveying to any persons who might be within hearing, the clearest possible notion of the catastrophe, ran off across the country at his utmost speed, screaming "Fire!" with all his might.

It was at this moment, when old Wardle and Sam Weller

were approaching the hole with cautious steps, and Mr Benjamin Allen was holding a hurried consultation with Mr Bob Sawyer, on the advisability of bleeding the company generally, as an improving little bit of professional practice—it was at this very moment that a face, head, and shoulders emerged from beneath the water, and disclosed the features and spectacles of Mr Pickwick.

"Keep yourself up for an instant—for only one instant!" bawled Mr Snodgrass.

"Yes, do; let me implore you—for my sake!" roared Mr Winkle, deeply affected. The adjuration was rather unnecessary; the probability being, that if Mr Pickwick had declined to keep himself up for anybody else's sake, it would have occurred to him that he might as well do so, for his own.

"Do you feel the bottom there, old fellow?" said Wardle.

"Yes, certainly," replied Mr Pickwick, wringing the water from his head and face, and gasping for breath. "I fell upon my back. I couldn't get on my feet at first."

The clay upon so much of Mr Pickwick's coat as was yet visible, bore testimony to the accuracy of this statement; and as the fears of the spectators were still further relieved by the fat boy's suddenly recollecting that the water was nowhere more than five feet deep, prodigies of valour were performed to get him out. After a vast quantity of splashing, and cracking, and struggling, Mr Pickwick was at length fairly extricated from his unpleasant position, and once more stood on dry land.

"Oh, he'll catch his death of cold," said Emily.

"Dear old thing!" said Arabella. "Let me wrap this shawl round you, Mr Pickwick."

"Ah, that's the best thing you can do," said Wardle; "and when you've got it on, run home as fast as your legs can carry you, and jump into bed directly."

A dozen shawls were offered on the instant. Three or four of the thickest having been selected, Mr Pickwick was wrapped up, and started off, under the guidance of Mr Weller: presenting the singular phenomenon of an elderly gentleman, dripping wet, and without a hat, with his arms bound down to his sides, skimming over the ground, without any clearly defined purpose, at the rate of six good English miles an hour.

Pickwick Papers

YESTERDAY we were up again shortly after seven and came on upon our journey by the Glasgow Mail which charged us the remarkably low sum of *six pounds, four* for two places inside. We had a very droll male companion until seven o'clock in the evening, and a most delicious lady's maid for twenty miles who implored us to keep a sharp look-out at the coach windows as she expected her carriage was coming to meet her and she was afraid of missing it. We had many delightful vauntings of the same kind; and in the end it is scarcely necessary to say that the coach did not come, and a very dirty girl did.

As we came further North, the snow grew deeper. About eight o'clock it began to fall heavily, and as we crossed the wild heaths hereabout, there was no vestige of a track. The Mail kept on well, however, and at eleven we reached a bare place with a house standing alone in the midst of a dreary moor, which the Guard informed us was Greta Bridge. I was in a perfect agony of apprehension, for it was fearfully cold and there were no outward signs of anybody being up in the house. But to our great joy we discovered a comfortable room with drawn curtains and a most blazing fire. In half an hour they gave us a smoking supper and a bottle of mulled port and then we retired to a couple of capital bedrooms in each of which was a rousing fire half way up the chimney.

We have had for breakfast, toasts, cakes, a Yorkshire pie, a piece of beef about the size and much the shape of my portmanteau, tea, coffee, ham and eggs—and are now going to look about us.

Letter to his Wife—from Greta Bridge 1838

YES! and the bedpost was his own. The bed was his own, the room was his own. Best and happiest of all, the Time before him was his own, to make amends in!

"I will live in the Past, the Present, and the Future!" Scrooge repeated as he scrambled out of bed. "The Spirits of all Three shall strive within me. Oh, Jacob Marley! Heaven and the Christmas Time be praised for this! I say it on my knees, old Jacob; on my knees!"

He was so fluttered and so glowing with his good intentions, that his broken voice would scarcely answer to his call. He had been sobbing violently in his conflict with the Spirit, and his face was wet with tears.

"They are not torn down," cried Scrooge, folding one of his bed-curtains in his arms, "they are not torn down, rings and all. They are here—I am here—the shadows of the things that would have been may be dispelled. They will be. I know they will!"

His hands were busy with his garments all this time; turning them inside out, putting them on upside down, tearing them, mislaying them, making them parties to every kind of extravagance.

"I don't know what to do!" cried Scrooge, laughing and crying in the same breath, and making a perfect Laocoön of himself with his stockings. "I am as light as a feather, I am as happy as an angel, I am as merry as a schoolboy. I am as giddy as a drunken man. A merry Christmas to everybody! A happy New Year to all the world! Hallo here! Whoop! Hallo!"

He had frisked into the sitting-room, and was now standing there, perfectly winded.

"There's the saucepan that the gruel was in!" cried Scrooge, starting off again, and going round the fire-place. "There's the door by which the Ghost of Jacob Marley entered! There's the corner where the Ghost of Christmas Present sat! There's the window where I saw the wandering Spirits! It's all right, it's all true, it all happened. Ha, ha, ha!"

Really, for a man who had been out of practice for so many years, it was a splendid laugh, a most illustrious laugh. The father of a long, long line of brilliant laughs!

"I don't know what day of the month it is," said Scrooge. "I don't know how long I have been among the Spirits. I don't know anything. I'm quite a baby. Never mind. I don't care. I'd rather be a baby. Hallo! Whoop! Hallo here!"

He was checked in his transports by the churches ringing out the lustiest peals he had ever heard. Clash, clash, hammer; ding, dong, bell! Bell, dong, ding; hammer, clang, clash! Oh, glorious, glorious!

Running to the window, he opened it, and put out his head. No fog, no mist; clear, bright, jovial, stirring, cold; cold, piping for the blood to dance to; Golden sun-light; Heavenly sky; sweet fresh air; merry bells. Oh, glorious! Glorious!

"What's today?" cried Scrooge, calling downward to a boy in Sunday clothes, who perhaps had loitered in to look about him.

"EH?" returned the boy with all his might of wonder.

"What's today, my fine fellow?" said Scrooge.

"Today!" replied the boy. "Why, CHRISTMAS DAY."

"It's Christmas Day!" said Scrooge to himself. "I haven't missed it. The Spirits have done it all in one night. They can do anything they like. Of course they can. Of course they can. Hallo, my fine fellow!"

"Hallo!" returned the boy.

"Do you know the Poulterer's in the next street but one, at the corner?" Scrooge inquired.

"I should hope I did," replied the lad.

"An intelligent boy!" said Scrooge. "A remarkable boy! Do you know whether they've sold the prize Turkey that was hanging up there?—Not the little prize Turkey: the big one?"

"What! the one as big as me? returned the boy.

"What a delightful boy!" said Scrooge. "It's a pleasure to talk to him. Yes, my buck!"

"It's hanging there now," replied the boy.

"Is it?" said Scrooge. "Go and buy it."

"Walk-ER!" exclaimed the boy.

"No, no," said Scrooge, "I am in earnest. Go and buy it, and tell 'em to bring it here, that I may give them the directions where to take it. Come back with the man, and I'll give you a shilling. Come back with him in less than five minutes, and I'll give you half-a-crown!"

The boy was off like a shot. He must have had a steady hand at a trigger who could have got a shot off half so fast.

"I'll send it to Bob Cratchit's," whispered Scrooge, rubbing his hands, and splitting with a laugh. "He shan't know who sends it. It's twice the size of Tiny Tim. Joe Miller never made such a joke as sending it to Bob's will be!"

The hand in which he wrote the address was not a steady one; but write it he did, somehow, and went downstairs to open the street-door, ready for the coming of the poulterer's man. As he stood there, waiting his arrival, the knocker caught his eye.

"I shall love it as long as I live!" cried Scrooge, patting it with his hand. "I scarcely ever looked at it before. What an honest expression it has in its face! It's a wonderful knocker!—Here's the Turkey. Hallo! Whoop! How are you? Merry Christmas!"

It *was* a Turkey! He never could have stood upon his legs, that bird. He would have snapped 'em short off in a minute, like sticks of sealing-wax.

"Why, it's impossible to carry that to Camden Town," said Scrooge. "You must have a cab."

The chuckle with which he said this, and the chuckle with which he paid for the Turkey, and the chuckle with which he paid for the cab, and the chuckle with which he recompensed the boy, were only to be exceeded by the chuckle with which he sat down breathless in his chair again, and chuckled till he cried.

Shaving was not an easy task, for his hand continued to shake very much; and shaving requires attention, even when you don't dance while you are at it. But, if he had cut the end of his nose off, he would have put a piece of sticking-plaster over it, and been quite satisfied.

He dressed himself "all in his best," and at last got out into the streets. The people were by this time pouring forth, as he had seen them with the Ghost of Christmas Present; and, walking with his hands behind him, Scrooge regarded every one with a delighted smile. He looked so irresistibly pleasant, in a word, that three or four good-humoured fellows said, "Good-morning, sir! A merry Christmas to you!" And Scrooge said often afterwards that, of all the blithe sounds he had ever heard, those were the blithest in his ears.

A Christmas Carol

The Masculine Point of View

PODSNAP always talks Britain, and talks as if he were a sort of Private Watchman employed, in the British interests, against the rest of the world. "We know what Russia means, sir," says Podsnap; "we know what France wants; we see what America is up to; but we know what England is. That's enough for us."

Our Mutual Friend

IT has been remarked that Mr Pecksniff was a moral man. So he was. Perhaps there never was a more moral man than Mr Pecksniff: especially in his conversation and correspondence. It was once said of him by a homely admirer, that he had a Fortunatus's purse of good sentiments in his inside. In this particular he was like the girl in the fairy tale, except that if they were not actual diamonds which fell from his lips, they were the very brightest paste, and shone prodigiously. He was a most exemplary man: fuller of virtuous precept than a copy-book. Some people likened him to a direction-post, which is always telling the way to a place, and never goes there: but these were his enemies; the shadows cast by his brightness; that was all. His very throat was moral. You saw a good deal of it. You looked over a very low fence of white cravat (where of no man had ever beheld the tie, for he fastened it behind), and there it lay, a valley between two jutting heights of collar, serene and whiskerless before you. It seemed to say, on the part of Mr Pecksniff, "There is no deception, ladies and gentlemen, all is peace, a holy calm pervades me." So did his hair, just grizzled with an iron-grey, which was all brushed off his fore-head, and stood bolt upright, or slightly drooped in kindred action with his heavy eyelids. So did his person, which was sleek though free from corpulency. So did his manner, which was soft and oily. In a word, even his plain black suit, and state of widower, and dangling double eyeglass, all tended to the same purpose, and cried aloud, "Behold the moral Pecksniff!"

Martin Chuzzlewit

THE night was bitter cold. The snow lay on the ground, frozen into a hard thick crust, so that only the heaps that had drifted into byways and corners were affected by the sharp wind that howled abroad, which, as if expending increased fury on such prey as it found, caught it savagely up in clouds, and, whirling it into a thousand misty eddies, scattered it in air. Bleak, dark, and piercing cold, it was a night for the well-housed and fed to draw round the bright fire and thank God they were at home; and for the homeless, starving wretch to lay him down and die. Many hunger-worn outcasts close their eyes in our bare streets at such times who, let their crimes have been what they may, can hardly open them in a more bitter world.

Such was the aspect of out-of-door affairs, when Mrs Corney, the matron of the workhouse to which our readers have been already introduced as the birthplace of Oliver Twist, sat herself down before a cheerful fire in her own little room, and glanced, with no small degree of complacency, at a small round table, on which stood a tray of corresponding size, furnished with all necessary materials for the most grateful meal that matrons enjoy. In fact, Mrs Corney was about to solace herself with a cup of tea. As she glanced from the table to the fireplace, where the smallest of all possible kettles was singing a small song in a small voice, her inward satisfaction evidently increased—so much so, indeed, that Mrs Corney smiled.

"Well!" said the matron, leaning her elbow on the table, and looking reflectively at the fire; "I'm sure we have all on us a great deal to be grateful for! A great deal, if we did but know it. Ah!"

Mrs Corney shook her head mournfully, as if deploring the mental blindness of those paupers who did not know it; and thrusting a silver spoon (private property) into the inmost recesses of a two-ounce tin tea-caddy, proceeded to make the tea.

How slight a thing will disturb the equanimity of our frail minds! The black teapot, being very small and easily filled, ran over while Mrs Corney was moralising; and the water slightly scalded Mrs Corney's hand.

"Drat the pot!" said the worthy matron, setting it down very hastily on the hob; "a little stupid thing, that only holds a couple of cups! What use is it of, to anybody! Except," said Mrs Corney, pausing, "except to a poor desolate creature like me. Oh dear!"

With these words, the matron dropped into her chair, and, once more resting her elbow on the table, thought of her solitary fate. The small teapot, and the single cup, had awakened in her mind sad recollections of Mr Corney (who had not been dead more than five-and-twenty years), and she was overpowered.

"I shall never get another!" said Mrs Corney pettishly; "I shall never get another—like him."

Whether this remark bore reference to the husband, or the teapot, is uncertain. It might have been the latter; for Mrs Corney looked at it as she spoke, and took it up afterwards. She had just tasted her first cup, when she was disturbed by a soft tap at the room-door.

"Oh, come in with you!" said Mrs Corney sharply. "Some of the old women dying, I suppose. They always die when I'm at meals. Don't stand there, letting the cold air in, don't. What's amiss now, eh?"

"Nothing, ma'am, nothing," replied a man's voice.

"Dear me!" exclaimed the matron, in a much sweeter tone, "is that Mr Bumble?"

"At your service, ma'am," said Mr Bumble, who had been stopping outside to rub his shoes clean, and to shake the snow off his coat; and who now made his appearance, bearing the cocked hat in one hand and a bundle in the other. "Shall I shut the door, ma'am?"

The lady modestly hesitated to reply, lest there should be any impropriety in holding an interview with Mr Bumble, with closed doors. Mr Bumble, taking advantage of the hesitation, and being very cold himself, shut it without permission.

"Hard weather, Mr Bumble," said the matron.

"Hard, indeed, ma'am," replied the beadle. "Anti-porochial weather this, ma'am. We have given away, Mrs Corney, we have given away a matter of twenty quartern loaves and a cheese and a half, this very blessed afternoon; and yet them paupers are not contented."

"Of course not. When would they be, Mr Bumble?" said the matron, sipping her tea.

"When, indeed, ma'am!" rejoined Mr Bumble. "Why here's one man that, in consideration of his wife and large family, has a quartern loaf and a good pound of cheese, full weight. Is he grateful, ma'am? Is he grateful? Not a copper farthing's worth of it! What does he do, ma'am, but ask for a few coals; if it's only a pocket handkerchief full, he says! Coals! What would he do with coals? Toast his cheese with 'em, and then come back for more. That's the way with these people, ma'am; give 'em a apron full of coals today, and they'll come back for another, the day after tomorrow, as brazen as alabaster!"

The matron expressed her entire concurrence in this intelligible simile, and the beadle went on.

"I never," said Mr Bumble, "see anything like the pitch it's got to. The day afore yesterday, a man—you have been a married woman, ma'am, and I may mention it to you—a man, with hardly a rag upon his back (here Mrs Corney looked at the floor), goes to our overseer's door when he has got company coming to dinner, and says he must be relieved, Mrs Corney. As he wouldn't go away, and shocked the company very much, our overseer sent him out a pound of potatoes and half a pint of oatmeal. 'My heart!' says the ungrateful villain, 'what's the use of *this* to me? You might as well give me a pair of iron spectacles!' 'Very good,' says our overseer, taking 'em away again, 'you won't get anything else here.' 'Then I'll die in the streets!' says the vagrant. 'Oh no, you won't,' says our overseer."

"Ha! ha! That was very good! So like Mr Grannett, wasn't it?" interposed the matron. "Well, Mr Bumble?"

"Well, ma'am," rejoined the beadle, "he went away; and he *did* die in the streets. There's an obstinate pauper for you!"

"It beats anything I could have believed," observed the matron emphatically. "But don't you think out-of-door relief a very bad thing, any way, Mr Bumble? You're a gentleman of experience, and ought to know. Come."

"Mrs Corney," said the beadle, smiling as men smile who are conscious of superior information, "out-of-door relief, properly managed—properly managed, ma'am—is the porochial safeguard. The great principle of out-of-door relief is, to give the paupers exactly what they don't want, and then they get tired of coming."

"Dear me!" exclaimed Mrs Corney. "Well, that is a good one, too!"

"Yes. Betwixt you and me, ma'am," returned Mr Bumble, "that's the great principle; and that's the reason why, if you look at any cases that get into them owdacious newspapers, you'll always observe that sick families have been relieved with slices of cheese. That's the rule now, Mrs Corney, all over the country. But, however," said the beadle, stopping to unpack his bundle, "these are official secrets, ma'am; not to be spoken of; except, as I may say, among the porochial officers, such as ourselves. This is the port wine, ma'am, that the board ordered for the infirmary; real, fresh, genuine port wine; only out of the cask this forenoon; clear as a bell; and no sediment!"

Having held the first bottle up to the light, and shaken it well to test its excellence, Mr Bumble placed them both on the top of a chest of drawers; folded the handkerchief in which they had been wrapped; put it carefully in his pocket; and took up his hat, as if to go.

"You'll have a very cold walk, Mr Bumble," said the matron.

"It blows, ma'am," replied Mr Bumble, turning up his coat-collar, "enough to cut one's ears off."

The matron looked from the little kettle to the beadle, who was moving towards the door; and as the beadle coughed, preparatory to bidding her good night, bashfully inquired whether—whether he wouldn't take a cup of tea?

Mr Bumble instantaneously turned back his collar again, laid his hat and stick upon a chair, and drew another chair up to the table. As he slowly seated himself, he looked at the lady. She fixed her eyes upon the little teapot. Mr Bumble coughed again, and slightly smiled.

Mrs Corney rose to get another cup and saucer from the closet. As she sat down, her eyes once again encountered those of the gallant beadle; she coloured, and applied herself to the task of making his tea. Again Mr Bumble coughed—louder this time than he had coughed yet.

"Sweet, Mr Bumble?" inquired the matron, taking up the sugar-basin.

"Very sweet, indeed, ma'am," replied Mr Bumble. He fixed his eyes on Mrs Corney as he said this; and if ever a beadle looked tender, Mr Bumble was that beadle at that moment.

The tea was made and handed in silence. Mr Bumble, having spread a handkerchief over his knees to prevent the crumbs from sullying the splendour of his shorts, began to eat and drink; varying these amusements, occasionally, by fetching a deep sigh; which, however, had no injurious effect upon his appetite, but, on the contrary, rather seemed to facilitate his operations in the tea and toast department.

"You have a cat, ma'am, I see," said Mr Bumble, glancing at one who, in the centre of her family, was basking before the fire; "and kittens too, I declare!"

"I am so fond of them, Mr Bumble, you can't think," replied the matron. "They're *so* happy, *so* frolicsome, and *so* cheerful, that they are quite companions for me."

"Very nice animals, ma'am," replied Mr Bumble approvingly; "so very domestic."

"Oh, yes!" rejoined the matron with enthusiasm; "so fond of their home too, that it's quite a pleasure, I'm sure."

"Mrs Corney, ma'am," said Mr Bumble slowly, and marking the time with his teaspoon, "I mean to say this, ma'am; that any cat, or kitten, that could live with you, ma'am, and *not* be fond of its home, must be an ass, ma'am."

"Oh, Mr Bumble!" remonstrated Mrs Corney.

"It's of no use disguising facts, ma'am," said Mr Bumble, slowly flourishing the teaspoon with a kind of amorous dignity which made him doubly impressive; "I would drown it myself, with pleasure."

"Then you're a cruel man," said the matron vivaciously, as she held out her hand for the beadle's cup; "and a very hard-hearted man besides."

"Hard-hearted, ma'am?" said Mr Bumble. "Hard?" Mr Bumble resigned his cup without another word; squeezed Mrs Corney's little finger as she took it; and inflicting two open-handed slaps upon his laced waistcoat, gave a mighty sigh, and hitched his chair a very little morsel farther from the fire.

It was a round table; and as Mrs Corney and Mr Bumble had been sitting opposite each other, with no great space between them, and fronting the fire, it will be seen that Mr Bumble in receding from the fire, and still keeping at the table, increased the distance between himself and Mrs Corney; which proceeding, some prudent readers will doubtless be disposed to admire, and to consider an act of great heroism on Mr Bumble's part: he being in some sort tempted by time, place, and opportunity, to give utterance to certain soft nothings, which however well they may become the lips of the light and thoughtless, do seem immeasurably beneath the dignity of the judges of the land, members of parliament, ministers of state, lord mayors, and other great public functionaries, but more particularly beneath the stateliness and gravity of a beadle, who (as is well known) should be the sternest and most inflexible among them all.

Whatever were Mr Bumble's intentions, however (and no doubt they were of the best), it unfortunately happened, as has been twice before remarked, that the table was a round one; consequently Mr Bumble, moving his chair by little and little, soon began to diminish the distance between himself and the matron; and continuing to travel round the outer edge of the circle, brought his chair, in time, close to that in which the matron was seated. Indeed, the two chairs touched; and when they did so, Mr Bumble stopped.

Now, if the matron had moved her chair to the right, she would have been scorched by the fire; and if to the left, she must have fallen into Mr Bumble's arms; so (being a discreet matron, and no doubt foreseeing these consequences at a glance) she remained where she was, and handed Mr Bumble another cup of tea.

"Hard-hearted, Mrs Corney?" said Mr Bumble, stirring his tea, and looking up into the matron's face; "are *you* hard-hearted, Mrs Corney?"

"Dear me!" exclaimed the matron, "what a very curious question from a single man. What can you want to know for, Mr Bumble?"

The beadle drank his tea to the last drop, finished a piece of toast, whisked the crumbs off his knees, wiped his lips, and deliberately kissed the matron.

"Mr Bumble!" cried that discreet lady in a whisper, for the fright was so great that she had quite lost her voice; "Mr Bumble, I shall scream!" Mr Bumble made no reply; but in a slow and signified manner, put his arm round the matron's waist.

As the lady had stated her intention of screaming, of course she would have screamed at this additional boldness, but that the exertion was rendered unnecessary by a hasty knocking at the door; which was no sooner heard, than Mr Bumble darted, with much agility, to the wine bottles, and began dusting them with great violence, while the matron sharply demanded who was there. It is worthy of remark, as a curious physical instance of the efficacy of a sudden surprise in counteracting the effects of extreme fear, that her voice had quite recovered all its official asperity.

"If you please, mistress," said a withered old female pauper, hideously ugly, putting her head in at the door, "Old Sally is agoing fast."

"Well, what's that to me?" angrily demanded the matron. "I can't keep her alive, can I?"

"No, no, mistress," replied the old woman, "nobody can; she's far beyond the reach of help. I've seen a many people die, little babes and great strong men, and I know when deaths' a-coming, well enough. But she's troubled in her mind; and when the fits are not on her—and that's not often, for she is dying very hard—she says she has got something to tell, which you must hear. She'll never die quiet till you come, mistress."

At this intelligence, the worthy Mrs Corney muttered a variety of invectives against old women would couldn't even die without purposely annoying their betters; and muffling herself in a thick shawl which she hastily caught up, briefly requested Mr Bumble to stay till she came back, lest anything particular should occur. Bidding the messenger walk fast, and not be all night hobbling up the stairs, she followed her from the room with a very ill grace, scolding all the way.

Mr Bumble's conduct on being left to himself was rather inexplicable. He opened the closet, counted the teaspoons, weighed the sugar-tongs, closely inspected a silver milk-pot to ascertain that it was of the genuine metal, and, having satisfied his curiosity on these points, put on his cocked-hat cornerwise, and danced with much gravity four distinct times round the table. Having gone through this very extraordinary performance, he took off the cocked hat again, and, spreading himself before the fire with his back towards it, seemed to be mentally engaged in taking an exact inventory of the furniture.

Oliver Twist

THUS arrested on the threshold as he was following his wife out of the room, Toodle returned and confronted Mr Dombey alone. He was a strong, loose, round-shouldered, shuffling, shaggy fellow, on whom his clothes sat negligently: with a good deal of hair and whisker deepened in its natural tint, perhaps by smoke and coal-dust: hard knotty hands: and a square forehead, as coarse in grain as the bark of an oak. A thorough contrast in all respects to Mr Dombey, who was one of those close-shaved close-cut moneyed gentlemen who are glossy and crisp like new bank-notes, and who seem to be artificially braced and tightened as by the stimulating action of golden shower-baths.

"You have a son, I believe?" said Mr Dombey.

"Four on 'em, Sir. Four hims and a her. All alive!"

"Why, it's as much as you can afford to keep them!" said Mr Dombey.

"I couldn't hardly afford but one thing in the world less, Sir."

"What is that?"

"To lose 'em, Sir."

Dombey and Son

"HELL'S fire!" cried Sikes, breaking fiercely from the Jew. "Let me go!"

Flinging the old man from him, he rushed from the room, and darted, wildly and furiously, up the stairs.

"Bill, Bill!" cried Fagin, following him hastily. "A word. Only a word."

The word would not have been exchanged, but that the housebreaker was unable to open the door, on which he was expending fruitless oaths and violence, when the Jew came panting up.

"Let me out," said Sikes. "Don't speak to me; it's not safe. Let me out, I say!"

"Hear me speak a word," rejoined Fagin, laying his hand upon the lock. "You won't be . . ."

"Well," replied the other.

"You won't be—too—violent, Bill?"

The day was breaking, and there was light enough for the men to see each other's faces. They exchanged one brief glance; there was a fire in the eyes of both, which could not be mistaken.

"I mean," said Fagin, showing that he felt all disguise was now useless, "not too violent for safety. Be crafty, Bill, and not too bold."

Sikes made no reply; but, pulling open the door, of which Fagin had turned the lock, dashed into the silent streets.

Without one pause, or moment's consideration; without once turning his head to the right or left, or raising his eyes to the sky, or lowering them to the ground, but looking straight before him with savage resolution; his teeth so tightly compressed that the strained jaw seemed starting through his skin; the robber held on his headlong course, nor muttered a word, nor relaxed a muscle, until he reached his own door. He opened it softly with a key, strode lightly up the stairs, and entering his own room, double-locked the door, and lifting a heavy table against it, drew back the curtain of the bed.

The girl was lying, half-dressed, upon it. He had roused her from her sleep, for she raised herself with a hurried and startled look.

"Get up!" said the man.

"It *is* you, Bill!" said the girl, with an expression of pleasure at his return.

"It is," was the reply. "Get up."

There was a candle burning, but the man hastily drew it from the candlestick, and hurled it under the grate. Seeing the faint light of early day without the girl rose to undraw the curtain.

"Let it be," said Sikes, thrusting his hand before her. "There's light enough for wot I've got to do."

"Bill," said the girl, in the low voice of alarm, "why do you look like that at me!"

The robber sat regarding her, for a few seconds, with dilated nostrils and heaving breast; and then, grasping her by the head and throat, dragged her into the middle of the room, and looking once towards the door, placed his heavy hand upon her mouth.

"Bill, Bill!" gasped the girl, wrestling with the strength of mortal fear—"I—I won't scream or cry—not once—hear me—speak to me—tell me what I have done."

"You know, you she devil!" returned the robber, suppressing his breath. "You were watched tonight: every word you said was heard."

"Then spare my life for the love of Heaven, as I spared yours," rejoined the girl, clinging to him. "Bill, dear Bill, you cannot have the heart to kill me. Oh! think of all I have given up, only this one night, for you. You *shall* have time to think, and save yourself this crime; I will not loose my hold, you cannot throw me off. Bill, Bill, for dear God's sake, for your own, for mine, stop before you spill my blood! I have been true to you, upon my guilty soul I have!"

The man struggled violently to release his arms; but those of the girl were clasped round his, and tear her as he would, he could not tear them away.

"Bill," cried the girl, striving to lay her head upon his breast, "the gentleman and that dear lady told me tonight of a home in some foreign country where I could end my days in solitude and peace. Let me see them again, and beg them, on my knees, to show the same mercy and goodness to you; and let us both leave this dreadful place, and far apart lead better lives, and forget how we have lived, except in prayers, and never see each other more. It is never too late to repent. They told me so—I feel it now—but we must have time—a little, little time!"

The housebreaker freed one arm, and grasped his pistol. The certainty of immediate detection if he fired flashed across his mind even in the midst of his fury; and he beat it twice with all the force he could summon, upon the upturned face that almost touched his own.

She staggered and fell: nearly blinded with the blood that rained down from a deep gash in her forehead; but raising herself, with difficulty, on her knees, drew from her bosom a white handkerchief—Rose Maylie's own—and holding it up, in her folded hands, as high towards Heaven as her feeble strength would allow, breathed one prayer for mercy to her Maker.

It was a ghastly figure to look upon. The murderer staggering backward to the wall, and shutting out the sight with his hand, seized a heavy club and struck her down.

Of all bad deeds that, under cover of the darkness, had been committed within wide London's bounds since night hung over it, that was the worst. Of all the horrors that rose with an ill scent upon the morning air, that was the foulest and most cruel.

The sun—the bright sun—that brings back, not light alone, but new life, and hope, and freshness to man—burst upon the crowded city in clear and radiant glory. Through costly-coloured glass and paper-mended window, through cathedral dome and rotten crevice, it shed its equal ray. It lighted up the room where the murdered woman lay. It did. He tried to shut it out, but it would stream in. If the sight had been a ghastly one in the dull morning, what was it, now, in all that brilliant light!

He had not moved; he had been afraid to stir. There had been a moan and motion of the hand; and, with terror added to rage, he had struck and struck again. Once he threw a rug over it; but it was worse to fancy the eyes, and imagine them moving towards him, than to see them glaring upward, as if watching the reflection of the pool of gore that quivered and danced in the sunlight on the ceiling. He had plucked it off again. And there was the body—mere flesh and blood, no more—but such flesh, and so much blood!

He struck a light, kindled the fire, and thrust the club into it. There was hair upon the end, which blazed and shrunk into a light cinder, and, caught by the air, whirled up the chimney. Even that frightened him, sturdy as he was; but he held the weapon till it broke, and then piled it on the coals to burn away, and smoulder into ashes. He washed himself, and rubbed his clothes; there were spots that would not be removed, but he cut the pieces out, and burnt them. How those stains were dispersed about the room! The very feet of the dog were bloody.

All this time he had, never once, turned his back upon the corpse; no, not for a moment. Such preparations completed, he moved, backward, towards the door: dragging the dog with him, lest he should soil his feet anew and carry out new evidences of the crime into the streets. He shut the door softly, locked it, took the key, and left the house.

He crossed over and glanced up at the window, to be sure that nothing was visible from the outside. There was the curtain still drawn, which she would have opened to admit the light she never saw again. It lay nearly under there. *He* knew that. God, how the sun poured down upon the very spot!

The glance was instantaneous. It was a relief to have got free of the room. He whistled on the dog, and walked rapidly away.

He went through Islington; strode up the hill at Highgate on which stands the stone in honour of Whittington; turned down to Highgate Hill, unsteady of purpose, and uncertain where to go; struck off to the right again, almost as soon as he began to descend it; and taking the footpath across the fields, skirted Caen Wood, and so came out on Hampstead Heath.

Traversing the hollow by the Vale of Health, he mounted the opposite bank, and crossing the road which joins the villages of Hampstead and Highgate, made along the remaining portion of the heath to the fields at North End, in one of which he laid himself down under a hedge, and slept.

Soon he was up again, and away—not far into the country, but back towards London by the high-road—then back again—then over another part of the same ground as he had already traversed—then wandering up and down in fields, and lying on ditches' brinks to rest, and starting up to make for some other spot, and do the same, and ramble on again.

Where could he go, that was near and not too public, to get some meat and drink? Hendon. That was a good place, not far off, and out of most people's way. Thither he directed his steps—running sometimes, and sometimes, with a strange perversity, loitering at a snail's pace, or stopping altogether and idly breaking the hedges with his stick. But when he got there, all the people he met—the very children at the doors—seemed to view him with suspicion. Back he turned again, without the courage to purchase bit or drop, though he had tasted no food for many hours; and once more he lingered on the Heath, uncertain where to go.

Oliver Twist

SOLOMON Gills rubbed his hands with an air of stealthy enjoyment, as he talked of the sea, though; and looked on the seafaring objects about him with inexpressible complacency.

"Think of this wine, for instance," said old Sol, "which has been to the East Indies and back, I'm not able to say how often, and has been once round the world. Think of the pitch-dark nights, the roaring winds, and rolling seas!"

"The thunder, lightning, rain, hail, storm of all kinds," said the boy.

"To be sure," said Solomon—"that this wine has passed

through. Think what a straining and creaking of timbers, and masts: what a whistling and howling of the gale through ropes and rigging!"

"What a clambering aloft of men, vying with each other who shall lie out first upon the yards to furl the icy sails, while the ship rolls and pitches, like mad!" cried his nephew.

"Exactly so," said Solomon: "has gone on, over the old cask that held this wine. Why, when the Charming Sally went down in the——"

"In the Baltic Sea, in the dead of night; five-and-twenty minutes past twelve when the captain's watch stopped in his pocket; he lying dead against the main-mast—on the fourteenth of February, seventeen forty-nine!" cried Walter, with great animation.

"Ay, to be sure!" cried old Sol, "quite right! Then, there were 500 casks of such wine aboard; and all hands (except the first mate, first lieutenant, two seamen, and a lady, in a leaky boat) going to work to stave the casks, got drunk and died drunk, singing 'Rule Britannia,' when she settled and went down, and ending with one awful scream in chorus."

"But when the George the Second drove ashore, Uncle, on the coast of Cornwall, in a dismal gale, two hours before day-break, on the fourth of March, 'seventy-one, she had near 200 horses aboard; and the horses breaking loose down below, early in the gale, and tearing to and fro, and trampling each other to death, made such noises, and set up such human cries, that the crew believing the ship to be full of devils, some of the best men, losing heart and head, went overboard in despair, and only two were left alive, at last, to tell the tale."

"And when," said old Sol, "when the Polyphemus——"

"Private West India trader, burden 350 tons, Captain, John Brown of Deptford. Owners, Wiggs and Co.," cried Walter.

"The same," said Sol; "when she took fire, four days' sail with a fair wind out of Jamaica Harbour, in the night,——"

"There were two brothers on board," interposed his nephew, speaking very fast and loud, "and there not being room enough for both of them in the only boat that wasn't swamped, neither of them would consent to go, until the elder took the younger by the waist and flung him in. And then the younger rising in the boat, cried out, 'Dear Edward, think of your promised wife at home. I'm only a boy. No one waits at home for me. Leap down into my place!' and flung himself into the sea!"

The kindling eye and heightened colour of the boy, who had risen from his seat in the earnestness of what he said and felt, seemed to remind old Sol of something he had forgotten, or that his encircling mist had hitherto shut out. Instead of proceeding with any more anecdotes, as he had evidently intended but a moment before, he gave a short dry cough, and said, "Well! suppose we change the subject."

The truth was, that the simple-minded uncle in his secret attraction towards the marvellous and adventurous—of which he was, in some sort, a distant relation, by his trade—had greatly encouraged the same attraction in the nephew; and that everything that had ever been put before the boy to deter him from a life of adventure, had had the usual unaccountable effect of sharpening his taste for it. This is invariable. It would seem as if there never was a book written, or a story told, expressly with the object of keeping boys on shore, which did not lure and charm them to the ocean, as a matter of course.

But an addition to the little party now made its appearance, in the shape of a gentleman in a wide suit of blue, with a hook instead of a hand attached to his right wrist; very bushy black eyebrows; and a thick stick in his left hand, covered all over (like his nose) with knobs. He wore a loose black silk handkerchief round his neck, and such a very large coarse shirt collar, that it looked like a small sail. He was evidently the person for whom the spare wine-glass was intended, and evidently knew it; for having taken off his rough outer coat, and hung up, on a particular peg behind the door, such a hard glazed hat as a sympathetic person's head might ache at the sight of, and which left a red rim round his own forehead as if he had been wearing a tight basin, he brought a chair to where the clean glass was, and sat himself down behind it. He was usually addressed as Captain, this visitor; and had been a pilot, or a skipper, or a privateer's-man, or all three perhaps; and was a very salt-looking man indeed.

His face, remarkable for a brown solidity, brightened as he shook hands with uncle and nephew; but he seemed to be of a laconic disposition, and merely said—"How goes it?"

Dombey and Son

WE had a beautiful little dinner. Quite an elegant dish of fish; the kidney-end of a loin of veal, roasted; fried sausage-meat; a partridge, and a pudding. There was wine, and there was strong ale; and after dinner Mrs Micawber made us a bowl of hot punch with her own hands.

Mr Micawber was uncommonly convivial. I never saw him such good company. He made his face shine with the punch, so that it looked as if it had been varnished all over. He got cheerfully sentimental about the town, and proposed success to it; observing, that Mrs Micawber and himself had been made extremely snug and comfortable there, and that he never should forget the agreeable hours they had passed in Canterbury. He proposed me afterwards; and he, and Mrs Micawber, and I, took a review of our past acquaintance, in the course of which we sold the property all over again. Then I proposed Mrs Micawber; or, at least, said modestly, "if you'll allow me, Mrs Micawber, I shall now have the pleasure of drinking *your* health, ma'am." On which Mr Micawber delivered an eulogium on Mrs Micawber's character, and said she had ever been his guide, philosopher, and friend, and that he would recommend me, when I came to a marrying-time of life, to marry such another woman, if such another woman could be found.

As the punch disappeared, Mr Micawber became still more friendly and convivial. Mrs Micawber's spirits becoming elevated, too, we sang "Auld Lang Syne." When we came to "Here's a hand, my trusty frere," we all joined hands round the table; and when we declared we would "take a right gude Willie

Waught," and hadn't the least idea what it meant, we were really affected.

In a word, I never saw anybody so thoroughly jovial as Mr Micawber was, down to the very last moment of the evening, when I took a hearty farewell of himself and his amiable wife. Consequently, I was not prepared, at seven o'clock next morning, to receive the following communication, dated half-past nine in the evening; a quarter of an hour after I had left him.

"My dear Young Friend,

"The die is cast—all is over. Hiding the ravages of care with a sickly mask of mirth, I have not informed you, this evening, that there is no hope of the remittance! Under these circumstances, alike humiliating to endure, humiliating to contemplate, and humiliating to relate, I have discharged the pecuniary liability contracted at this establishment, by giving a note of hand, made payable fourteen days after date, at my residence, Pentonville, London. When it becomes due, it will not be taken up. The result is destruction. The bolt is impending, and the tree must fall.

"Let the wretched man who now addresses you, my dear Copperfield, be a beacon to you through life. He writes with that intention, and in that hope. If he could think himself of so much use, one gleam of day might, by possibility, penetrate into the cheerless dungeon of his remaining existence—though his longevity is, at present (to say the least of it), extremely problematical.

"This is the last communication, my dear Copperfield, you will ever receive

"From

"The

"Beggared Outcast,

"Wilkins Micawber."

I was so shocked by the contents of this heart-rending letter, that I ran off directly towards the little hotel with the intention of taking it on my way to Dr Strong's, and trying to soothe Mr Micawber with a word of comfort. But, half-way there, I met the London coach with Mr and Mrs Micawber up behind; Mr Micawber, the very picture of tranquil enjoyment, smiling at Mrs Micawber's conversation, eating walnuts out of a paper bag, with a bottle sticking out of his breast pocket. As they did not see me, I thought it best, all things considered, not to see them. So, with a great weight taken off my mind, I turned into a bye-street that was the nearest way to school, and felt, upon the whole, relieved that they were gone; thought I still liked them very much, nevertheless.

David Copperfield

"WE have no Faith left, positively," said Mrs Skewton. We have no Faith in the dear old Barons, who were the most delightful creatures—or in the dear old Priests, who were the most warlike of men—or even in the days of that inestimable Queen Bess, upon the wall there, which were so extremely golden. Dear creature! She was all heart! And that charming father of hers! I hope you dote on Harry the Eighth!"

"I admire him very much," said Carker.

"So bluff!" cried Mrs Skewton, "wasn't he? So burly. So truly English. Such a picture, too, he makes, with his dear little peepy eyes, and his benevolent chin!"

Dombey and Son

MR QUILP withdrew to the adjoining room, and turning back his coat-collar, proceeded to smear his countenance with a damp towel of very unwholesome appearance, which made his complexion rather more cloudy than it had been before. But, while he was thus engaged, his caution and inquisitiveness did not forsake him. With a face as sharp and cunning as ever, he often stopped, even in this short process, and stood listening for any conversation in the next room, of which he might be the theme.

"Ah!" he said after a short effort of attention, "it was not the towel over my ears, I thought it wasn't. I'm a little hunchy villain and a monster, am I, Mrs Jiniwin? Oh!"

The pleasure of this discovery called up the old doglike smile in full force. When he had quite done with it, he shook himself in a very doglike manner, and rejoined the ladies.

Mr Quilp now walked up to the front of a looking-glass, and was standing there, putting on his neckerchief, when Mrs Jiniwin, happening to be behind him, could not resist the inclination she felt to shake her fist at her tyrant son-in-law. It was the gesture of an instant, but as she did so and accompanied the action with a menacing look, she met his eye in the glass, catching her in the very act. The same glance at the mirror conveyed to her the reflection of a horribly grotesque and distorted face with the tongue lolling out: and the next instant the dwarf, turning about, with a perfectly bland and placid look, inquired in a tone of great affection,

"How are you now, my dear old darling?"

Slight and ridiculous as the incident was, it made him appear such a little fiend and withal such a keen and knowing one, that the old woman felt too much afraid of him to utter a single word, and suffered herself to be led with extraordinary politeness to the breakfast-table. Here, he by no means diminished the impression he had just produced, for he ate hard eggs, shell and all, devoured gigantic prawns with the heads and tails on, chewed tobacco and water-cresses at the same time and with extraordinary greediness, drank boiling tea without winking, bit his fork and spoon till they bent again, and in short performed so many horrifying and uncommon acts that the women were nearly frightened out of their wits and began to doubt if he were really a human creature. At last, having gone through these proceedings and many others which were equally a part of his system, Mr Quilp left them, reduced to a very obedient and humbled state, and betook himself to the river-side, where he took boat for the wharf on which he had bestowed his name.

It was flood tide when Daniel Quilp sat himself down in the wherry to cross to the opposite shore. A fleet of barges were coming lazily on, some wideways, some head first, some stern first; all in a wrong-headed, dogged, obstinate way, bumping up against the larger craft, running under the bows of steam-boats, getting into every kind of nook and corner where they had no business, and being crunched on all sides like so many walnut-shells; while each, with its pair of long sweeps struggling and splashing in the water, looked like some lumbering fish in pain. In some of the vessels at anchor all hands were busily engaged in coiling ropes, spreading out sails to dry, taking in or discharging their cargoes; in others, no life was visible but two or three tarry boys, and perhaps a barking dog running to and fro upon the deck or scrambling up to look over the side and bark the louder for the view. Coming slowly on through the forests of masts, was a great steam ship, beating the water in short impatient strokes with her heavy paddles, as though she wanted room to breathe, and advancing in her huge bulk like a sea monster among the minnows of the Thames. On either hand, were long black tiers of colliers; between them, vessels slowly working out of harbour with sails glistening in the sun, and creaking noise on board, re-echoed from a hundred quarters. The water and all upon it was in active motion, dancing and buoyant and bubbling up; while the old grey Tower and piles of building on the shore, with many a church-spire shooting up between, looked coldly on, and seemed to disdain their chafing neighbour.

Daniel Quilp, who was not much affected by a bright morning save in so far as it spared him the trouble of carrying an umbrella, caused himself to be put ashore hard by the wharf, and proceeded thither, through a narrow lane which, partaking of the amphibious character of its frequenters, had as much water as mud in its composition, and a very liberal supply of both. Arrived at his destination, the first object that presented itself to his view was a pair of very imperfectly shod feet elevated in the air with the soles upwards, which remarkable appearance was referable to the boy, who being of an eccentric spirit and having a natural taste for tumbling was now standing on his head and contemplating the aspect of the river under these uncommon circumstances. He was speedily brought on his heels by the sound of his master's voice, and as soon as his head was in its right position, Mr. Quilp, to speak expressively in the absence of a better verb, "punched it" for him.

"Come, you let me alone," said the boy, parrying Quilp's hand with both his elbows alternatively. "You'll get something you won't like if you don't, and so I tell you."

"You dog," snarled Quilp, "I'll beat you with an iron rod, I'll scratch you with a rusty nail, I'll pinch your eyes, if you talk to me. I will!"

With these threats he clenched his hand again, and dexterously diving in between the elbows and catching the boy's head as it dodged from side to side, gave it three or four good hard knocks. Having now carried his point and insisted on it, he left off.

"You won't do it again," said the boy, nodding his head and drawing back, with the elbows ready in case of the worst; "now!"

"Stand still, you dog," said Quilp. "I won't do it again, because I've done it as often as I want. Here. Take the key."

"Why don't you hit one of your own size?" said the boy, approaching very slowly.

"Where is there one of my size, you dog?" returned Quilp. "Take the key, or I'll brain you with it." Indeed he gave him a smart tap with the handle as he spoke. "Now, open the counting-house."

The boy sulkily complied, muttering at first, but desisting when he looked round and saw that Quilp was following him with a steady look. And here it may be remarked, that between this boy and the dwarf there existed a strange kind of mutual liking. How born or bred, or how nourished upon blows and threats on one side, and retorts and defiances on the other, is not to the purpose. Quilp would certainly suffer nobody to contradict him but the boy, and the boy would assuredly not have submitted to be so knocked about by anybody but Quilp, when he had the power to run away at any time he chose.

"Now," said Quilp, passing into the wooden counting-house,

"you mind the wharf. Stand upon your head again, and I'll cut one of your feet off."

The boy made no answer, but directly Quilp had shut himself in, stood on his head before the door, then walked on his hands to the back and stood on his head there, and then to the opposite side and repeated the performance.

The Old Curiosity Shop

THE church Walter had chosen for the purpose, was a mouldy old church in a yard, hemmed in by a labyrinth of back streets and courts, with a little burying-ground round it, and itself buried in a kind of vault, formed by the neighbouring houses, and paved with echoing stones. It was a great dim, shabby pile, with high old oaken pews, among which about a score of people lost themselves every Sunday; while the clergyman's voice drowsily resounded through the emptiness, and the organ rumbled and rolled as if the church had got the colic, for want of a congregation to keep the wind and damp out. But so far was this City church from languishing for the company of other churches, that spires were clustered round it, as the masts of shipping cluster on the river. It would have been hard to count them from its steeple-top, they were so many. In almost every yard and blind-place near, there was a church. The confusion of bells when Susan and Mr Toots betook themselves towards it on the Sunday morning, was deafening. There were twenty churches close together, clamouring for people to come in.

The two stray sheep in question were penned by a beadle in a commodious pew, and, being early, sat for some time counting the congregation, listening to the disappointed bell high up in the tower, or looking at a shabby little old man in the porch behind the screen, who was ringing the same, like the Bull in Cock Robin, with his foot in a stirrup. Mr Toots, after a lengthened survey of the large books on the reading-desks, whispered Miss Nipper that he wondered where the banns were kept, but that young lady merely shook her head and frowned; repelling for the time all approaches of a temporal nature.

Mr Toots, however, appearing unable to keep his thoughts from the banns, was evidently looking out for them during the whole preliminary portion of the service. As the time for reading them approached, the poor young gentleman manifested great anxiety and trepidation, which was not diminished by the unexpected apparition of the Captain in the front row of the gallery. When the clerk handed up a list to the clergyman, Mr Toots, being then seated, held on by the seat of the pew; but when the names of Walter Gay and Florence Dombey were read aloud as being in the third and last stage of that association, he was so entirely conquered by his feelings as to rush from the church without his hat, followed by the beadle and pew-opener, and two gentlemen of the medical profession, who happened to be present; of whom the first-named presently returned for that article, informing Miss Nipper in a whisper that she was not to make herself uneasy about the gentleman, as the gentleman said his indisposition was of no consequence.

Miss Nipper, feeling that the eyes of that integral portion of Europe which lost itself weekly among the high-backed pews, were upon her, would have been sufficiently embarrassed by this incident, though it had terminated here; the more so, as the Captain in the front row of the gallery, was in a state of unmitigated consciousness which could hardly fail to express to the congregation that he had some mysterious connexion with it. But the extreme restlessness of Mr Toots painfully increased and protracted the delicacy of her situation. That young gentleman, incapable, in his state of mind, of remaining alone in the churchyard, a prey to solitary meditation, and also desirous, no doubt, of testifying his respect for the offices he had in some measure interrupted, suddenly returned—not coming back to the pew, but stationing himself on a free seat in the aisle, between two elderly females who were in the habit of receiving their portion of a weekly dole of bread then set forth on a shelf in the porch. In this conjunction Mr Toots remained, greatly disturbing the congregation, who felt it impossible to avoid looking at him, until his feelings overcame him again, when he departed silently and suddenly. Not venturing to trust himself in the church any more, and yet wishing to have some social participation in what was going on there, Mr Toots was, after this, seen from time to time, looking in, with a lorn aspect, at one or other of the windows; and as there were several windows accessible to him from without, and as his restlessness was very great, it not only became difficult to conceive at which window he would appear next, but likewise became necessary, as it were, for the whole congregation to speculate upon the chances of the different windows, during the comparative leisure afforded them by the sermon. Mr Toots's movements in the churchyard were so eccentric that, he seemed generally to defeat all calculation, and to appear, like the conjurer's figure, where he was least expected; and the effect of these mysterious presentations was much increased by its being difficult to him to see in, and easy to everybody else to see out: which occasioned his remaining, every time, longer than might have been expected, with his face close to the glass, until he all at once became aware that all eyes were upon him, and vanished.

These proceedings on the part of Mr Toots, and the strong individual consciousness of them that was exhibited by the Captain, rendered Miss Nipper's position so responsible a one, that she was mightily relieved by the conclusion of the service; and was hardly so affable to Mr Toots as usual, when he informed her and the Captain, on the way back, that now he was sure he had no hope, you know, he felt more comfortable—at least not exactly more comfortable, but more comfortably and completely miserable.

Dombey and Son

MR PODSNAP was well to do, and stood very high in Mr Podsnap's opinion. Beginning with a good inheritance, he had married a good inheritance, and had thriven exceedingly in the Marine Insurance way, and was quite satisfied. He never could make out why everybody was not quite satisfied, and he felt conscious that he set a brilliant social example in being particularly well satisfied with most things, and, above all other things, with himself.

Thus happily acquainted with his own merit and importance, Mr Podsnap settled that whatever he put behind him he put out of existence. There was a dignified conclusiveness—not to add a grand convenience—in this way of getting rid of disagreeables, which had done much towards establishing Mr Podsnap in his lofty place in Mr Podsnap's satisfaction. "I don't want to know about it; I don't choose to discuss it; I don't admit it!" Mr Podsnap had even acquired a peculiar flourish of his right arm in often clearing the world of its most difficult problems, by sweeping them behind him (and consequently sheer away) with those words and a flushed face. For they affronted him.

Mr Podsnap's world was not a very large world, morally; no, nor even geographically: seeing that although his business was sustained upon commerce with other countries, he considered other countries, with that important reservation, a mistake, and of their manners and customs would conclusively observe, "Not English!" when, PRESTO! with a flourish of the arm, and a flush of the face, they were swept away. Elsewise, the world got up at eight, shaved close at a quarter-past, breakfasted at nine, went to the City at ten, came home at half-past five, and dined at seven. Mr Podsnap's notions of the Arts in their integrity might have been stated thus. Literature; large print, respectively descriptive of getting up at eight, shaving close at a quarter-past, breakfasting at nine, going to the City at ten, coming home at half-past five, and dining at seven. Painting and Sculpture; models and portraits representing Professors of getting up at eight, shaving close at a quarter-past, breakfasting at nine, going to the City at ten, coming home at half-past five, and dining at seven. Music; a respectable performance (without variations) on stringed and wind instruments, sedately expressive of getting up at eight, shaving close at a quarter-past, breakfasting at nine, going to the City at ten, coming home at half-past five, and dining at seven. Nothing else to be permitted to those same vagrants the Arts, on pain of excommunication. Nothing else To Be—anywhere!

As a so eminently respectable man, Mr Podsnap was sensible of its being required of him to take Providence under his protection. Consequently he always knew exactly what Providence meant. Inferior and less respectable men might fall short of that mark, but Mr Podsnap was always up to it. And it was very remarkable (and must have been very comfortable) that what Providence meant, was invariably what Mr Podsnap meant.

These may be said to have been the articles of a faith and school which the present chapter takes the liberty of calling, after its representative man, Podsnappery. They were confined within close bounds, as Mr Podsnap's own head was confined by his shirt-collar; and they were enunciated with a sounding pomp that smacked of the creaking of Mr Podsnap's own boots.

There was a Miss Podsnap. And this young rocking-horse was being trained in her mother's art of prancing in a stately manner without ever getting on. But the high parental action was not yet imparted to her, and in truth she was but an undersized damsel, with high shoulders, low spirits, chilled elbows, and a rasped surface of nose, who seemed to take occasional frosty peeps out of childhood into womanhood, and to shrink back again, overcome by her mother's head-dress and her father from head to foot—crushed by the mere dead-weight of Podsnappery.

A certain institution in Mr Podsnap's mind which he called "the young person" may be considered to have been embodied in Miss Podsnap, his daughter. It was an inconvenient and exacting institution, as requiring everything in the universe to be filed down and fitted to it. The question about everything was, would it bring a blush into the cheek of the young person? And the inconvenience of the young person was, that, according to Mr Podsnap, she seemed always liable to burst into blushes when there was no need at all. There appeared to be no line of demarcation between the young person's excessive innocence, and another person's guiltiest knowledge. Take Mr Podsnap's word for it, and the soberest tints of drab, white, lilac, and grey, were all flaming red to this troublesome Bull of a young person.

The Podsnaps lived in a shady angle adjoining Portman Square. They were a kind of people certain to dwell in the shade, wherever they dwelt. Miss Podsnap's life had been, from her first appearance on this planet, altogether of a shady order; for, Mr Podsnap's young person was likely to get little good out of association with other young persons, and had therefore been restricted to companionship with not very congenial older persons, and with massive furniture. Miss Podsnap's early views of life being principally derived from the reflections of it in her father's boots, and in the walnut and rosewood tables of the dim drawing-rooms, and in their swarthy giants of looking-glasses, were of a sombre cast; and it was not wonderful that now when she was on most days solemnly tooled through the Park by the side of her mother in a great tall custard-coloured phaeton, she showed above the apron of that vehicle like a dejected young person sitting up in bed to take a startled look at things in general, and very strongly desiring to get her head under the counterpane again.

Said Mr Podsnap to Mrs Podsnap, "Georgiana is almost eighteen."

Said Mrs Podsnap to Mr Podsnap, assenting, "Almost eighteen."

Said Mr Podsnap then to Mrs Podsnap, "Really I think we should have some people on Georgiana's birthday."

Said Mrs Podsnap then to Mr Podsnap, "Which will enable us to clear off all those people who are due."

So it came to pass that Mr and Mrs Podsnap requested the honour of the company of seventeen friends of their souls at dinner; and that they substituted other friends of their souls for such of the seventeen original friends of their souls as deeply regretted that a prior engagement prevented their having the honour of dining with Mr and Mrs Podsnap, in pursuance of their kind invitation; and that Mrs Podsnap said of all of these inconsolable personages, as she checked them off with a pencil in her list. "Asked at any rate, and got rid of;" and that they successfully disposed of a good many friends of their souls in this way, and felt their consciences much lightened.

There were still other friends of their souls who were not entitled to be asked to dinner, but had a claim to be invited to come and take a haunch of mutton vapour-bath at half-past nine. For the clearing off of these worthies, Mrs Podsnap added a small and early evening to the dinner, and looked in at the music-shop to bespeak a well conducted automaton to come and play quadrilles for a carpet dance.

Mr and Mrs Veneering and Mr and Mrs Veneering's bran-new bride and bridegroom, were of the dinner company; but the Podsnap establishment had nothing else in common with the Veneerings. Mr Podsnap could tolerate taste in a mush-room man who stood in need of that sort of thing, but was far above it himself. Hideous solidity was the characteristic of the Podsnap plate. Everything was made to look as heavy as it could, and to take up as much room as possible. Everything said boastfully, "Here you have as much of me in my ugliness as if I were only lead; but I am so many ounces of precious metal worth so much an ounce;—wouldn't you like to melt me down?" A corpulent straddling epergne, blotched all over as if it had broken out in an eruption rather than been ornamented, delivered this address from an unsightly silver platform in the centre of the table. Four silver wine-coolers, each furnished with four staring heads, each head obtrusively carrying a big silver ring in each of its ears, conveyed the sentiment up and down the table, and handed it on to the pot-belled silver salt-cellars. All the big silver spoons and forks widened the mouths of the company expressly for the purpose of thrusting the sentiment down their throats with every morsel they ate.

The majority of the guests were like the plate, and included several heavy articles weighing ever so much. But there was a foreign gentleman among them: whom Mr Podsnap had in-invited after much debate with himself—believing the whole European continent to be in mortal alliance against the young person—and there was a droll disposition, not only on the part of Mr Podsnap, but of everybody else, to treat him as if he were a child who was hard of hearing.

As a delicate concession to this unfortunately-born foreigner, Mr Podsnap, in receiving him, had presented his wife as "Madame Podsnap"; also his daughter as "Mademoiselle Podsnap," with some inclination to add "ma fille," in which bold venture, however, he checked himself. The Veneerings being at that time the only other arrivals, he had added (in a condescendingly explanatory manner), "Monsieur Vey-nair-reeng," and had then subsided into English.

"How do you like London?" Mr Podsnap now inquired from his station of host, as if he were administering something in the nature of a powder or potion to the deaf child; "London, Londres, London?"

The foreign gentleman admired it.

"You find it Very Large?" said Mr Podsnap, spaciously.

The foreign gentleman found it very large.

"And Very Rich?"

The foreign gentleman found it, without doubt, enormément riche.

"Enormously Rich, We say," returned Mr Podsnap, in a condescending manner. "Our English adverbs do Not terminate in Mong, and We Pronounce the 'ch' as if there were a 't' before it. We say Ritch."

"Reetch," remarked the foreign gentleman.

"And Do You Find, Sir," pursued Mr Podsnap, with dignity, "Many Evidences that Strike You, of our British Constitution in the Streets of The World's Metropolis, London, Londres, London?"

The foreign gentleman begged to be pardoned, but did not altogether understand.

"The Constitution Britannique," Mr Podsnap explained, as if he were teaching in an infant school. "We Say British, But You Say Britannique, You Know" (forgivingly, as if that were not his fault). "The Constitution, Sir."

The foreign gentleman said, "Mais, yees; I know eem."

A youngish sallowish gentleman in spectacles, with a lumpy forehead, seated in a supplementary chair at a corner of the table, here caused a profound sensation by saying, in a raised voice, "ESKER," and then stopping dead.

"Mais oui," said the foreign gentleman, turning towards him. "Est-ce que? Quoi donc?"

But the gentleman with the lumpy forehead having for the time delivered himself of all that he found behind his lumps, spake for the time no more.

"I Was Inquiring," said Mr Podsnap, resuming the thread of his discourse, "Whether You Have Observed in our Streets as We should say, Upon our Pavvy as You would say, any Tokens . . ."

The foreign gentleman with patient courtesy entreated pardon; "But what was tokenz?"

"Marks," said Mr Podsnap; "Signs, you know, Appearances—Traces."

"Ah! Of a Orse?" inquired the foreign gentleman.

"We call it Horse," said Mr Podsnap, with forbearance. "In England, Angleterre, England, We Aspirate the 'H', and We Say 'Horse.' Only our Lower Classes Say 'Orse!' "

"Pardon," said the foreign gentleman; "I am alwiz wrong!"

"Our Language," said Mr Podsnap, with a gracious consciousness of being always right, "is Difficult. Ours is a copious Language, and Trying to Strangers. I will not Pursue my Question."

But the lumpy gentleman, unwilling to give it up, again madly said, "ESKER," and again spake no more.

"It merely referred," Mr Podsnap explained, with a sense of meritorious proprietorship, "to Our Constitution, Sir. We Englishmen are Very Proud of our Constitution, Sir. It Was Bestowed Upon Us By Providence. No Other Country is so Favoured as This Country."

"And ozer countries?"—— the foreign gentleman was beginning, when Mr Podsnap put him right again.

"We do not say Ozer; we say Other: the letters are 'T' and 'H'; you say Tay and Aish, You Know;" (still with clemency). "The sound is 'th'—'th'!"

"And *other* countries," said the foreign gentleman. "They do how?"

"They do, Sir," returned Mr Podsnap, gravely shaking his head; "they do—I am sorry to be obliged to say it—*as* they do."

"It was a little particular of Providence," said the foreign gentleman, laughing; "for the frontier is not large."

"Undoubtedly," assented Mr Podsnap; "But So it is. It was the Charter of the Land. This Island was Blest, Sir, to the Direct Exclusion of such Other Countries as—as there may happen to be. And if we were all Englishmen present, I would say," added Mr Podsnap, looking round upon his compatriots, and sounding solemnly with his theme, "that there is in the Englishman a combination of qualities, a modesty, an independence, a responsibility, a repose, combined with an absence of everything calculated to call a blush into the cheek of a young person, which one would seek in vain among the Nations of the Earth."

Our Mutual Friend

THE court was paved, from floor to roof, with human faces. Inquisitive and eager eyes peered from every inch of space. From the rail before the dock, away into the sharpest angle of the smallest corner in the galleries, all looks were fixed upon one man—Fagin. Before him and behind: above, below, on the right and on the left: he seemed to stand surrounded by a firmament, all bright with gleaming eyes.

He stood there, in all this glare of living light, with one hand resting on the wooden slab before him, the other held to his ear, and his head thrust forward to enable him to catch with greater distinctness every word that fell from the presiding judge, who was delivering his charge to the jury. At times he turned his eyes sharply upon them to observe the effect of the slightest featherweight in his favour; and when the points against him were stated with terrible distinctness, looked towards his counsel, in mute appeal that he would, even then, urge something in his behalf. Beyond these manifestations of anxiety he stirred not hand or foot. He had scarcely moved since the trial began; and now that the judge ceased to speak he still remained in the same strained attitude of close attention, with his gaze bent on him, as though he listened still.

A slight bustle in the court recalled him to himself. Looking round, he saw that the jurymen had turned together, to consider of their verdict. As his eyes wandered to the gallery he could see the people rising above each other to see his face, some hastily applying their glasses to their eyes, and others whispering their neighbours with looks expressive of abhorrence. A few there were who seemed unmindful of him, and looked only to the jury, in impatient wonder how they could delay. But in no one face—not even among the women, of whom there were many there—could he read the faintest sympathy with himself, or any feeling but one of all-absorbing interest that he should be condemned.

As he saw all this in one bewildered glance the death-like stillness came again, and looking back, he saw that the jurymen had turned towards the judge. Hush!

They only sought permission to retire.

He looked, wistfully, into their faces, one by one, when they passed out, as though to see which way the greater number leant; but that was fruitless. The jailer touched him on the shoulder. He followed mechanically to the end of the dock, and sat down on a chair. The man pointed it out, or he would not have seen it.

He looked up into the gallery again. Some of the people were eating, and some fanning themselves with handkerchiefs; for the crowded place was very hot. There was one young man sketching his face in a little note-book. He wondered whether it was like, and looked on when the artist broke his pencil-point, and made another with his knife, as any idle spectator might have done.

In the same way, when he turned his eyes towards the judge, his mind began to busy itself with the fashion of his dress, and what it cost, and how he put it on. There was an old fat gentleman on the bench, too, who had gone out, some half-an-hour before, and now come back. He wondered within himself whether this man had been to get his dinner, what he had had, and where he had had it; and pursued this train of careless thought until some new object caught his eye and roused another.

Not that, all this time, his mind was, for an instant, free from one oppressive overwhelming sense of the grave that opened at his feet; it was ever present to him, but in a vague and general way, and he could not fix his thoughts upon it. Thus, even while he trembled, and turned burning hot at the idea of speedy death, he fell to counting the iron spikes before him, and wondering how the head of one had been broken off, and whether they would mend it, or leave it as it was. Then he thought of all the horrors of the gallows and the scaffold—and stopped to watch a man sprinkling the floor to cool it—and then went on to think again.

At length there was a cry of silence, and a breathless look from all towards the door. The jury returned, and passed him close. He could glean nothing from their faces; they might as well have been of stone. Perfect stillness ensued—not a rustle—not a breath—Guilty.

The building rang with a tremendous shout, and another, and another, and then it echoed loud groans, that gathered strength as they swelled out, like angry thunder. It was a peal of joy from the populace outside, greeting the news that he would die on Monday.

The noise subsided, and he was asked if he had anything to say why sentence of death should not be passed upon him. He had resumed his listening attitude, and looked intently at his questioner while the demand was made; but it was twice repeated before he seemed to hear it, and then he only muttered that he was an old man—an old man—an old man—and so, dropping into a whisper, was silent again.

The judge assumed the black cap, and the prisoner still stood with the same air and gesture. A woman in the gallery uttered some exclamation, called forth by this dread solemnity; he looked hastily up as if angry at the interruption, and bent forward yet more attentively. The address was solemn and impressive; the sentence fearful to hear. But he stood like a marble figure, without the motion of a nerve. His haggard face was still thrust forward, his under-jaw hanging down, and his eyes staring out before him, when the jailer put his hand upon his arm, and beckoned him away. He gazed stupidly at him for an instant, and obeyed.

They led him through a paved room under the court, where some prisoners were waiting till their turns came, and others were talking to their friends, who crowded round a grate which looked into the open yard. There was nobody there to speak to *him*; but, as he passed the prisoners fell back to render him more visible to the people who were clinging to the bars: and they assailed him with opprobrious names, and screeched and hissed. He shook his fist, and would have spat upon them; but his conductors hurried him on through a gloomy passage, lighted by a few dim lamps, into the interior of the prison.

Here he was searched, that he might not have about him the means of anticipating the law; this ceremony performed, they led him to one of the condemned cells, and left him there—alone.

He sat down on a stone bench opposite the door, which served for seat and bedstead; and casting his bloodshot eyes upon the ground, tried to collect his thoughts. After a while, he began to remember a few disjointed fragments of what the judge had said: though it had seemed to him, at the time, that he could not hear a word. These gradually fell into their proper places, and by degrees suggested more: so that in a little time he had the whole, almost as it was delivered. To be hanged by the neck till he was dead—that was the end. To be hanged by the neck till he was dead.

As it came on very dark he began to think of all the men he had known who had died upon the scaffold; some of them through his means. They rose up, in such quick succession, he could hardly count them. He had seen some of them die—and had joked, too, because they died with prayers upon their lips. With what a rattling noise the drop went down; and how suddenly they changed from strong and vigorous men to dangling heaps of clothes!

Some of them might have inhabited that very cell—sat upon that very spot. It was very dark; why didn't they bring a light? The cell had been built for many years. Scores of men must have passed their last hours there. It was like sitting in a vault strewn with dead bodies—the cap, the noose, the pinioned arms, the faces that he knew, even beneath that hideous veil.—Light, light!

At length, when his hands were raw with beating against the heavy door and walls, two men appeared: one bearing a candle, which he thrust into an iron candlestick fixed against the wall: the other dragging in a mattress on which to pass the night; for the prisoner was to be left alone no more.

Then came night—dark, dismal, silent night. Other watchers are glad to hear the church-clocks strike, for they tell of life and coming day. To him they brought despair. The boom of every iron bell came laden with the one deep, hollow sound—Death. What availed the noise and bustle of cheerful morning, which penetrated even there, to him? It was another form of knell, with mockery added to the warning.

The day passed off. Day? There was no day; it was gone as soon as come—and night came on again; night so long, and yet so short; long in its dreadful silence, and short in its fleeting hours. At one time he raved and blasphemed; and at another howled and tore his hair. Venerable men of his own persuasion had come to pray beside him, but he had driven them away with curses. They renewed their charitable efforts, and he beat them off.

Saturday night. He had only one night more to live. And as he thought of this the day broke—Sunday.

It was not until the night of this last awful day that a withering sense of his helpless, desperate state came in its full intensity upon his blighted soul; not that he had ever held any defined or positive hope of mercy, but that he had never been able to consider more than the dim probability of dying so soon. He had spoken little to either of the two men, who relieved each other in their attendance upon him: and they, for their parts, made no effort to rouse his attention. He had sat there, awake, but dreaming. Now, he started up, every minute, and with gasping mouth and burning skin, hurried to and fro, in such a paroxysm of fear and wrath that even they—used to such sights—recoiled from him with horror. He grew so terrible, at last, in all the tortures of his evil conscience, that one man could not bear to sit there, eyeing him alone; and so the two kept watch together.

He cowered down upon his stone bed, and thought of the past. He had been wounded with some missiles from the crowd on the day of his capture, and his head was bandaged with a linen cloth. His red hair hung down upon his bloodless face; his beard was torn and twisted into knots; his eyes shone with a terrible light; his unwashed flesh crackled with the fever that burnt him up. Eight—nine—ten. If it was not a trick to frighten him, and those were the real hours treading on each other's heels, where would he be when they came round again! Eleven! Another struck, before the voice of the previous hour had ceased to vibrate. At eight he would be the only mourner in his own funeral train; at eleven——

Those dreadful walls of Newgate, which have hidden so much misery and such unspeakable anguish, not only from the eyes, but, too often, and too long, from the thoughts, of men, never held so dread a spectacle as that. The few who lingered as they passed, and wondered what the man was doing who was to be hanged tomorrow, would have slept but ill that night, if they could have seen him.

Oliver Twist

"BY the bye, what is your name, my good soul? You are called Hugh, I know, of course—your other name?"

"I have no other name."

"A very strange fellow! Do you mean that you never knew one, or that you don't choose to tell it? Which?"

"I'd tell it if I could," said Hugh, quickly. "I can't. I have been always called Hugh; nothing more. I never knew, nor saw, nor thought about a father; and I was a boy of six—that's not very old—when they hung my mother up at Tyburn for a couple of thousand men to stare at. They might have let her live. She was poor enough."

"How very sad!" exclaimed his patron, with a condescending smile. "I have no doubt she was an exceedingly fine woman."

"You see that dog of mine?" said Hugh, abruptly.

"Faithful, I dare say?" rejoined his patron, looking at him through his glass; "and immensely clever? Virtuous and gifted animals, whether man or beast, always are so very hideous."

"Such a dog as that, and one of the same breed, was the only living thing except me that howled that day," said Hugh. "Out of the two thousand odd—there was a larger crowd for its being a woman—the dog and I alone had any pity. If he'd have been a man, he'd have been glad to be quit of her, for she had been forced to keep him lean and half-starved; but being a dog, and not having a man's sense, he was sorry."

"It was dull of the brute, certainly," said Mr Chester, "and very like a brute."

Barnaby Rudge

MONSEIGNEUR, one of the great lords in power at the Court, held his fortnightly reception in his grand hotel in Paris. Monseigneur was in his inner room, his sanctuary of sanctuaries, the Holiest of Holiests to the crowd of worshippers in the suite of rooms without. Monseigneur was about to take his chocolate. Monseigneur could swallow a great many things with ease, and was by some few sullen minds supposed to be rather rapidly swallowing France; but, his morning's chocolate could not so much as get into the throat of Monseigneur, without the aid of four strong men besides the Cook.

Yes, it took four men, all four a-blaze with gorgeous decoration, and the Chief of them unable to exist with fewer than two gold watches in his pocket, emulative of the noble and chaste fashion set by Monseigneur, to conduct the happy chocolate to Monseigneur's lips. One lacquey carried the chocolate-pot into the sacred presence; a second, milled and frothed the chocolate with the little instrument he bore for that function; a third, presented the favoured napkin; a fourth (he of the two gold watches), poured the chocolate out. It was impossible for Monseigneur to dispense with one of these attendants on the chocolate and hold his high place under the admiring Heavens. Deep would have been the blot upon his escutcheon if his chocolate had been ignobly waited on by only three men; he must have died of two.

A Tale of Two Cities

QUITE unconscious that his master was looking on from the dark corner by the parlour door, Sim threw off the paper cap, sprang from his seat, and in two extraordinary steps, something between skating and minuet dancing, bounded to a washing-place at the other end of the shop, and there removed from his face and hands all traces of his previous work—practising the same step all the time with the utmost gravity. This done, he drew from some concealed place a little scrap of looking-glass, and with its assistance arranged his hair, and ascertained the exact state of a little carbuncle on his nose. Having now completed his toilet, he placed the fragment of mirror on a low bench, and looked over his shoulder at so much of his legs as could be reflected in that small compass, with the greatest possible complacency and satisfaction.

Sim, as he was called in the locksmith's family, or Mr Simon Tappertit, as he called himself, and required all men to style him out of doors, on holidays, and Sundays out,—was an old-fashioned, thin-faced, sleek-haired, sharp-nosed, small-eyed little fellow, very little more than five feet high, and thoroughly convinced in his own mind that he was above the middle size; rather tall, in fact, than otherwise. Of his figure, which was well enough formed, though somewhat of the leanest, he entertained the highest admiration; and with his legs, which, in knee-breeches, were perfect curiosities of littleness, he was enraptured to a degree amounting to enthusiasm. He also had some majestic, shadowy ideas, which had never been quite fathomed by his most intimate friends, concerning the power of his eye. Indeed he had been known to go so far as to boast that he could utterly quell and subdue the haughtiest beauty by a simple process, which he termed "eyeing her over"; but it must be added, that neither of this faculty, nor of the power he claimed to have, through the same gift, of vanquishing and heaving down dumb animals, even in a rabid state, had he ever furnished evidence which could be deemed quite satisfactory and conclusive.

It may be inferred from these premises, that in the small body of Mr Tappertit there was locked up an amibitious and aspiring soul. As certain liquors, confined in casks too cramped in their dimensions, will ferment, and fret, and chafe in their imprisonment, so the spiritual essence or soul of Mr. Tappertit would sometimes fume within that precious cask, his body, until, with great foam and froth and splutter, it would force a vent, and carry all before it. It was his custom to remark, in reference to any one of these occasions, that his soul had got into his head; and in this novel kind of intoxication many scrapes and mishaps befell him, which he had frequently concealed with no small difficulty from his worthy master.

Sim Tappertit, among the other fancies upon which his before-mentioned soul was for ever feasting and regaling itself (and which fancies, like the liver of Prometheus, grew as they were fed upon), had a mighty notion of his order; and had been heard by the servant-maid openly expressing his regret that the 'prentices no longer carried clubs wherewith to mace the citizens: that was his strong expression. He was likewise reported to have said that in former times a stigma had been cast upon the body by the execution of George Barnwell, to which they should not have basely submitted, but should have demanded him of the legislature—temperately at first; then by an appeal to arms, if necessary—to be dealt with as they in their wisdom might think fit. These thoughts always led him to consider what a glorious engine the 'prentices might yet become if they had but a master spirit at their head; and then he would darkly, and to the terror of his hearers, hint at certain reckless fellows that he knew of, and at a certain Lion Heart ready to become their captain, who, once afoot, would make the Lord Mayor tremble on his throne.

In respect of dress and personal decoration, Sim Tappertit was no less of an adventurous and enterprising character. He had been seen, beyond dispute, to pull off ruffles of the finest quality at the corner of the street on Sunday nights, and to put them carefully in his pocket before returning home; and it was quite notorious that on all great holiday occasions it was his habit to exchange his plain steel knee-buckles for a pair of glittering paste, under cover of a friendly post, planted most conveniently in that same spot. Add to this that he was in years just twenty, in his looks much older, and in conceit at least two hundred; that he had no obection to be jested with, touching his admiration of his master's daughter; and had even, when called upon at a certain obscure tavern to pledge the lady whom he honoured with his love, toasted, with many winks and leers, a fair creature whose Christian name, he said, began with a D—;—and as much is known of Sim Tappertit, who has by this time followed the locksmith in to breakfast, as is necessary to be known in making his acquaintance.

Barnaby Rudge

MRS Merdle's first husband had been a colonel, under whose auspices the bosom had entered into competition with the snows of North America, and had come off at little disadvantage in point of whiteness, and at none in point of coldness. The colonel's son was Mrs Merdle's only child. He was of a chuckle-headed high-shouldered make, with a general appearance of being, not so much a young man as a swelled boy. He had given so few signs of reason, that a by-word went among his companions that his brain had been frozen up in a mighty frost which prevailed at St John's, New Brunswick, at the period of his birth there, and had never thawed from that hour. Another by-word represented him as having in his infancy, through the negligence of a nurse, fallen out of a high window on his head, which had been heard by responsible witnesses to crack. It is probable that both these representations were of ex post facto origin; the young gentleman (whose expressive name was Sparkler) being monomaniacal in offering marriage to all manner of undesirable young ladies, and in remarking of every successive young lady to whom he tendered a matrimonial proposal that she was "a doosed fine gal—well educated too—with no biggodd nonsense about her."

Little Dorrit

AT the first stroke of twelve the prison bell began to toll. Then the roar—mingled now with cries of "Hats off!" and "Poor fellows!" and, from some specks in the great concourse, with a shriek or groan—burst forth again. It was terrible to see—if any one in that distraction of excitement could have seen—the world of eager eyes, all strained upon the scaffold and the beam.

The hollow murmuring was heard within the jail as plainly as without. The three were brought forth into the yard, together, as it resounded through the air; and knew its import well.

"D'ye hear?" cried Hugh, undaunted by the sound. "They expect us! I heard them gathering when I woke in the night, and turned over on t'other side and fell asleep again. We shall see how they welcome the hangman, now that it comes home to him. Ha, ha, ha!"

The Ordinary coming up at this moment, reproved him for his indecent mirth, and advised him to alter his demeanour.

"And why, master?" said Hugh. "Can I do better than bear it easily? *You* bear it easily enough. Oh! never tell me," he cried, as the other would have spoken, "for all your sad look and your solemn air, you think little enough of it! They say you're the best maker of lobster salads in London. Ha, ha, ha! I've heard that, you see, before now. Is it a good one, this morning—is your hand in? How does the breakfast look? I hope there's enough, and to spare, for all this hungry company that'll sit down to it, when the sight's over."

"I fear," observed the clergyman, shaking his head, "that you are incorrigible."

"You're right. I am," rejoined Hugh, sternly. "Be no hypocrite, master! You make a merry-making of this, every month; let me be merry, too. If you want a frightened fellow there's one that'll suit you. Try your hand upon him."

He pointed, as he spoke, to Dennis, who, with his legs trailing on the ground, was held between two men; and who trembled so, that all his joints and limbs seemed racked by spasms. Turning from this wretched spectacle, he called to Barnaby, who stood apart.

"What cheer, Barnaby? Don't be downcast, lad. Leave that to *him*."

"Bless you," cried Barnaby, stepping lightly towards him, "I'm not frightened, Hugh. I'm quite happy. I wouldn't desire to live now, if they'd let me. Look at me! Am I afraid to die? Will they see *me* tremble?"

Hugh gazed for a moment at his face, on which there was a strange, unearthly smile; and at his eye, which sparkled brightly; and interposing between him and the Ordinary, gruffly whispered to the latter:

"I wouldn't say much to him, master, if I was you. He may spoil your appetite for breakfast, though you *are* used to it."

Barnaby Rudge

THE subject that worked in Mr Willet's mind, and occasioned these demonstrations, was no other than his son's bodily disfigurement, which he had never yet got himself thoroughly to believe, or comprehend. Shortly after their first meeting, he had been observed to wander, in a state of great perplexity, to the kitchen, and to direct his gaze towards the fire, as if in search of his usual adviser in all matters of doubt and difficulty. But there being no boiler at the Black Lion, and the rioters having so beaten and battered his own that it was quite unfit for further service, he wandered out again, in a perfect bog of uncertainty and mental confusion, and in that state took the strangest means of resolving his doubts: such as feeling the sleeve of his son's greatcoat as deeming it possible that his arm might be there; looking at his own arms and those of everybody else, as if to assure himself that two and not one was the usual allowance; sitting by the hour together in a brown study, as if he were endeavouring to recall Joe's image in his younger days, and to remember whether he really had in those times one arm or a pair; and employing himself in many other speculations of the same kind.

Finding himself at this supper, surrounded by faces with which he had been so well acquainted in old times, Mr Willet recurred to the subject with uncommon vigour; apparently resolved to understand it now or never. Sometimes, after every two or three mouthfuls, he laid down his knife and fork, and stared at his son with all his might—particularly at his maimed side; then, he looked slowly round the table until he caught some person's eye, when he shook his head with great solemnity, patted his shoulder, winked, or as one may say—for winking was a very slow process with him—went to sleep with one eye for a minute or two; and so, with another solemn shaking of his head, took up his knife and fork again, and went on eating. Sometimes he put his food into his mouth abstractedly, and, with all his faculties concentrated on Joe, gazed at him in a fit of stupefaction as he cut his meat with one hand, until he was recalled to himself by symptoms of choking on his own part, and was by that means restored to consciousness. At other times he resorted to such small devices as asking him for the salt, the pepper, the vinegar, the mustard—anything that was on his maimed side—and watching him as he handed it. By dint of these experiments, he did at last so satisfy and convince himself, that, after a longer silence than he had yet maintained, he laid down his knife and fork on either side his plate, drank a long draught from a tankard beside him still keeping his eyes on Joe, and, leaning backward in his chair and fetching a long breath, said, as he looked all round the board:

"It's been took off!"

"By George!" said the Black Lion, striking the table with his hand, "he's got it!"

"Yes, sir," said Mr Willet, with the look of a man who felt that he had earned a compliment, and deserved it. "That's where it is. It's been took off."

"Tell him where it was done," said the Black Lion to Joe.

"At the defence of the Savannah, father."

"At the defence of the Salwanners," repeated Mr Willet, softly; again looking round the table.

"In America, where the war is," said Joe.

"In America where the war is," repeated Mr Willet. "It was took off in the defence of the Salwanners in America where the war is." Continuing to repeat these words to himself in a low tone of voice (the same information had been conveyed to him in the same terms, at least fifty times before), Mr Willet arose from table; walked round to Joe; felt his empty sleeve all the way up, from the cuff, to where the stump of his arm remained; shook his hand; lighted his pipe at the fire, took a long whiff, walked to the door; turned round once when he had reached it, wiped his left eye with the back of his forefinger, and said, in a faltering voice: 'My son's arm—was took off—at the defence of the—Salwanners—in America—where the war is"—with which he withdrew, and returned no more that night.

Barnaby Rudge

"AN idiot, eh?" said the gentleman, looking at Barnaby as he spoke. "And how long hast thou been an idiot?"

"She knows," was Barnaby's timid answer, pointing to his mother—"I—always, I believe."

"From his birth," said the widow.

"I don't believe it," cried the gentleman, "not a bit of it. It's an excuse not to work. There's nothing like flogging to cure that disorder. I'd make a difference in him in ten minutes, I'll be bound."

"Heaven has made none in more than twice ten years, sir," said the widow mildly.

"Then why don't you shut him up? we pay enough for county institutions, damn 'em. But thou'd rather drag him about to excite charity—of course. Ay, I know thee."

Now, this gentleman had various endearing appellations among his intimate friends. By some he was called "a country gentleman of the true school," by some "a fine old country gentleman," by some "a sporting gentleman," by some "a thorough-bred Englishman," by some "a genuine John Bull"; but they all agreed in one respect, and that was, that it was a pity there were not more like him, and that because there were not, the country was going to rack and ruin every day. He was in the commission of the peace, and could write his name almost legibly; but his greatest qualifications were, that he was more severe with poachers, was a better shot, a harder rider, had better horses, kept better dogs, could eat more solid food, drink more strong wine, go to bed every night more drunk and get up every morning more sober, than any man in the county. In knowledge of horseflesh he was almost equal to a farrier, in stable learning he surpassed his own head groom, and in gluttony not a pig on his estate was a match for him. He had no seat in Parliament himself, but he was extremely patriotic, and usually drove his voters up to the poll with his own hands. He was warmly attached to the Church, and never appointed to the living in his gift any but a three-bottle man and a first-rate fox-hunter. He mistrusted the honesty of all poor people who could read and write, and had a secret jealousy of his own wife (a young lady whom he had married for what his friends called "the good old English reason," that her father's property adjoined his own) for possessing those accomplishments in a greater degree than himself. In short, Barnaby being an idiot, and Grip a creature of mere brute instinct, it would be very hard to say what this gentleman was.

Barnaby Rudge

PERHAPS there never was a man, in this troublesome world, so troublesome for the imagination to picture as a boy. And yet he had changed very little in his progress through life. Confronting him, in the room in which he sat, was a boy's portrait, which anybody seeing him would have identified as Master Christopher Casby, aged ten: though disguised with a haymaking rake, for which he had had, at any time, as much taste or use as for a diving-bell; and sitting (on one of his own legs) upon a bank of violets, moved to precocious contemplation by the spire of a village church. There was the same smooth face and forehead, the same calm blue eye, the same placid air. The shining bald head, which looked so very large because it shone so much; and the long grey hair at its sides and back, like floss silk or spun glass, which looked so very benevolent because it was never cut; were not, of course, to be seen in the boy as in the old man. Nevertheless, in the Seraphic creature with the haymaking rake, were clearly to be discerned the rudiments of the Patriarch with the list shoes.

Patriarch was the name which many people delighted to give him. Various old ladies in the neighbourhood spoke of him as The Last of the Patriarchs. So grey, so slow, so quiet, so impassionate, so very bumpy in the head, Patriarch was the word for him. He had been accosted in the streets, and respectfully solicited to become a Patriarch for painters and for sculptors; with so much importunity, in sooth, that it would appear to be beyond the Fine Arts to remember the points of a Patriarch, or to invent one. Philanthropists of both sexes had asked who he was, and on being informed, "Old Christopher Casby, formerly Town-agent to Lord Decimus Tite Barnacle," had cried in a rapture of disappointment, "Oh! why, with that head, is he not a benefactor to his species! Oh! why, with that head, is he not a father to the orphan and a friend to the friendless!" With that head, however, he remained old Christopher Casby, proclaimed by common report rich in house property; and with that head, he now sat in his silent parlour. Indeed it would be the height of unreason to expect him to be sitting there without that head.

Little Dorrit

And the Feminine

MR PECKSNIFF had been to the undertaker, and was now upon his way to another officer in the train of mourning: a female functionary, a nurse, and watcher, and performer of nameless offices about the persons of the dead: whom he had recommended. Her name, as Mr Pecksniff gathered from a scrap of writing in his hand, was Gamp; her residence in Kingsgate Street, High Holborn. So Mr Pecksniff, in a hackney cab, was rattling over Holborn stones, in quest of Mrs Gamp.

This lady lodged at a bird-fancier's, next door but one to the celebrated mutton-pie shop, and directly opposite to the original cat's meat warehouse; the renown of which establishments was duly heralded on their respective fronts. It was a little house, and this was the more convenient; for Mrs Gamp being, in her highest walk of art, a monthly nurse, or, as her sign-board boldly had it, "Midwife," and lodging in the first-floor front, was easily assailable at night by pebbles, walking-sticks, and fragments of tobacco-pipe: all much more efficacious than the street-door knocker, which was so constructed as to wake the street with ease, and even spread alarms of fire in Holborn, without making the smallest impression on the premises to which it was addressed.

It chanced on this particular occasion, that Mrs Gamp had been up all the previous night, in attendance upon a ceremony to which the usage of gossips has given that name which expresses, in two syllables, the curse pronounced on Adam. It chanced that Mrs Gamp had not been regularly engaged, but had been called in at a crisis, in consequence of her great repute, to assist another professional lady with her advice; and thus it happened that, all points of interest in the case being over, Mrs Gamp had come home again to the bird-fancier's, and gone to bed. So when Mr Pecksniff drove up in the hackney cab, Mrs Gamp's curtains were drawn close, and Mrs Gamp was fast asleep behind them.

If the bird-fancier had been at home, as he ought to have been, there would have been no great harm in this; but he was out, and his shop was closed. The shutters were down certainly; and in every pane of glass there was at least one tiny bird in a tiny bird-cage, twittering and hopping his little ballet of despair, and knocking his head against the roof: while one unhappy goldfinch who lived outside a red villa with his name on the door, drew the water for his own drinking, and mutely appealed to some good man to drop a farthing's-worth of poison in it. Still, the door was shut. Mr Pecksniff tried the latch, and shook it, causing a cracked bell inside to ring most mournfully; but no one came. The bird-fancier was an easy shaver also, and a fashionable hairdresser also; and perhaps he had been sent for, express, from the court end of the town, to trim a lord, or cut and curl a lady; but however that might be, there, upon his own ground, he was not; nor was there any more distinct trace of him to assist the imagination of an inquirer, than a professional print or emblem of his calling (much favoured in the trade), representing a hairdresser of easy manners curling a lady of distinguished fashion, in the presence of a patent upright grand pianoforte.

Noting these circumstances, Mr Pecksniff, in the innocence of his heart, applied himself to the knocker; but at the first double knock every window in the street became alive with female heads; and before he could repeat the performance whole troops of married ladies (some about to trouble Mrs Gamp themselves very shortly) came flocking round the steps, all crying out with one accord, and with uncommon interest, "Knock at the winder, sir, knock at the winder. Lord bless you, don't lose no more time than you can help; knock at the winder!"

Acting upon this suggestion, and borrowing the driver's whip for the purpose, Mr Pecksniff soon made a commotion among the first-floor flower-pots and roused Mrs Gamp, whose voice—to the great satisfaction of the matrons—was heard to say, "I'm coming."

"He's as pale as a muffin," said one lady, in allusion to Mr Pecksniff.

"So he ought to be, if he's the feelings of a man," observed another.

A third lady (with her arms folded) said she wished he had chosen any other time for fetching Mrs Gamp, but it always happened so with *her*.

It gave Mr Pecksniff much uneasiness to find, from these remarks, that he was supposed to have come to Mrs Gamp upon an errand touching—not the close of life, but the other end. Mrs Gamp herself was under the same impression, for throwing open the window, she cried behind the curtains, as she hastily attired herself:

"Is it Mrs Perkins?"

"No!" returned Mr Pecksniff, sharply. "Nothing of the sort."

"What, Mr Whilks!" cried Mrs Gamp. "Don't say it's you, Mr Whilks, and that poor creetur Mrs Whilks with not even a pincushion ready. Don't say it's you, Mr Whilks!"

"It isn't Mr Whilks," said Pecksniff. "I don't know the man. Nothing of the kind. A gentleman is dead; and some person being wanted in the house, you have been recommended by Mr Mould the undertaker."

As she was by this time in a condition to appear, Mrs Gamp, who had a face for all occasions, looked out of the window with her mourning countenance, and said she would be down directly. But the matrons took it very ill that Mr Pecksniff's mission was of so unimportant a kind; and the lady with her arms folded rated him in good round terms, signifying that she would be glad to know what he meant by terrifying delicate females "with his corpses"; and giving it as her opinion that he was quite ugly enough to know better. The other ladies were not at all behind-hand in expressing similar sentiments; and the children, of whom some scores had now collected, hooted and defied Mr Pecksniff quite savagely. So when Mrs Gamp appeared, the unoffending gentleman was glad to hustle her with very little ceremony into the cabriolet, and drive off, overwhelmed with popular execration.

Mrs Gamp had a large bundle with her, a pair of pattens, and a species of gig umbrella; the latter article in colour like a faded leaf, except where a circular patch of a lively blue had been dexterously let in at the top. She was much flurried by the haste she had made, and laboured under the most erroneous views of cabriolets, which she appeared to confound with mail-coaches or stage-waggons, inasmuch as she was constantly endeavouring for the first half mile to force her luggage through the little front window, and clamouring to the driver to "put it in the boot." When she was disabused of this idea, her whole being resolved itself into an absorbing anxiety about her pattens, with which she played innumerable games at quoits on Mr Pecksniff's legs. It was not until they were close upon the house of mourning that she had enough composure to observe:

"And so the gentleman's dead, sir! Ah! The more's the pity." She didn't even know his name. "But it's what we must all come to. It's as certain as being born, except that we can't make our calculations as exact. Ah! Poor dear!"

She was a fat old woman, this Mrs Gamp, with a husky voice and a moist eye, which she had a remarkable power of turning up, and only showing the white of it. Having very little neck, it cost her some trouble to look over herself, if one may say so, at those to whom she talked. She wore a very rusty black gown, rather the worse for snuff, and a shawl and bonnet to correspond. In these dilapidated articles of dress she had, on principle, arrayed herself, time out of mind, on such occasions as the present; for this at once expressed a decent amount of veneration for the deceased, and invited the next of kin to present her with a fresher suit of weeds: an appeal so frequently successful, that the very fetch and ghost of Mrs Gamp, bonnet and all, might be seen hanging up, any hour in the day in at least a dozen of the second-hand clothes shops about Holborn. The face of Mrs Gamp—the nose in particular—was somewhat red and swollen, and it was difficult to enjoy her society without becoming conscious of a smell of spirits. Like most persons who have attained to great eminence in their profession, she took to hers very kindly; insomuch that, setting aside her natural predilections as a woman, she went to a lying-in, or a laying-out with equal zest and relish.

"Ah!" repeated Mrs Gamp; for it was always a safe sentiment in cases of mourning. "Ah, dear! When Gamp was summoned to his long home, and I see him a-lying in Guy's Hospital with a penny-piece on each eye, and his wooden leg under his left arm, I thought I should have fainted away. But I bore up."

If certain whispers current in the Kingsgate Street circles had any truth in them, she had indeed borne up surprisingly; and had exerted such uncommon fortitude as to dispose of Mr Gamp's remains for the benefit of science. But it should be added, in fairness, that this had happened twenty years before; and that Mr and Mrs Gamp had long been separated on the ground of incompatibility of temper in their drink.

"You have become indifferent since then, I suppose?" said Mr Pecksniff. "Use is second nature, Mrs Gamp."

"You may well say second natur, sir," returned that lady. "One's first ways is to find sich things a trial to the feelings, and so is one's lasting custom. If it wasn't for the nerve a little sip of liquor gives me (I never was able to do more than taste it),

I never could go through with what I sometimes has to do. 'Mrs Harris,' I says, at the very last case as ever I acted in, which it was but a young person, 'Mrs Harris,' I says, 'leave the bottle on the chimley-piece and don't ask me to take none, but let me put my lips to it when I am so dispoged, and then I will do what I'm engaged to do, according to the best of my ability,' 'Mrs Gamp,' she says, in answer, 'if there ever was a sober creetur to be got at eighteen pence a day for working people, and three and six for gentlefolks—night watching,' " said Mrs Gamp, with emphasis, ' "being a extra charge—you are that inwallable person.' 'Mrs Harris,' I says to her, 'don't name the charge, for if I could afford to lay all my feller creeturs out for nothink, I would glady do it, sich is the love I bears 'em. But what I always says to them as had the management of matters, Mrs Harris:' " here she kept her eye on Mr Pecksniff: " 'be they gents or be they ladies, is, don't ask me whether I won't take none, or whether I will, but leave the bottle on the chimley-piece, and let me put my lips to it when I am so dispoged.' "

Martin Chuzzlewit

CAPTAIN CUTTLE lived on the brink of a little canal near the India Docks, where there was a swivel bridge which opened now and then to let some wandering monster of a ship come roaming up the street like a stranded leviathan. The gradual change from land to water, on the approach to Captain Cuttle's lodgings, was curious. It began with the erection of flagstaffs, as appurtenances to public-houses; then came slopseller's shops, with Guernsey shirts, sou'wester hats, and canvas pantaloons, at once the tightest and the loosest of their order, hanging up outside. These were succeeded by anchor and chain-cable forges, where sledge-hammers were dinging upon iron all day long. Then came rows of houses, with little vane-surmounted masts uprearing themselves from among the scarlet beans. Then, ditches. Then, pollard willows. Then, more ditches. Then, unaccountable patches of dirty water, hardly to be descried, for the ships that covered them. Then, the air was perfumed with chips; and all other trades were swallowed up in mast, oar, and block making, and boat building. Then, the ground grew marshy and unsettled. Then, there was nothing to be smelt but rum and sugar. Then, Captain Cuttle's lodgings—at once a first floor and a top story, in Brig Place—were close before you.

The Captain was one of those timber-looking men, suits of oak as well as hearts, whom it is almost impossible for the liveliest imagination to separate from any part of their dress, however insignificant. Accordingly, when Walter knocked at the door, and the Captain instantly poked his head out of one of his little front windows, and hailed him, with the hard glazed hat already on it, and the shirt-collar like a sail, and the wide suit of blue, all standing as usual, Walter was as fully persuaded that he was always in that state, as if the Captain had been a bird and those had been his feathers.

"Wal'r, my lad!" said Captain Cuttle. "Stand by and knock again. Hard! It's washing day."

Walter, in his impatience, gave a prodigious thump with the knocker.

"Hard it is!" said Captain Cuttle, and immediately drew in his head, as if he expected a squall.

Nor was he mistaken: for a widow lady, with her sleeves rolled up to the shoulders and her arms frothy with soapsuds and smoking with hot water, replied to the summons with startling rapidity. Before she looked at Walter she looked at the knocker, and then, measuring him with her eyes from head to foot, said she wondered he had left any of it.

"Captain Cuttle's at home, I know," said Walter, with a conciliatory smile.

"Is he?" replied the widow lady. "In-deed!"

"He has just been speaking to me," said Walter in breathless explanation.

"Has he?" replied the widow lady. "Then p'raps you'll give him Mrs MacStinger's respects, and say that the next time he lowers himself and his lodgings by talking out of winder she'll thank him to come down and open the door too." Mrs MacStinger spoke loud, and listened for any observations that might be offered from the first floor.

"I'll mention it," said Walter, "if you'll have the goodness to let me in, Ma'am."

For he was repelled by a wooden fortification extending across the doorway, and put there to prevent the little MacStingers in their moments of recreation from tumbling down the steps.

"A boy that can knock my door down," said Mrs MacStinger, contemptuously, "can get over that, I should hope!" But Walter, taking this as a permission to enter, and getting over it, Mrs MacStinger immediately demanded whether an Englishwoman's house was her castle or not; and whether she was to be broke in upon by "raff." On these subjects her thirst for information was still very importunate, when Walter, having made his way up the little staircase through an artificial fog occasioned by the washing, which covered the bannisters with a clammy perspiration, entered Captain Cuttle's room, and found that gentleman in ambush behind the door.

"Never owed her a penny, Wal'r," said Captain Cuttle in a low voice, and with visible marks of trepidation on his countenance. "Done her a world of good turns, and the children too. Vixen at times, though. Whew!"

"*I* should go away, Captain Cuttle," said Walter.

"Dursn't do it, Wal'r," returned the Captain. "She'd find me out wherever I went. Sit down. How's Gills?"

The Captain was dining (in his hat) off cold loin of mutton, porter, and some smoking hot potatoes, which he had cooked himself, and took out of a little saucepan before the fire as he wanted them. He unscrewed his hook at dinner-time, and screwed a knife into its wooden socket instead, with which he had already begun to peel one of these potatoes for Walter. His rooms were very small, and strongly impregnated with tobacco-smoke, but snug enough: everything being stowed away, as if there were an earthquake regularly every half-hour.

Dombey and Son

MISS TOX inhabited a dark little house that had been squeezed, at some remote period of English history, into a fashionable neighbourhood at the west end of the town, where it stood in the shade like a poor relation of the great street round the corner, coldly looked down upon by mighty mansions. It was not exactly in a court, and it was not exactly in a yard; but it was in the dullest of No-Thoroughfares, rendered anxious and haggard by distant double knocks. The name of this retirement, where grass grew between the chinks in the stone pavement, was Princess's Place; and in Princess's Place was Princess's Chapel, with a tinkling bell, where sometimes as many as five-and-twenty people attended service on a Sunday. The Princess's Arms was also there, and much resorted to by splendid footmen. A sedan chair was kept inside the railing before the Princess's Arms, but it had never come out within the memory of man; and on fine mornings, the top of every rail (there were eight-and-forty, as Miss Tox had often counted) was decorated with a pewter-pot.

There was another private house besides Miss Tox's in Princess's Place: not to mention an immense pair of gates, with an immense pair of lion-headed knockers on them, which were never opened by any chance, and were supposed to constitute a disused entrance to somebody's stables. Indeed, there was a smack of stabling in the air of Princess's Place; and Miss Tox's bedroom (which was at the back) commanded a vista of mews, where hostlers, at whatever sort of work engaged, were continually accompanying themselves with effervescent noises; and where the most domestic and confidential garments of coachmen and their wives and families, usually hung, like Macbeth's banners, on the outward walls.

At this other private house in Princess's Place, tenanted by a retired butler who had married a housekeeper, apartments were let Furnished, to a single gentleman: to wit, a wooden-featured, blue-faced Major, with his eyes starting out of his head, in whom Miss Tox recognized, as she herself expressed it, "something so truly military;" and between whom and herself, an occasional interchange of newspapers and pamphlets, and such

Platonic dalliance, was effected through the medium of a dark servant of the Major's, whom Miss Tox was quite content to classify as a "native," without connecting him with any geographical idea whatever.

Perhaps there never was a smaller entry and staircase, than the entry and staircase of Miss Tox's house. Perhaps, taken altogether, from top to bottom, it was the most inconvenient little house in England, and the crookedest; but then, Miss Tox said, what a situation! There was very little daylight to be got there in the winter: no sun at the best of times: air was out of the question, and traffic was walled out. Still Miss Tox said, think of the situation! So said the blue-faced Major, whose eyes were starting out of his head: who gloried in Princess's Place: and who delighted to turn the conversation at his club, whenever he could, to something connected with some of the great people in the great street round the corner, that he might have the satisfaction of saying they were his neighbours.

The dingy tenement inhabited by Miss Tox was her own; having been devised and bequeathed to her by the deceased owner of the fishy eye in the locket, of whom a miniature portrait, with a powdered head and a pigtail, balanced the kettle-holder on opposite sides of the parlour fireplace. The greater part of the furniture was of the powdered-head and pigtail period: comprising a plate-warmer, always languishing and sprawling its four attenuated bow legs in somebody's way; and an obsolete harpsichord, illuminated round the maker's name with a painted garland of sweet peas.

Although Major Bagstock had arrived at what is called in polite literature, the grand meridian of life, and was proceeding on his journey downhill with hardly any throat, and a very rigid pair of jaw-bones, and long-flapped elephantine ears, and his eyes and complexion in the state of artificial excitement already mentioned, he was mightily proud of awakening an interest in Miss Tox, and tickled his vanity with the fiction that she was a splendid woman who had her eye on him. This he had several times hinted at the club: in connexion with little jocularities, of which old Joe Bagstock, old Joey Bagstock, old

J. Bagstock, old Josh Bagstock, or so forth, was the perpetual theme: it being, as it were, the Major's stronghold and donjon-keep of light humour, to be on the most familiar terms with his own name.

"Joey B., Sir," the Major would say, with a flourish of his walking-stick, "is worth a dozen of you. If you had a few more of the Bagstock breed among you, Sir, you'd be none the worse for it. Old Joe, Sir, needn't look far for a wife even now, if he was on the look-out; but he's hard-hearted, Sir, is Joe—he's tough, Sir, tough, and de-vilish sly!" After such a declaration, wheezing sounds would be heard; and the Major's blue would deepen into purple, while his eyes strained and started convulsively.

Notwithstanding his very liberal laudation of himself, however, the Major was selfish. It may be doubted whether there ever was a more entirely selfish person at heart; or at stomach is perhaps a better expression, seeing that he was more decidedly endowed with that latter organ than with the former. He had no idea of being overlooked or slighted by anybody; least of all, had he the remotest comprehension of being overlooked and slighted by Miss Tox.

And yet, Miss Tox, as it appeared, forgot him—gradually forgot him. She began to forget him soon after her discovery of the Toodle family. She continued to forget him up to the time of the christening. She went on forgetting him with compound interest after that. Something or somebody had superseded him as a source of interest.

"Good morning, Ma'am," said the Major, meeting Miss Tox in Princess's Place, some weeks after the changes chronicled in the last chapter.

"Good morning, Sir," said Miss Tox; very coldly.

"Joe Bagstock, Ma'am," observed the Major, with his usual gallantry, "has not had the happiness of bowing to you at your window, for a considerable period. Joe has been hardly used, Ma'am. His sun has been behind a cloud."

Miss Tox inclined her head; but very coldly indeed.

"Joe's luminary has been out of town, Ma'am, perhaps," inquired the Major.

"I? out of town? oh no, I have not been out of town," said Miss Tox. "I have been much engaged lately. My time is nearly all devoted to some very intimate friends. I am afraid I have none to spare, even now. Good morning, Sir!"

As Miss Tox, with her most fascinating step and carriage, disappeared from Princess's Place, the Major stood looking after her with a bluer face than ever: muttering and growling some not at all complimentary remarks.

"Why, damme, Sir," said the Major, rolling his lobster eyes round and round Princess's Place, and apostrophizing its fragrant air, "six months ago, the woman loved the ground Josh Bagstock walked on. What's the meaning of it?"

The Major decided, after some consideration, that it meant man-traps; that it meant plotting and snaring; that Miss Tox was digging pitfalls. "But you won't catch Joe, Ma'am," said the Major. "He's tough, Ma'am, tough, is J. B. Tough, and de-vilish sly!" over which reflection he chuckled for the rest of the day.

But, still, when that day and many other days were gone and past, it seemed that Miss Tox took no heed whatever of the Major, and thought nothing at all about him. She had been wont, once upon a time, to look out at one of her little dark windows by accident, and blushingly return the Major's greeting; but now, she never gave the Major a chance, and cared nothing at all whether he looked over the way or not. Other changes had come to pass too. The Major, standing in the shade of his own apartment, could make out that an air of greater smartness had recently come over Miss Tox's house; that a new cage with gilded wires had been provided for the ancient little canary bird; that divers ornaments, cut out of coloured card-boards and paper, seemed to decorate the chimney-piece and tables; that a plant or two had suddenly sprung up in the windows; that Miss Tox occasionally practised on the harpsichord, whose garland of sweet peas was always displayed ostentatiously, crowned with the Copenhagen and Bird Waltzes in a Music Book of Miss Tox's own copying.

Over and above all this, Miss Tox had long been dressed

with uncommon care and elegance in slight mourning. But this helped the Major out of his difficulty; and he determined within himself that she had come into a small legacy and grown proud.

It was on the very next day after he had eased his mind by arriving at this decision, that the Major, sitting at his breakfast, saw an apparition so tremendous and wonderful in Miss Tox's little drawing-room, that he remained for some time rooted to his chair; then, rushing into the next room, returned with a double-barrelled opera-glass, through which he surveyed it intently for some minutes.

"It's a baby, Sir," said the Major, shutting up the glass again, "for fifty thousand pound!"

The Major couldn't forget it. He could do nothing but whistle, and stare to that extent, that his eyes compared with what they now became, had been in former times quite cavernous and sunken. Day after day, two, three, four times a week, this baby reappeared. The Major continued to stare and whistle. To all other intents and purposes he was alone in Princess's Place. Miss Tox had ceased to mind what he did. He might have been black as well as blue, and it would have been of no consequence to her.

The perseverance with which she walked out of Princess's Place to fetch this baby and its nurse, and walked back with them, and walked home with them again, and continually mounted guard over them; and the perseverance with which she nursed it herself, and fed it, and played with it, and froze its young blood with airs upon the harpischord; was extraordinary. At about this same period too, she was seized with a passion for looking at a certain bracelet; also with a passion for looking at the moon, of which she would take long observations from her chamber window. But whatever she looked at; sun, moon, stars, or bracelets; she looked no more at the Major. And the Major whistled, and stared, and wondered, and dodged about his room, and could make nothing of it.

Dombey and Son

AT the appointed time in the evening Mr Micawber re-appeared. I washed my hands and face, to do the greater honour to his gentility, and we walked to our house, as I suppose I must now call it, together; Mr Micawber impressing the names of streets, and the shapes of corner houses upon me as we went along, that I might find my way back, easily, in the morning.

Arrived at his house in Windsor Terrace (which I noticed was shabby like himself, but also, like himself, made all the show it could), he presented me to Mrs Micawber, a thin and faded lady, not at all young, who was sitting in the parlour (the first floor was altogether unfurnished, and the blinds were kept down to delude the neighbours), with a baby at her breast. This baby was one of twins; and I may remark here that I hardly ever, in all my experience of the family, saw both the twins detached from Mrs Micawber at the same time. One of them was always taking refreshment.

There were two other children; Master Micawber, aged about four, and Miss Micawber, aged about three. These, and a dark-complexioned young woman, with a habit of snorting, who was servant to the family, and informed me, before half-an-hour had expired, that she was "a Orfling," and came from St Luke's workhouse, in the neighbourhood, completed the establishment. My room was at the top of the house, at the back: a close chamber; stencilled all over with an ornament which my young imagination represented as a blue muffin; and very scantily furnished.

"I never thought," said Mrs Micawber, when she came up, twin and all, to show me the apartment, and sat down to take breath, "before I was married, when I lived with papa and mama, that I should ever find it necessary to take a lodger. But Mr Micawber being in difficulties, all considerations of private feeling must give way."

I said, "Yes, ma'am."

"Mr Micawber's difficulties are almost overwhelming, just at present," said Mrs Micawber; "and whether it is possible to bring him through them, I don't know. When I lived at home with papa and mama, I really should have hardly understood what the word meant, in the sense in which I now employ it, but experientia does it—as papa used to say."

I cannot satisfy myself whether she told me that Mr Micawber had been an officer in the Marines, or whether I have imagined it. I only know that I believe to this hour that he *was* in the Marines once upon a time, without knowing why. He was a sort of town traveller for a number of miscellaneous houses, now; but made little or nothing of it, I am afraid.

"If Mr Micawber's creditors *will not* give him time," said Mrs Micawber, "they must take the consequences; and the sooner they bring it to an issue the better. Blood cannot be obtained from a stone, neither can anything on account be obtained at present (not to mention law expenses) from Mr Micawber."

I never can quite understand whether my precocious self-dependence confused Mrs Micawber in reference to my age, or whether she was so full of the subject that she would have talked about it to the very twins if there had been nobody else to communicate with, but this was the strain in which she began, and she went on accordingly all the time I knew her.

Poor Mrs Micawber! She said she had tried to exert herself; and so, I have no doubt, she had. The centre of the street-door was perfectly covered with a great brass-plate, on which was engraved, "Mrs Micawber's Boarding Establishment for Young Ladies": but I never found that any young lady had ever been to school there; or that any young lady ever came, or proposed to come; or that the least preparation was ever made to receive any young lady. The only visitors I ever saw or heard of, were creditors. *They* used to come at all hours, and some of them were quite ferocious. One dirty-faced man, I think he was a bootmaker, used to edge himself into the passage as early as seven o'clock in the morning, and call up the stairs to Mr Micawber: "Come! You ain't out yet, you know. Pay us, will you? Don't hide, you know; that's mean. I wouldn't be mean if I was you. Pay us, will you? You just pay us, d'ye hear? Come!" Receiving no answer to these taunts, he would mount in his wrath to the words "swindlers" and "robbers"; and these being ineffectual too, would sometimes go to the extremity of crossing the street, and roaring up at the windows of the second floor, where he knew Mr Micawber was. At these times, Mr Micawber would be transported with grief and mortification, even to the length (as I was once made aware by a scream from his wife) of making motions at himself with a razor; but within half-an-hour afterwards, he would polish up his shoes with extraordinary pains, and go out, humming a tune with a greater air of gentility than ever. Mrs Micawber was quite as elastic. I have known her to be thrown into fainting fits by the king's taxes at three o'clock, and to eat lamb-chops, breaded, and drink warm ale (paid for with two teaspoons that had gone to the pawnbroker's) at four. On one occasion, when an execution had just been put in, coming home through some chance as early as six o'clock, I saw her lying (of course with a twin) under the grate in a swoon, with her hair all torn about her face; but I never heard her more cheerful than she was, that very same night, over a veal-cutlet before the kitchen fire telling me stories about her papa and mama, and the company they used to keep.

David Copperfield

"*Dotheboys Hall,*
"*Thursday Morning.*

"Sir,

"My pa requests me to write to you, the doctors considering it doubtful whether he will ever recuvver the use of his legs which prevents his holding a pen.

"We are in a state of mind beyond everything, and my pa is one mask of brooses both blue and green likewise two forms are steepled in his Goar. We were kimpelled to have him carried down into the kitchen where he now lays. You will judge from this that he has been brought very low.

"When your nevew that you recommended for a teacher had done this to my pa and jumped upon his body with his feet and also langwedge which I will not pollewt my pen with describing, he assaulted my ma with dreadful violence, dashed her to the earth, and drove her back comb several inches into her head. A very little more and it must have entered her skull. We have a medical certifiket that if it had, the tortershell would have affected the brain.

"Me and my brother were then the victims of his feury since which we have suffered very much which leads us to the arrowing belief that we have received some injury in our insides, especially as no marks of violence are visible externally. I am screaming out loud all the time I write and so is my brother which takes off my attention rather and I hope will excuse mistakes.

"The monster having sasiated his thirst for blood ran away, taking with him a boy of desperate character that he had excited to rebellyon, and a garnet ring belonging to my ma, and not having been apprehended by the constables is supposed to have been took up by some stage-coach. My pa begs that if he comes to you the ring may be returned, and that you will let the thief and assassin go, as if we prosecuted him he would only be transported, and if he is let go he is sure to be hung before long which will save us trouble and be much more satisfactory. Hoping to hear from you when convenient.

"I remain
"Yours and cetrer
"FANNY SQUEERS.

"P.S. I pity his ignorance and despise him."

Nicholas Nickleby

SHE determined not to go to bed until Edith returned, and if she could not speak to her, at least to be sure that she was safe at home. What indistinct and shadowy dread moved Florence to this resolution, she did not know, and did not dare to think. She only knew that until Edith came back, there was no repose for her aching head or throbbing heart.

The evening deepened into night: midnight came; no Edith.

Florence could not read, or rest a moment. She paced her

own room, opened the door and paced the staircase-gallery outside, looked out of window on the night, listened to the wind blowing and the rain falling, sat down and watched the faces in the fire, got up and watched the moon flying like a storm-driven ship through the sea of clouds.

All the house was gone to bed, except two servants who were waiting the return of their mistress, downstairs.

One o'clock. The carriages that tumbled in the distance, turned away, or stopped short, or went past; the silence gradually deepened, and was more and more rarely broken, save by a rush of wind or sweep of rain. Two o'clock. No Edith!

Florence, more agitated, paced her room; and paced the gallery outside; and looked out at the night, blurred and wavy with the rain drops on the glass, and the tears in her own eyes; and looked up at the hurry in the sky, so different from the repose below, and yet so tranquil and solitary. Three o'clock! There was a terror in every ash that dropped out of the fire. No Edith yet.

Much and more agitated, Florence paced her room, and paced the gallery, and looked out at the moon with a new fancy of her likeness to a pale fugitive hurrying away and hiding her guilty face. Four struck! Five! No Edith yet.

But now there was some cautious stir in the house; and Florence found that Mrs Pipchin had been awakened by one of those who sat up, had risen and had gone down to her father's door. Stealing lower down the stairs, and observing what passed, she saw her father come out in his morning gown, and start when he was told his wife had not come home. He despatched a messenger to the stable to inquire whether the coachman was there; and while the man was gone, dressed himself very hurriedly.

The man came back, in great haste, bringing the coachman with him, who said he had been at home and in bed since ten o'clock. He had driven his mistress to her old house in Brook Street, where she had been met by Mr Carker——

Florence stood upon the very spot where she had seen him coming down. Again she shivered with the nameless terror of that sight, and had hardly steadiness enough to hear and understand what followed.

—Who had told him, the man went on to say, that his mistress would not want the carriage to go home in; and had dismissed him.

She saw her father turn white in the face, and heard him ask in a quick trembling voice for Mrs Dombey's maid. The whole house was roused; for she was there, in a moment, very pale too, and speaking incoherently.

She said she had dressed her mistress early—full two hours before she went out—and had been told, as she often was, that she would not be wanted at night. She had just come from her mistress's rooms, but——

"But what! what was it?" Florence heard her father demand like a madman.

"But the inner dressing-room was locked and the key gone."

Her father seized a candle that was flaming on the ground—some one had put it down there, and forgotten it—and came running upstairs with such fury, that Florence, in her fear, had hardly time to fly before him. She heard him striking in the door as she ran on, with her hands widely spread, and her hair streaming, and her face like a distracted person's, back to her own room.

When the door yielded, and he rushed in, what did he see there? No one knew. But thrown down in a costly mass upon the ground, was every ornament she had had, since she had been his wife; every dress she had worn; and everything she had possessed. This was the room in which he had seen, in yonder mirror, the proud face discard him. This was the room in which he had wondered, idly, how these things would look when he should see them next!

Heaping them back into the drawers, and locking them up in a rage of haste, he saw some papers on the table. The deed of settlement he had executed on the marriage, and a letter. He read that she was gone. He read that he was dishonoured. He read that she had fled, upon her shameful wedding-day, with the man whom she had chosen for her humiliation; and he tore out of the room, and out of the house, with a frantic idea of finding her yet, at the place to which she had been taken, and beating all trace of beauty out of the triumphant face with his bare hand.

Florence, not knowing what she did, put on a shawl and bonnet, in a dream of running through the streets until she found Edith, and then clasping her in her arms, to save and bring her back. But when she hurried out upon the staircase, and saw the frightened servants going up and down with lights, and whispering together, and falling away from her father as he passed down, she awoke to a sense of her own powerlessness; and hiding in one of the great rooms that had been made gorgeous for *this*, felt as if her heart would burst with grief.

Compassion for her father was the first distinct emotion that made head against the flood of sorrow which overwhelmed her. Her constant nature turned to him in his distress, as fervently and faithfully as if, in his prosperity, he had been the embodiment of that idea which had gradually become so faint and dim. Although she did not know, otherwise than through the suggestions of a shapeless fear, the full extent of his calamity, he stood before her wronged and deserted; and again her yearning love impelled her to his side.

He was not long away: for Florence was yet weeping in the great room and nourishing these thoughts, when she heard him come back. He ordered the servants to set about their ordinary occupations, and went into his own apartment, where he trod so heavily that she could hear him walking up and down from end to end.

Yielding at once to the impulse of her affection, timid at all other times, but bold in its truth to him in his adversity, and undaunted by past repulse, Florence, dressed as she was, hurried downstairs. As she set her light foot in the hall, he came out of his room. She hastened towards him unchecked with her arms stretched out, and crying "Oh dear, dear Papa!" as if she would have clasped him round the neck.

And so she would have done. But in his frenzy, he lifted up his cruel arm, and struck her, crosswise, with that heaviness that she tottered on the marble floor; and as he dealt the blow, he told her what Edith was, and bade her follow her, since they had always been in league.

She did not sink down at his feet; she did not shut out the sight of him with her trembling hands; she did not weep; she did not utter one word of reproach. But she looked at him, and a cry of desolation issued from her heart. For as she looked, she saw him murdering that fond idea to which she had held in spite of him. She saw his cruelty, neglect, and hatred dominant above it, and stamping it down. She saw she had no father upon earth, and ran out, orphaned, from his house.

Dombey and Son

MRS GAMP'S apartment in Kingsgate Street, High Holborn, wore, metaphorically speaking, a robe of state. It was swept and garnished for the reception of a visitor. That visitor was Betsey Prig: Mrs Prig, of Bartlemy's: or as some said, Barklemy's, or as some said, Bardlemy's; for by all these endearing and familiar appellations had the hospital of Saint Bartholomew become a household word among the sisterhood which Betsey Prig adorned.

Mrs Gamp's apartment was not a spacious one, but, to a contented mind, a closet is a palace; and the first-floor front at Mr Sweedlepipe's may have been, in the imagination of Mrs Gamp, a stately pile. If it were not exactly that, to restless intellects, it at least comprised as much accommodation as any person, not sanguine to insanity, could have looked for in a room of its dimensions. For only keep the bedstead always in your mind; and you were safe. That was the grand secret. Remembering the bedstead, you might even stoop to look under the little round table for anything you had dropped, without hurting yourself much against the chest of drawers, or qualifying as a patient of Saint Bartholomew, by falling into the fire.

Visitors were much assisted in their cautious efforts to preserve an unflagging recollection of this piece of furniture, by its size: which was great. It was not a turn-up bedstead, nor yet a French bedstead, nor yet a four-post bedstead, but what is poetically called a tent: the sacking whereof was low and bulgy, insomuch that Mrs Gamp's box would not go under it, but stopped half-way, in a manner which, while it did violence to the reason, likewise endangered the legs of a stranger. The frame too, which would have supported the canopy and hangings if there had been any, was ornamented with divers pippins carved in timber, which on the slightest provocation, and frequently on none at all, came tumbling down; harassing the peaceful guest with inexplicable terrors.

The bed itself was decorated with a patchwork quilt of great antiquity; and at the upper end, upon the side nearest to the door, hung a scanty curtain of blue check, which prevented the Zephyrs that were abroad in Kingsgate Street, from visiting Mrs Gamp's head too roughly. Some rusty gowns and other articles of that lady's wardrobe depended from the posts; and these had so adapted themselves by long usage to her figure, that more than one impatient husband coming in precipitately, at about the time of twilight, had been for an instant stricken dumb by the supposed discovery that Mrs Gamp had hanged herself. One gentleman, coming on the usual hasty errand, had said indeed, that they looked like guardian angels "watching of her in her sleep." But that, as Mrs Gamp said, "was his first;" and he never repeated the sentiment, though he often repeated his visit.

The chairs in Mrs Gamp's apartment were extremely large and broad-backed, which was more than a sufficient reason for there being but two in number. They were both elbow-chairs of ancient mahogany; and were chiefly valuable for the slippery nature of their seats, which had been originally horse-hair, but were now covered with a shiny substance of a bluish tint, from which the visitor began to slide away with a dismayed countenance, immediately after sitting down. What Mrs Gamp wanted in chairs she made up in bandboxes; of which she had a great collection, devoted to the reception of various miscellaneous valuables, which were not, however, as well protected as the good woman, by a pleasant fiction, seemed to think: for, though every bandbox had a carefully closed lid, not one among them had a bottom: owing to which cause the property within was merely, as it were, extinguished. The chest of drawers having been originally made to stand upon the top of another chest, had a dwarfish, elfin look, alone; but in regard of its security it had a great advantage over the bandboxes, for as all the handles had been long ago pulled off, it was very difficult to get at its contents. This indeed was only to be done by one or two devices; either by tilting the whole structure forward until all the drawers fell out together, or by opening them singly with knives, like oysters.

Mrs Gamp stored all her household matters in a little cupboard by the fire-place; beginning below the surface (as in nature) with the coals, and mounting gradually upwards to the spirits, which, from motives of delicacy, she kept in a teapot. The chimney-piece was ornamented with a small almanack, marked here and there in Mrs Gamp's own hand with a memorandum of the date at which some lady was expected to fall due. It was also embellished with three profiles: one, in colours, of Mrs Gamp herself in early life; one, in bronze, of a lady in feathers, supposed to be Mrs Harris, as she appeared when dressed for a ball; and one, in black, of Mr Gamp, deceased. The last was a full length, in order that the likeness might be rendered more obvious and forcible by the introduction of the wooden leg.

A pair of bellows, a pair of pattens, a toasting-fork, a kettle, a pap-boat, a spoon for the administration of medicine to the refractory, and lastly, Mrs Gamp's umbrella, which as something of great price and rarity, was displayed with particular ostentation, completed the decorations of the chimney-piece and adjacent wall. Towards these objects Mrs Gamp raised her eyes in satisfaction when she had arranged the tea-board, and had concluded her arrangements for the reception of Betsey Prig, even unto the setting forth of two pounds of Newcastle salmon, intensely pickled.

"There! Now drat you, Betsey, don't be long!" said Mrs Gamp, apostrophising her absent friend. "For I can't abear to wait, I do assure you. To wotever place I goes, I sticks to this one mortar, 'I'm easy pleased; it is but little as I wants; but I must have that little of the best, and to the minute when the clock strikes, else we do not part as I could wish, but bearin' malice in our arts.' "

Her own preparations were of the best, for they comprehended a delicate new loaf, a plate of fresh butter, a basin of fine white sugar, and other arrangements on the same scale. Even the snuff with which she now refreshed herself, was so choice in quality that she took a second pinch.

"My precious Betsey," said Mrs Gamp, "how late you are!"

The worthy Mrs Prig replied, with some asperity, "that if perwerse people went off dead, when they was least expected, it warn't no fault of her'n." And further, "that it was quite aggrawation enough to be made late when one was dropping for one's tea, without hearing on it again."

Mrs Gamp, deriving from this exhibition of repartee some clue to the state of Mrs Prig's feelings, instantly conducted her up-stairs: deeming that the sight of pickled salmon might work a softening change.

But Betsey Prig expected pickled salmon. It was obvious that she did; for her first words, after glacing at the table, were: "I know'd she wouldn't have a cowcumber!"

Mrs Gamp changed colour, and sat down upon the bedstead.

"Lord bless you, Betsey Prig, your words is true. I quite forgot it!"

Mrs Prig looked steadfastly at her friend, put her hand in her pocket, and with an air of surly triumph drew forth either the oldest of lettuces or youngest of cabbages, but at any rate, a green vegetable of an expansive nature, and of such magnificent proportions that she was obliged to shut it up like an umbrella before she could pull it out. She also produced a handful of mustard and cress, a trifle of the herb called dandelion, three bunches of radishes, an onion rather larger than an average turnip, three substantial slices of beetroot, and a short prong or antler of celery; the whole of this garden-stuff having been publicly exhibited, but a short time before, as a twopenny salad, and purchased by Mrs Prig on condition that the vendor could get it all into her pocket. Which had been happily accomplished, in High Holborn, to the breathless interest of a hackney-coach stand. And she laid so little stress on this surprising forethought, that she did not even smile, but returning her pocket into its accustomed sphere, merely recommended that these productions of nature should be sliced up, for immediate consumption, in plenty of vinegar.

"And don't go a-droppin' none of your snuff in it," said Mrs Prig. "In gruel, barley-water, apple tea, mutton-broth, and that, it don't signify. It stimilates a patient. But I don't relish it myself."

"Why, Betsey Prig!" cried Mrs Gamp, "how *can* you talk so!"

"Why, ain't your patients, wotever their disease is, always a-sneezin' their wery heads off, along of your snuff?" said Mrs Prig.

"And wot if they are!" said Mrs Gamp.

"Nothing if they are," said Mrs Prig. "But don't deny it, Sairah."

"Who deniges of it?" Mrs Gamp inquired.

Mrs Prig returned no answer.

"WHO deniges of it, Betsey?" Mrs Gamp inquired again. Then Mrs Gamp, by reversing the question, imparted a deeper and more awful character of solemnity to the same. "Betsey, who deniges of it?"

It was the nearest possible approach to a very decided difference of opinion between these ladies; but Mrs Prig's impatience for the meal being greater at the moment than her impatience of contradiction, she replied, for the present, "Nobody, if you don't, Sairah," and prepared herself for tea. For a quarrel can be taken up at any time, but a limited quantity of salmon cannot.

Her toilet was simple. She had merely to "chuck" her bonnet and shawl upon the bed; give her hair two pulls, one upon the right side and one upon the left, as if she were ringing a couple of bells; and all was done. The tea was already made, Mrs Gamp was not long over the salad, and they were soon at the height of their repast.

The temper of both parties was improved, for the time being, by the enjoyments of the table. When the meal came to a termination (which it was pretty long in doing), and Mrs Gamp having cleared away, produced the tea-pot from the top-shelf, simultaneously with a couple of wine-glasses, they were quite amiable.

"Betsey," said Mrs Gamp, filling her own glass, and passing the teapot, "I will now propoge a toast. My frequent pardner, Betsey Prig!"

"Which, altering the name to Sairah Gamp; I drink," said Mrs Prig, "with love and tenderness."

From this moment symptoms of inflammation began to lurk in the nose of each lady; and perhaps, notwithstanding all appearances to the contrary, in the temper also.

"Now, Sairah," said Mrs Prig, "joining business with pleasure, wot is this case in which you wants me?"

Mrs Gamp betraying in her face some intention of returning an evasive answer, Betsey added:

"*Is* it Mrs Harris?"

"No, Betsey Prig, it ain't," was Mrs Gamp's reply.

"Well!" said Mrs Prig, with a short laugh. "I'm glad of that, at any rate."

"Why should you be glad of that, Betsey?" Mrs Gamp retorted, warmly. "She is unbeknown to you except by hearsay, why should you be glad? If you have anythink to say contrairy to the character of Mrs Harris, which well I knows behind her back, afore her face, or anywheres, is not to be impeaged, out with it, Betsey. I have know'd that sweetest and best of women," said Mrs Gamp, shaking her head, and shedding tears, "ever since afore her First, which Mr Harris who was dreadful timid went and stopped his ears in an empty dog-kennel, and never took his hands away or come out once till he was showed the baby, wen bein' took with fits, the doctor collared him and laid him on his back upon the airy stones, and she was told to ease her mind, his owls was organs. And I have know'd her, Betsey Prig, when he has hurt her feelin' art by sayin' of his Ninth that it was one too many, if not two, while that dear innocent was cooin' in his face, which thrive it did though bandy, but I have never know'd as you had occagion to be glad, Betsey, on accounts of Mrs Harris not requiring you. Require she never will, depend upon it, for her constant words in sickness is, and will be, 'Send for Sairey!' "

During this touching address, Mrs Prig adroitly feigning to be the victim of that absence of mind which has its origin in excessive attention to one topic, helped herself from the teapot without appearing to observe it. Mrs Gamp observed it, however, and came to a premature close in consequence.

"Well, it ain't her, it seems," said Mrs Prig, coldly: "who is it then?"

"You have heerd me mention, Betsey," Mrs Gamp replied, after glancing in an expressive and marked manner at the teapot, "a person as I took care on at the time as you and me was pardners off and on, in that there fever at the Bull?"

"Old Snuffey," Mrs Prig observed.

Sarah Gamp looked at her with an eye of fire, for she saw in this mistake of Mrs Prig, another wilful and malignant stab at that same weakness or custom of hers, an ungenerous allusion to which, on the part of Betsey, had first disturbed their harmony that evening. And she saw it still more clearly, when, politely but firmly correcting that lady by the distinct enunciation of the word "Chuffey," Mrs Prig received the correction with a diabolical laugh.

The best among us have their failings, and it must be conceded of Mrs Prig, that if there were a blemish in the goodness of her disposition, it was a habit she had of not bestowing all its sharp and acid properties upon her patients (as a thoroughly amiable woman would have done), but of keeping a considerable remainder for the service of her friends. Highly pickled salmon, and lettuces chopped up in vinegar, may, as viands possessing some acidity of their own, have encouraged and increased this failing in Mrs Prig; and every application to the teapot certainly did; for it was often remarked of her by her friends, that she was most contradictory when most elevated. It is certain that her countenance became about this time derisive and defiant, and that she sat with her arms folded, and one eye shut up, in a somewhat offensive, because obtrusively intelligent, manner.

Mrs Gamp observing this, felt it the more necessary that Mrs Prig should know her place, and be made sensible of her exact station in society, as well as of her obligations to herself. She therefore assumed an air of greater patronage and importance, as she went on to answer Mrs Prig a little more in detail.

"Mr Chuffey, Betsey," said Mrs Gamp, "is weak in his mind. Excuge me if I makes remark, that he may neither be so weak as people thinks, nor people may not think he is so weak as they pretends, and what I knows, I knows; and what you don't, you don't; so do not ask me, Betsey. But Mr Chuffey's friends has made propojals for his bein' took care on, and has said to me, 'Mrs Gamp, *will* you undertake it? We couldn't think,' they says, 'of trusting him to nobody but you, for, Sairey, you are gold as has passed the furnage. Will you undertake it, at your own price, day and night, and by your own self?' 'No,' I says, 'I will not. Do not reckon on it. There is,' I says, 'but one creetur in the world as I would undertake on such terms, and her name is Harris. But,' I says, 'I am acquainted with a friend, whose name is Betsey Prig, that I can recommend, and will assist me. Betsey,' I says 'is always to be trusted, under me, and will be guided as I could desire.' "

Here Mrs Prig, without any abatement of her offensive manner, again counterfeited abstraction of mind, and stretched out her hand to the teapot. It was more than Mrs Gamp could bear. She stopped the hand of Mrs Prig with her own, and said, with great feeling:

"No, Betsey! Drink fair, wotever you do!"

Mrs Prig, thus baffled, threw herself back in her chair, and closing the same eye more emphatically, and folding her arms tighter, suffered her head to roll slowly from side to side, while she surveyed her friend with a contemptuous smile.

Mrs Gamp resumed:

"Mrs Harris, Betsey—"

"Bother Mrs Harris!" said Betsey Prig.

Mrs Gamp looked at her with amazement, incredulity, and indignation; when Mrs Prig, shutting her eye still closer, and folding her arms still tighter, uttered these memorable and tremendous words:

"I don't believe there's no sich a person!"

After the utterance of which expressions, she leaned forward, and snapped her fingers once, twice, thrice; each time nearer to the face of Mrs Gamp, and then rose to put on her bonnet, as one who felt that there was now a gulf between them, which nothing could ever bridge across.

The shock of this blow was so violent and sudden, that Mrs Gamp sat staring at nothing with uplifted eyes, and her mouth open as if she were gasping for breath, until Betsey Prig had put on her bonnet and her shawl, and was gathering the latter about her throat. Then Mrs Gamp rose—morally and physically rose—and denounced her.

"What!" said Mrs Gamp, "you bage creetur, have I know'd Mrs Harris five and thirty year, to be told at last that there ain't no sech a person livin'! Have I stood her friend in all her troubles, great and small, for it to come at last to sech a end as this, which her own sweet picter hanging up afore you all the time, to shame your Bragian words! But well you mayn't believe there's no sech a creetur, for she wouldn't demean herself to look at you, and often has she said, when I have made mention of your name, which, to my sinful sorrow, I have done, 'What, Sairey Gamp! debage yourself to *her*!' Go along with you!"

"I'm a-goin', ma'am, ain't I?" said Mrs Prig, stopping as she said it.

"You had better, ma'am," said Mrs Gamp.

"Do you know who you're talking to, ma'am?" inquired her visitor.

"Aperiently," said Mrs Gamp, surveying her with scorn from head to foot, "to Betsey Prig. Aperiently so. *I* know her. No one better. Go along with you!"

"And *you* was a-goin' to take me under you!" cried Mrs Prig, surveying Mrs Gamp from head to foot in her turn. "*You* was, was you? Oh, how kind! Why, deuce take your imperence," said Mrs Prig, with a rapid change from banter to ferocity, "what do you mean?"

"Go along with you!" said Mrs Gamp. "I blush for you."

"You had better blush a little for yourself, while you *are* about it!" said Mrs Prigg. You and your Chuffeys! What, the poor old creetur isn't mad enough, isn't he? Aha!"

"He'd very soon be made enough, if you had anything to do with him," said Mrs Gamp.

"And that's what I was wanted for, is it?" cried Mrs Prig, triumphantly. "Yes. But you'll find yourself deceived. I won't go near him. We shall see how you get on without me. I won't have nothink to do with him."

"You never spoke a truer word than that!" said Mrs Gamp. "Go along with you!"

She was prevented from witnessing the actual retirement of Mrs Prig from the room, notwithstanding the great desire she had expressed to behold it, by that lady, in her angry withdrawal, coming into contact with the bedstead, and bringing down the previously mentioned pippins; three or four of which came rattling on the head of Mrs Gamp so smartly, that when she recovered from this wooden showerbath, Mrs Prig was gone.

Martin Chuzzlewit

As to Dolly, there she was again, the very pink and pattern of good looks, in a smart little cherry-coloured mantle, with a hood of the same drawn over her head, and upon the top of that hood, a little straw hat trimmed with cherry-coloured ribbons, and worn the merest trifle on one side—just enough, in short, to make it the wickedest and most provoking head-dress that ever malicious milliner devised. And not to speak of the manner in which these cherry-coloured decorations brightened her eyes, or vied with her lips, or shed a new bloom on her face, she wore such a cruel little muff, and such a heart-rending pair of shoes, and was so surrounded and hemmed in, as it were, by aggravations of all kinds, that when Mr Tappertit, holding the horse's head, saw her come out of the house alone, such impulses came over him to decoy her into the chaise and drive off like mad, that he would unquestionably have done it, but for certain uneasy doubts besetting him as to the shortest way to Gretna Green; whether it was up the street or down, or up the right-hand turning or the left; and whether, supposing all the turnpikes to be carried by storm, the blacksmith in the end would marry them on credit; which by reason of his clerical office appeared, even to his excited imagination, so unlikely, that he hesitated. And while he stood hesitating, and looking postchaises-and-six at Dolly, out came his master and his mistress, and the constant Miggs, and the opportunity was gone for ever.

Barnaby Rudge

THERE was a fourth and most original figure in the Patriarchal tent, who also appeared before dinner. This was an amazing little old woman, with a face like a staring wooden doll too cheap for expression, and a stiff yellow wig perched unevenly on the top of her head, as if the child who owned the doll had driven a tack through it anywhere, so that it only got fastened on. Another remarkable thing in this little old woman was, that the same child seemed to have damaged her face in two or three places with some blunt instrument in the nature of a spoon; her countenance, and particularly the tip of her nose, presenting the phenomena of several dints, generally answering to the bowl of that article. A further remarkable thing in this little old woman was, that she had no name but Mr F's Aunt.

She broke upon the visitor's view under the following circumstances: Flora said when the first dish was being put on the table, perhaps Mr Clennam might not have heard that Mr F had left her a legacy? Clennam in return implied his hope that Mr F had endowed the wife whom he adored, with the greater part of his wordly substance, if not with all. Flora said oh yes, she didn't mean that, Mr F had made a beautiful will, but he had left her as a separate legacy, his Aunt. She then went out of the room to fetch the legacy, and, on her return, rather triumphantly presented "Mr F's Aunt."

The major characteristics discoverable by the stranger in Mr F's Aunt, were extreme severity and grim taciturnity; sometimes interrupted by a propensity to offer remarks in a deep warning voice, which, being totally uncalled for by anything said by anybody, and traceable to no association of ideas, confounded and terrified the mind. Mr F's Aunt may have thrown in these observations on some system of her own, and it may have been ingenious, or even subtle; but the key to it was wanted.

The neatly-served and well-cooked dinner (for everything about the Patriarchal household promoted quiet digestion) began with some soup, some fried soles, a butter-boat of shrimp sauce, and a dish of potatoes. The conversation still turned on the receipt of rents. Mr F's Aunt, after regarding the company for ten minutes with a malevolent gaze, delivered the following fearful remark.

"When we lived at Henley, Barnes's gander was stole by tinkers."

Mr Pancks courageously nodded his head and said, "All right, ma'am." But the effect of this mysterious communication upon Clennam was absolutely to frighten him. And another circumstance invested this old lady with peculiar terrors. Though she was always staring, she never acknowledged that she saw any individual. The polite and attentive stranger would desire, say, to consult her inclinations on the subject of potatoes. His expressive action would be hopelessly lost upon her, and what could he do? No man could say, "Mr F's Aunt, will you permit me?" Every man retired from the spoon, as Clennam did, cowed and baffled.

There was mutton, a steak, and an apple-pie—nothing in the

remotest way connected with ganders—and the dinner went on like a disenchanted feast, as it truly was. Once upon a time Clennam had sat at that table taking no heed of anything but Flora; now the principal heed he took of Flora was, to observe, against his will, that she was very fond of porter, that she combined a great deal of sherry with sentiment, and that if she were a little overgrown, it was upon substantial grounds. The last of the Patriarchs had always been a mighty eater, and he disposed of an immense quantity of solid fuel with the benignity of a good soul who was feeding some one else. Mr Pancks, who was always in a hurry, and who referred at intervals to a little dirty note-book which he kept beside him (perhaps containing the names of the defaulters he meant to look up by way of dessert), took in his victuals much as if he were coaling; with a good deal of noise, a good deal of dropping about, and a puff and a snort occasionally, as if he were nearly ready to steam away.

All through dinner, Flora combined her present appetite for eating and drinking, with her past appetite for romantic love, in a way that made Clennam afraid to lift his eyes from his plate; since he could not look towards her without receiving some glance of mysterious meaning or warning, as if they were engaged in a plot. Mr F's Aunt sat silently defying him with an aspect of the greatest bitterness, until the removal of the cloth and the appearance of the decanters, when she originated another observation—struck into the conversation like a clock, without consulting anybody.

Flora had just said, "Mr Clennam, will you give me a glass of port for Mr F's Aunt."

"The Monument near London Bridge," that lady instantly proclaimed, "was put up after the Great Fire of London; and the Great Fire of London was not the fire in which your uncle George's workshops was burned down."

Mr Pancks, with his former courage, said "Indeed, ma'am? All right!" But appearing to be incensed by imaginary contradiction, or other ill-usage, Mr F's Aunt, instead of relapsing into silence, made the following additional proclamation.

"I hate a fool!"

She imparted to this sentiment, in itself almost Solomonic, so extremely injurious and personal a character, by levelling it straight at the visitor's head, that it became necessary to lead Mr F's Aunt from the room. This was quietly done by Flora; Mr F's Aunt offering no resistance, but inquiring on her way out "What he come there for, then?" with implacable animosity.

Little Dorrit

MY shoes were by this time in a woeful condition. The soles had shed themselves bit by bit, and the upper leathers had broken and burst until the very shape and form of shoes had departed from them. My hat (which had served me for a night-cap, too) was so crushed and bent, that no old battered handleless saucepan on a dunghill need have been ashamed to vie with it. My shirt and trousers, stained with heat, dew, grass, and the Kentish soil on which I had slept—and torn besides—might have frightened the birds from my aunt's garden, as I stood at the gate. My hair had known no comb or brush since I left London. My face, neck, and hands, from unaccustomed exposure to the air and sun, were burnt to a berry-brown. From head to foot I was powdered almost as white with chalk and dust, as if I had come out of a lime-kiln. In this plight, and with a strong consciousness of it, I waited to introduce myself to, and make my first impression on, my formidable aunt.

The unbroken stillness of the parlour-window leading me to infer, after awhile, that she was not there, I lifted up my eyes to the window above it, where I saw a florid, pleasant-looking gentleman, with a grey head, who shut up one eye in a grotesque manner, nodded his head at me several times, shook it at me as often, laughed, and went away.

I had been discomposed enough before; but I was so much the more discomposed by this unexpected behaviour, that I was on the point of slinking off, to think how I'd best proceed, when there came out of the house a lady with a handkerchief tied over her cap, and a pair of gardening gloves on her hands, wearing a gardening pocket like a toll-man's apron, and carrying a great knife. I knew her immediately to be Miss Betsey, for she came stalking out of the house, exactly as my poor mother had so often described her stalking up our garden at Blunderstone Rookery.

"Go away!" said Miss Betsey, shaking her head, and making a distant chop in the air with her knife. "Go along! No boys here!"

I watched her with my heart at my lips, as she marched to a corner of her garden, and stooped to dig up some little root there. Then, without a scrap of courage, but with a great deal of desperation, I went softly in and stood beside her, touching her with my finger.

"If you please, ma'am," I began.

She started, and looked up.

"If you please, aunt."

"Eh?" exclaimed Miss Betsey, in a tone of amazement I have never heard approached.

"If you please, aunt, I am your nephew."

"Oh, Lord!" said my aunt, and sat flat down in the garden-path.

"I am David Copperfield, of Blunderstone, in Suffolk—where you came, on the night when I was born, and saw my dear mama. I have been very unhappy since she died. I have been slighted, and taught nothing, and thrown upon myself, and put to work not fit for me. It made me run away to you. I was robbed at first setting out, and have walked all the way, and have never slept in a bed since I began the journey." Here my self-support gave way all at once; and with a movement of my hands, intended to show her my ragged state, and call it to witness that I had suffered something, I broke into a passion of crying, which I suppose had been pent up within me all the week.

My aunt, with every sort of expression but wonder discharged from her countenance, sat on the gravel, staring at me, until I began to cry; when she got up in a great hurry, collared me, and took me into the parlour. Her first proceeding there was to unlock a tall press, bring out several bottles, and pour some of the contents of each into my mouth. I think they must have been taken out at random, for I am sure I tasted aniseed water, anchovy sauce, and salad dressing. When she had administered these restoratives, as I was still quite hysterical, and unable to control my sobs, she put me on the sofa, with a shawl under my head, and the handkerchief from her own head under my feet, lest I should sully the cover; and then, sitting herself down behind the green fan or screen I have already mentioned, so that I could not see her face, ejaculated at intervals, "Mercy on us!" letting those exclamations off like minute guns.

David Copperfield

Children's Corner

CONSCIENCE is an elastic and very flexible article, which will bear a deal of stretching and adapt itself to a great variety of circumstances. Some people by prudent management and leaving it off piece by piece, like a flannel waistcoat in warm weather, even contrive, in time, to dispense with it altogether; but there be others who can assume the garment and throw it off at pleasure; and this, being the greatest and most convenient improvement, is the one most in vogue.

The Old Curiosity Shop

THE room in which the boys were fed, was a large stone hall, with a copper at one end; out of which the master, dressed in an apron for the purpose, and assisted by one or two women, ladled the gruel at mealtimes. Of this festive composition each boy had one porringer, and no more—except on occasions of great public rejoicing, when he had two ounces and a quarter of bread besides. The bowls never wanted washing. The boys polished them with their spoons till they shone again; and when they had performed this operation (which never took very long, the spoons being nearly as large as the bowls), they would sit staring at the copper, with such eager eyes, as if they could have devoured the very bricks of which it was composed; employing themselves, meanwhile, in sucking their fingers most assiduously, with the view of catching up any stray splashes of gruel that might have been cast thereon. Boys have generally excellent appetites. Oliver Twist and his companions suffered the tortures of slow starvation for three months: at last they got so voracious and wild with hunger, that one boy, who was tall for his age and hadn't been used to that sort of thing (for his father had kept a small cook-shop), hinted darkly to his companions, that unless he had another basin of gruel *per diem*, he was afraid he might some night happen to eat the boy who slept next him, who happened to be a weakly youth of tender age. He had a wild, hungry eye; and they implicitly believed him. A council was held; lots were cast who should walk up to the master after supper that evening, and ask for more; and it fell to Oliver Twist.

The evening arrived; the boys took their places. The master, in his cook's uniform, stationed himself at the copper; his pauper assistants ranged themselves behind him; the gruel was served out; and a long grace was said over the short commons. The gruel disappeared; the boys whispered each other, and winked at Oliver; while his next neighbours nudged him. Child as he was, he was desperate with hunger, and reckless with misery. He rose from the table; and advancing to the master, basin and spoon in hand, said, somewhat alarmed at his own temerity:

"Please, sir, I want some more."

The master was a fat, healthy man; but he turned very pale. He gazed in stupefied astonishment on the small rebel for some seconds, and then clung for support to the copper. The assistants were paralysed with wonder; the boys with fear.

"What!" said the master at length, in a faint voice.

"Please, sir," replied Oliver, "I want some more."

The master aimed a blow at Oliver's head with the ladle; pinioned him in his arms; and shrieked aloud for the beadle.

The board were sitting in solemn conclave, when Mr Bumble rushed into the room in great excitement, and addressing the gentleman in the high chair, said,

"Mr Limbkins, I beg your pardon, sir! Oliver Twist has asked for more!"

There was a general start. Horror was depicted on every countenance.

"For *more?*" said Mr Limbkins. "Compose yourself, Bumble, and answer me distinctly. Do I understand that he asked for more, after he had eaten the supper allotted by the dietary?"

"He did, sir," replied Bumble.

"That boy will be hung," said the gentleman in the white waistcoat. "I know that boy will be hung."

Nobody controverted the prophetic gentleman's opinion. An animated discussion took place. Oliver was ordered into instant confinement; and a bill was next morning pasted on the outside of the gate, offering a reward of five pounds to anybody who would take Oliver Twist off the hands of the parish. In other words, five pounds and Oliver Twist were offered to any man or woman who wanted an apprentice to any trade, business or calling.

"I never was more convinced of anything in my life," said the gentleman in the white waistcoat, as he knocked at the gate and read the bill next morning: "I never was more convinced of anything in my life, than I am that that boy will come to be hung."

Oliver Twist

"DAMN that boy," said the old gentleman, "he's gone to sleep again."

"Very extraordinary boy, that," said Mr Pickwick, "does he always sleep in this way?"

"Sleep!" said the old gentleman, "he's always asleep. Goes on errands fast asleep, and snores as he waits at table."

"How very odd!" said Mr Pickwick.

"Ah! odd indeed," returned the old gentleman; "I'm proud of that boy—wouldn't part with him on any account—he's a natural curiosity! Here, Joe—Joe—take these things away, and open another bottle—d'ye hear?"

The fat boy rose, opened his eyes, swallowed the huge piece of pie he had been in the act of masticating when he last fell asleep, and slowly obeyed his master's orders—gloating languidly over the remains of the feast, as he removed the plates and deposited them in the hamper.

Pickwick Papers

"YOU'RE the wax-work child, are you not?" said Miss Monflathers.

"Yes, ma'am," replied Nell, colouring deeply, for the young ladies had collected about her, and she was the centre on which all eyes were fixed.

"And don't you think you must be a very wicked little child," said Miss Monflathers, who was of rather uncertain temper and lost no opportunity of impressing moral truths upon the tender minds of the young ladies, "to be a waxwork child at all?"

Poor Nell had never viewed her position in this light, and not knowing what to say, remained silent, blushing more deeply than before.

"Don't you know," said Miss Monflathers, "that it's very naughty and unfeminine, and a perversion of the properties wisely and benignantly transmitted to us, with expansive powers to be roused from their dormant state through the medium of cultivation?"

The two teachers murmured their respectful approval of this home-thrust, and looked at Nell as though they would have said that there indeed Miss Monflathers had hit her very hard. Then they smiled and glanced at Miss Monflathers, and then, their eyes meeting, they exchanged looks which plainly said that each considered herself smiler in ordinary to Miss Monflathers, and regarded the other as having no right to smile, and that her so doing was an act of presumption and impertinence.

"Don't you feel how naughty it is of you," resumed Miss Monflathers, "to be a wax-work child, when you might have the proud consciousness of assisting, to the extent of your infant powers, the manufactures of your country; of improving your mind by the constant contemplation of the steam-engine; and of earning a comfortable and independent subsistence of from two and ninepence to three shillings per week? Don't you know that the harder you are at work, the happier you are?"

"'How doth the little——'" murmured one of the teachers, in quotation from Doctor Watts.

"Eh?" said Miss Monflathers, turning smartly round. "Who said that?"

Of course the teacher who had not said it, indicated the rival who had, whom Miss Monflathers frowningly requested to hold her peace; by that means throwing the informing teacher into raptures of joy.

"The little busy bee," said Miss Monflathers, drawing herself up, "is applicable only to genteel children.

'In books, or work, or healthful play'

is quite right as far as they are concerned; and the work means painting on velvet, fancy needle-work, or embroidery. In such cases as these," pointing to Nell, with her parasol, "and in the case of all poor people's children, we should read it thus:

'In work, work, work. In work alway
Let my first years be past,
That I may give for ev'ry day
Some good account at last.'"

The Old Curiosity Shop

WHENEVER a young gentleman was taken in hand by Doctor Blimber, he might consider himself sure of a pretty tight squeeze. The Doctor only undertook the charge of ten young gentlemen, but he had, always ready, a supply of learning for a hundred, on the lowest estimate; and it was at once the business and delight of his life to gorge the unhappy ten with it.

In fact, Doctor Blimber's establishment was a great hothouse, in which there was a forcing apparatus incessantly at work. All the boys blew before their time. Mental green-peas were produced at Christmas, and intellectual asparagus all the year round. Mathematical gooseberries (very sour ones too) were common at untimely seasons, and from mere sprouts of bushes, under Doctor Blimber's cultivation. Every description of Greek and Latin vegetable was got off the driest twigs of boys, under the frostiest circumstances. Nature was of no consequence at all. No matter what a young gentleman was intended to bear, Doctor Blimber made him bear to pattern, somehow or other.

This was all very pleasant and ingenious, but the system of forcing was attended with its usual disadvantages. There was not the right taste about the premature productions, and they didn't keep well. Moreover, one young gentleman, with a swollen nose and an excessively large head (the oldest of the ten who had "gone through" everything), suddenly left off blowing one day, and remained in the establishment a mere stalk. And people did say that the Doctor had rather overdone it with young Toots, and that when he began to have whiskers he left off having brains.

There young Toots was, at any rate; possessed of the gruffest of voices and the shrillest of minds; sticking ornamental pins into his shirt, and keeping a ring in his waistcoat pocket to put on his little finger by stealth, when the pupils went out walking; constantly falling in love by sight with nursery-maids, who had no idea of his existence; and looking at the gas-lighted world over the little iron bars in the left-hand corner window of the front three pairs of stairs, after bedtime, like a greatly overgrown cherub who had sat up aloft much too long.

The Doctor was a portly gentleman in a suit of black, with strings at his knees, and stockings below them. He had a bald head, highly polished; a deep voice; and a chin so very double, that it was a wonder how he ever managed to shave into the creases. He had likewise a pair of little eyes that were always half shut up, and a mouth that was always half expanded into a grin, as if he had, that moment, posed a boy, and were waiting to convict him from his own lips. Insomuch that when the Doctor put his right hand into the breast of his coat, and with his other hand behind him, and a scarcely perceptible wag of his head, made the commonest observation to a nervous stranger, it was like a sentiment from the Sphynx, and settled his business.

The Doctor's was a mighty fine house, fronting the sea. Not a joyful style of house within, but quite the contrary. Sad-coloured curtains, whose proportions were spare and lean, hid themselves despondently behind the windows. The tables and chairs were put away in rows, like figures in a sum; fires were so rarely lighted in the rooms of ceremony, that they felt like wells, and a visitor represented the bucket; the dining-room seemed the last place in the world where any eating or drinking was likely to occur; there was no sound through all the house but the ticking of a great clock in the hall, which made itself audible in the very garrets; and sometimes a dull cooing of young gentlemen at their lessons like the murmurings of an assemblage of melancholy pigeons.

Miss Blimber, too, although a slim and graceful maid, did no soft violence to the gravity of the house. There was no light nonsense about Miss Blimber. She kept her hair short and crisp, and wore spectacles. She was dry and sandy with working in the graves of deceased languages. None of your live languages for Miss Blimber. They must be dead—stone dead—and then Miss Blimber dug them up like a ghoul.

Mrs Blimber, her mamma, was not learned herself, but she pretended to be, and that did quite as well. She said at evening parties, that if she could have known Cicero, she thought she could have died contented. It was the steady joy of her life to see the Doctor's young gentlemen go out walking, unlike all other young gentlemen, in the largest possible shirt-collars, and the stiffest possible cravats. It was so classical, she said.

As to Mr Feeder, B.A., Dr Blimber's assistant, he was a kind of human barrel-organ, with a little list of tunes at which he was continually working, over and over again, without any variation. He might have been fitted up with a change of barrels, perhaps, in early life, if his destiny had been favourable; but it had not been; and he had only one, with which, in a monotonous round, it was his occupation to bewilder the young ideas of Dr Blimber's young gentlemen. The young gentlemen were prematurely full of carking anxieties. They knew no rest from the pursuit of stony-hearted verbs, savage noun-substantives, inflexible syntactic passages, and ghosts of exercises that appeared to them in their dreams. Under the forcing system, a young gentleman usually took leave of his spirits in three weeks. He had all the cares of the world on his head in three months. He conceived bitter sentiments against his parents or guardians in four; he was an old misanthrope, in five; he envied Curtis that blessed refuge in the earth, in six; and at the end of the first twelvemonth had arrived at the conclusion, from which he never afterwards departed, that all the fancies of the poets, and lessons of the sages, were a mere collection of words and grammar, and had no other meaning in the world.

But he went on, blow, blow, blowing, in the Doctor's hot-house, all the time; and the Doctor's glory and reputation were great, when he took his wintry growth home to his relations and friends.

Upon the Doctor's door-steps one day, Paul stood with a fluttering heart, and with his small right hand in his father's. His other hand was locked in that of Florence. How tight the tiny pressure of that one; and how loose and cold the other!

Mrs Pipchin hovered behind the victim, with her sable plumage and her hooked beak, like a bird of ill omen. She was out of breath—for Mr Dombey, full of great thoughts, had walked fast—and she croaked hoarsely as she waited for the opening of the door.

"Now, Paul," said Mr Dombey exultingly. "This is the way indeed to be Dombey and Son, and have money. You are almost a man already."

"Almost," returned the child.

Even his childish agitation could not master the sly and quaint yet touching look, with which he accompanied the reply.

It brought a vague expression of dissatisfaction into Mr Dombey's face; but the door being opened, it was quickly gone.

"Doctor Blimber is at home, I believe?" said Mr Dombey.

The man said yes; and as they passed in, looked at Paul as if he were a little mouse, and the house were a trap. He was a weak-eyed young man, with the first faint streaks or early dawn of a grin on his countenance. It was mere imbecility; but Mrs Pipchin took it into her head that it was impudence, and made a snap at him directly.

"How dare you laugh behind the gentleman's back?" said Mrs Pipchin. "And what do you take me for?"

"I ain't a laughing at nobody, and I'm sure I don't take you for nothing, ma'am," returned the young man, in consternation.

"A pack of idle dogs!" said Mrs Pipchin, "only fit to be turn-spits. Go and tell your master that Mr Dombey's here, or it'll be worse for you!"

The weak-eyed young man went, very meekly, to discharge himself of this commission; and soon came back to invite them to the Doctor's study.

"You're laughing again, sir," said Mrs Pipchin, when it came to her turn, bringing up the rear, to pass him in the hall.

"I *ain't*," returned the young man, grievously oppressed. "I never see such a thing as this!"

"What is the matter, Mrs Pipchin?" said Mr Dombey, looking round. "Softly! Pray!"

Mrs Pipchin, in her deference, merely muttered at the young man, as she passed on, and said, "Oh! he was a precious fellow"—leaving the young man, who was all meekness and incapacity, affected even to tears by the incident. But Mrs Pipchin had a way of falling foul of all meek people; and her friends said who could wonder at it, after the Peruvian mines!

The Doctor was sitting in his portentous study, with a globe at each knee, books all round him, Homer over the door, and Minerva on the mantel-shelf. "And how do you, sir?" he said to Mr Dombey, "and how is my little friend?" Grave as an organ was the Doctor's speech; and when he ceased the great clock in the hall seemed (to Paul at least) to take him up, and to go on saying, "how, is, my, lit, tle, friend? how, is, my, lit, tle, friend?" over and over and over again.

The little friend being something too small to be seen at all from where the Doctor sat, over the books on his table, the Doctor made several futile attempts to get a view of him round the legs; which Mr Dombey perceiving, relieved the Doctor from his embarrassment by taking Paul up in his arms, and sitting him on another little table, over against the Doctor, in the middle of the room.

"Ha!" said the Doctor, leaning back in his chair with his hand in his breast. "Now I see my little friend. How do you do, my little friend?"

The clock in the hall wouldn't subscribe to this alteration in the form of words, but continued to repeat "how, is, my, lit, tle, friend? how, is ,my, lit, tle, friend?"

"Very well, I thank you, sir," returned Paul, answering the clock quite as much as the Doctor.

"Ha!" said Doctor Blimber. "Shall we make a man of him?"

"Do you hear, Paul?" added Mr Dombey; Paul being silent.

"Shall we make a man of him?" repeated the Doctor.

"I had rather be a child," replied Paul.

"Indeed!" said the Doctor. "Why?"

The child sat on the table looking at him, with a curious expression of suppressed emotion in his face, and beating one hand proudly on his knee as if he had the rising tears beneath it, and crushed them. But his other hand strayed a little way the while, a little farther—farther from him yet—until it lighted on the neck of Florence. "This is why," it seemed to say, and then the steady look was broken up and gone; the working lip was loosened; and the tears came streaming forth.

"Mrs Pipchin," said his father, in a querulous manner, "I am really very sorry to see this."

"Come away from him, do, Miss Dombey," quoth the matron.

"Never mind," said the Doctor, blandly nodding his head, to keep Mrs Pipchin back, "Ne-ver mind; we shall substitute new cares and new impressions, Mr Dombey, very shortly. You would still wish my little friend to acquire——"

"Everything, if you please, Doctor," returned Mr Dombey, firmly.

"Yes," said the Doctor, who, with his half-shut eyes, and his usual smile, seemed to survey Paul with the sort of interest that might attach to some choice little animal he was going to stuff. "Yes, exactly. Ha! We shall impart a great variety of information to our little friend, and bring him quickly forward, I dare say. I dare say. Quite a virgin soil, I believe you said, Mr Dombey?"

"Except some ordinary preparation at home, and from this lady," replied Mr Dombey, introducing Mrs Pipchin, who instantly communicated a rigidity to her whole muscular system, and snorted defiance beforehand, in case the Doctor should disparage her; "except so far, Paul has, as yet, applied himself to no studies at all."

Doctor Blimber inclined his head, in gentle tolerance of such insignificant poaching as Mrs Pipchin's, and said he was glad to hear it. It was much more satisfactory, he observed, rubbing his hands, to begin at the foundation. And again he leered at Paul, as if he would have liked to tackle him with the Greek alphabet on the spot.

"That circumstance, indeed, Doctor Blimber," pursued Mr Dombey, glancing at his little son, "and the interview I have already had the pleasure of holding with you, renders any further explanation, and consequently, any further intrusion on your valuable time, so unnecessary, that——"

"Now, Miss Dombey!" said the acid Pipchin.

"Permit me," said the Doctor, "one moment. Allow me to present Mrs Blimber and my daughter, who will be associated with the domestic life of our young pilgrim to Parnassus. Mrs Blimber," for the lady, who had perhaps been in waiting, opportunely entered, followed by her daughter, that fair sexton in spectacles, "Mr Dombey. My daughter Cornelia, Mr Dombey. Mr Dombey, my love," pursued the Doctor, turning to his wife, "is so confiding as to—do you see our little friend?"

Mrs Blimber, in an access of politeness, of which Mr Dombey was the object, apparently did not, for she was backing against the little friend and very much endangering his position on the table. But, on this hint, she turned to admire his classical and intellectual lineaments, and turning again to Mr Dombey, said, with a sigh, that she envied his dear son.

"Like a bee, sir," said Mrs Blimber, with uplifted eyes, "about to plunge into a garden of the choicest flowers, and sip the sweets for the first time. Virgil, Horace, Ovid, Terence, Plautus, Cicero. What a world of honey have we here. It may appear remarkable, Mr Dombey, in one who is a wife—the wife of such a husband——"

"Hush, hush," said Doctor Blimber. "Fie for shame."

"Mr Dombey will forgive the partiality of a wife," said Mrs Blimber, with an engaging smile.

Mr Dombey answered "Not at all": applying those words, it is to be presumed, to the partiality, and not to the forgiveness.

"—And it may seem remarkable in one who is a mother also," resumed Mrs Blimber.

"And such a mother," observed Mr Dombey, bowing with some confused idea of being complimentary to Cornelia.

"But really," pursued Mrs Blimber, "I think if I could have known Cicero, and been his friend, and talked with him in his retirement at Tusculum (beautiful Tusculum!), I could have died contented."

A learned enthusiast is so very contagious that Mr Dombey half believed this was exactly his case; and even Mrs Pipchin, who was not, as we have seen, of an accommodating disposition generally, gave utterance to a little sound between a groan and a sigh, as if she would have said that nobody but Cicero could have proved a lasting consolation under that failure of the

Peruvian mines, but that he indeed would have been a very Davy-lamp of refuge.

Cornelia looked at Mr Dombey through her spectacles, as if she would have liked to crack a few quotations with him from the authority in question. But this design, if she entertained it, was frustrated by a knock at the room door.

"Who is that?" said the Doctor. "Oh! Come in, Toots; come in. Mr Dombey, sir." Toots bowed. "Quite a coincidence!" said Doctor Blimber. "Here we have the beginning and the end. Alpha and Omega. Our head boy, Mr Dombey."

The Doctor might have called him their head and shoulders boy, for he was at least that much taller than any of the rest. He blushed very much at finding himself among strangers, and chuckled aloud.

"An addition to our little portico, Toots," said the Doctor; "Mr Dombey's son."

Young Toots blushed again; and finding, from a solemn silence which prevailed, that he was expected to say something, said to Paul, "How are you?" in a voice so deep, and a manner so sheepish, that if a lamb had roared it couldn't have been more surprising.

"Ask Mr Feeder, if you please, Toots," said the Doctor, "to prepare a few introductory volumes for Mr Dombey's son, and to allot him a convenient seat for study. My dear, I believe Mr Dombey has not seen the dormitories."

"If Mr Dombey will walk upstairs," said Mrs Blimber, "I shall be more than proud to show him the dominions of the drowsy god."

With that, Mrs Blimber, who was a lady of great suavity, and a wiry figure, and who wore a cap composed of sky-blue materials, proceeded upstairs with Mr Dombey and Cornelia; Mrs Pipchin following, and looking out sharp for her enemy the footman.

While they were gone, Paul sat upon the table, holding Florence by the hand, and glancing timidly from the Doctor round and round the room, while the Doctor, leaning back in his chair, with his hand in his breast as usual, held a book from him at arm's-length, and read. There was something very awful in this manner of reading. It was such a determined, unimpassioned, inflexible, cold-blooded way of going to work. It left the Doctor's countenance exposed to view; and when the Doctor smiled suspiciously at his author, or knit his brows, or shook his head and made wry faces at him, as much as to say, "Don't tell me, sir. I know better," it was terrific.

Toots, too, had no business to be outside the door, ostentatiously examining the wheels in his watch, and counting his half-crowns. But that didn't last long; for Doctor Blimber, happening to change the position of his tight plump legs, as if he were going to get up, Toots swiftly vanished, and appeared no more.

Mr Dombey and his conductress were soon heard coming downstairs again, talking all the way; and presently they re-entered the Doctor's study.

"I hope, Mr Dombey," said the Doctor, laying down his book, "that the arrangements meet your approval."

"They are excellent, sir," said Mr Dombey.

"Very fair, indeed," said Mrs Pipchin, in a low voice; never disposed to give too much encouragement.

"Mrs Pipchin," said Mr Dombey, wheeling round, "will, with your permission, Doctor and Mrs Blimber, visit Paul now and then."

"Whenever Mrs Pipchin pleases," observed the Doctor.

"Always happy to see her," said Mrs Blimber.

"I think," said Mr Dombey, "I have now given all the trouble I need, and may take my leave. Paul, my child," he went close to him, as he sat upon the table. "Good-bye."

"Good-bye, Papa."

The limp and careless little hand that Mr Dombey took in his, was singularly out of keeping with the wistful face. But he had no part in its sorrowful expression. It was not addressed to him. No, no. To Florence—all to Florence.

If Mr Dombey in his insolence of wealth, had ever made an enemy, hard to appease and cruelly vindictive in his hate, even such an enemy might have received the pang that wrung his proud heart then, as compensation for his injury.

He bent down over his boy, and kissed him. If his sight were dimmed as he did so, by something that for a moment blurred the little face, and made it indistinct to him, his mental vision may have been, for that short time, the clearer perhaps.

"I shall see you soon, Paul. You are free on Saturdays and Sundays, you know."

"Yes, Papa," returned Paul: looking at his sister. "On Saturdays and Sundays."

"And you'll try and learn a great deal here, and be a clever man," said Mr Dombey; "won't you?"

"I'll try," returned the child wearily.

"And you'll soon be grown up now!" said Mr Dombey.

"Oh! very soon!" replied the child. Once more the old, old look passed rapidly across his features like a strange light. It fell on Mrs Pipchin, and extinguished itself in her black dress. That excellent ogress stepped forward to take leave and to bear off Florence, which she had long been thirsting to do. The move on her part roused Mr Dombey, whose eyes were fixed on Paul. After patting him on the head, and pressing his small hand again, he took leave of Doctor Blimber, Mrs Blimber, and Miss Blimber, with his usual polite frigidity, and walked out of the study.

Despite his entreaty that they would not think of stirring, Doctor Blimber, Mrs Blimber, and Miss Blimber all pressed forward to attend him to the hall; and thus Mrs Pipchin got into a state of entanglement with Miss Blimber and the Doctor, and was crowded out of the study before she could clutch Florence. To which happy accident Paul stood afterwards indebted for the dear remembrance, that Florence ran back to throw her arms round his neck, and that hers was the last face in the doorway: turned towards him with a smile of encouragement, the brighter for the tears through which it beamed.

It made his childish bosom heave and swell when it was gone; and sent the globes, the books, blind Homer and Minerva, swimming round the room. But they stopped, all of a sudden; and then he heard the loud clock in the hall still gravely inquiring "how, is, my, lit, tle, friend? how, is, my, lit, tle, friend?" as it had done before.

He sat with folded hands, upon his pedestal, silently listening. But he might have answered "weary, weary! very lonely, very sad!" And there, with an aching void in his young heart, and all outside so cold, and bare, and strange, Paul sat as if he had taken life unfurnished, and the upholsterer were never coming.

Dombey and Son

AS Mrs Vincent Crummles recrossed back to the table, there bounded on to the stage from some mysterious inlet, a little girl in a dirty white frock, with tucks up to the knees, short trousers, sandaled shoes, white spencer, pink gauze bonnet, green veil and curl-papers; who turned a pirouette, cut twice in the air, turned another pirouette, then, looking off at the opposite wing, shrieked, bounded forward to within six inches of the footlights, and fell into a beautiful attitude of terror, as a shabby gentleman in an old pair of buff slippers came in at one powerful slide, and chattering his teeth, fiercely brandished a walking-stick.

"They are going through the Indian Savage and the Maiden," said Mrs Crummles.

"Oh!" said the manager, "the little ballet interlude. Very good, go on. A little this way, if you please, Mr Johnson. That'll do. Now!"

The manager clapped his hands as a signal to proceed, and the savage, becoming ferocious, made a slide towards the maiden; but the maiden avoided him in six twirls, and came down, at the end of the last one, upon the very points of her toes. This seemed to make some impression upon the savage; for, after a little more ferocity and chasing of the maiden into corners, he began to relent, and stroked his face several times with his right thumb and four fingers, thereby intimating that he was struck with admiration of the maiden's beauty. Acting upon the impulse of this passion, he (the savage) began to hit himself severe thumps in the chest, and to exhibit other indications of being desperately in love, which being rather a prosy proceeding, was very likely the cause of the maiden's falling asleep; whether it was or no, asleep she did fall, sound as a church, on a sloping bank, and the savage perceiving it, leant his left ear on his left hand, and nodded sideways, to intimate to all whom it might concern that she *was* asleep, and no shamming. Being left to himself, the savage had a dance, all alone. Just as he left off, the maiden woke up, rubbed her eyes, got off the bank, and had a dance all alone too—such a dance that the savage looked on in ecstasy all the while, and when it was done, plucked from a neighbouring tree some botanical curiosity, resembling a small pickled cabbage, and offered it to the maiden, who at first wouldn't have it, but on the savage shedding tears relented. Then the savage jumped for joy; then the maiden jumped for rapture at the sweet smell of the pickled cabbage. Then the savage and the maiden danced violently together, and, finally, the savage dropped down on one knee, and the maiden stood on one leg upon his other knee; thus concluding the ballet, and leaving the spectators in a state of pleasing uncertainty, whether she would ultimately marry the savage, or return to her friends.

"Very well indeed," said Mr Crummles; "bravo!"

"Bravo!" cried Nicholas, resolved to make the best of everything. "Beautiful!"

"This, sir," said Mr Vincent Crummles bringing the maiden forward, "this is the infant phenomenon—Miss Ninetta Crummles."

"Your daughter?" inquired Nicholas.

"My daughter—my daughter," replied Mr Vincent Crummles; "the idol of every place we go into, sir. We have had complimentary letters about this girl, sir, from the nobility and gentry of almost every town in England."

"I am not surprised at that," said Nicholas; "she must be quite a natural genius."

"Quite a——!" Mr Crummles stopped: language was not powerful enough to describe the infant phenomenon.

"I'll tell you what, sir," he said; "the talent of this child is not to be imagined. She must be seen, sir—seen—to be ever so faintly appreciated. There; go to your mother, my dear."

"May I ask how old she is?" inquired Nicholas.

"You may, sir," replied Mr Crummles, looking steadily in his questioner's face, as some men do when they have doubts about being implicitly believed in what they are going to say. "She is ten years of age, sir."

"Not more!"

"Not a day."

"Dear me!" said Nicholas, "it's extraordinary."

It was; for the infant phenomenon, though of short stature, had a comparatively aged countenance, and had moreover been precisely the same age—not perhaps to the full extent of the memory of the oldest inhabitant, but certainly for five good years. But she had been kept up late every night, and put upon an unlimited allowance of gin-and-water from infancy, to prevent her growing tall, and perhaps this system of training had produced in the infant phenomenon these additional phenomena.

Nicholas Nickleby

GRACE having been said by the Doctor, dinner began. There was some nice soup; also roast meat, boiled meat, vegetables, pie, and cheese. Every young gentleman had a massive silver fork, and a napkin; and all the arrangements were stately and handsome. In particular, there was a butler in a blue coat and bright buttons, who gave quite a winey flavour to the table beer; he poured it out so superbly.

Nobody spoke, unless spoken to, except Doctor Blimber, Mrs Blimber, and Miss Blimber, who conversed occasionally. Whenever a young gentleman was not actually engaged with his knife and fork or spoon, his eye, with an irresistible attraction, sought the eye of Doctor Blimber, Mrs Blimber, or Miss Blimber, and modestly rested there. Toots appeared to be the only exception to this rule. He sat next Mr Feeder on Paul's side of the table, and frequently looked behind and before the intervening boys to catch a glimpse of Paul.

Only once during dinner was there any conversation that included the young gentlemen. It happened at the epoch of the cheese, when the Doctor, having taken a glass of port wine and hemmed twice or thrice, said:

"It is remarkable, Mr Feeder, that the Romans——"

At the mention of this terrible people, their implacable enemies, every young gentleman fastened his gaze upon the Doctor, with an assumption of the deepest interest. One of the number who happened to be drinking, and who caught the Doctor's eye glaring at him through the side of his tumbler, left off so hastily that he was convulsed for some moments, and in the sequel ruined Doctor Blimber's point.

"It is remarkable, Mr Feeder," said the Doctor, beginning again slowly, "that the Romans, in those gorgeous and profuse entertainments of which we read in the days of the Emperors, when luxury had attained a height unknown before or since, and when whole provinces were ravaged to supply the splendid means of one Imperial Banquet——"

Here the offender, who had been swelling and straining, and waiting in vain for a full stop, broke out violently.

"Johnson," said Mr Feeder, in a low reproachful voice, "take some water."

The Doctor, looking very stern, made a pause until the water was brought, and then resumed:

"And when, Mr Feeder——"

But Mr Feeder, who saw that Johnson must break out again, and who knew that the Doctor would never come to a period before the young gentlemen until he had finished all he meant to say, couldn't keep his eye off Johnson; and thus was caught in the act of not looking at the Doctor, who consequently stopped.

"I beg your pardon, sir," said Mr Feeder, reddening. "I beg your pardon, Doctor Blimber."

"And when," said the Doctor, raising his voice, "when, sir, as we read, and have no reason to doubt—incredible as it may appear to the vulgar of our time—the brother of Vitellius prepared for him a feast, in which were served, of fish, two thousand dishes——"

"Take some water, Johnson—dishes, sir," said Mr Feeder.

"Of various sorts of fowl, five thousand dishes."

"Or try a crust of bread," said Mr Feeder.

"And one dish," pursued Doctor Blimber, raising his voice still higher as he looked all round the table, "called, from its enormous dimensions, the Shield of Minerva, and made, among other costly ingredients, of the brains of pheasants——"

"Ow, ow, ow!" (from Johnson).

"Woodcocks,——"

"Ow, ow, ow!"

"The sounds of the fish called scari,——"

"You'll burst some vessel in your head," said Mr Feeder. "You had better let it come."

"And the spawn of the lamprey, brought from the Carpathian Sea," pursued the Doctor, in his severest voice; "when we read of costly entertainments such as these, and still remember that we have a Titus,——"

"What would be your mother's feelings if you died of apoplexy!" said Mr Feeder.

"A Domitian,——"

"And you're blue, you know," said Mr Feeder.

"A Nero, a Tiberius, a Caligula, a Heliogabalus, and many more," pursued the Doctor; "it is, Mr Feeder—if you are doing me the honour to attend—remarkable; VERY remarkable, sir——"

But Johnson, unable to suppress it any longer, burst at that moment into such an overwhelming fit of coughing, that, although both his immediate neighbours thumped him on the back, and Mr Feeder himself held a glass of water to his lips, and the butler walked him up and down several times between his own chair and the sideboard, like a sentry, it was full five minutes before he was moderately composed. Then there was a profound silence.

"Gentlemen," said Doctor Blimber, "rise for grace! Cornelia, lift Dombey down"—nothing of whom but his scalp was accordingly seen above the table-cloth. "Johnson will repeat to me tomorrow morning before breakfast, without book, and from the Greek Testament, the first chapter of the epistle of Saint Paul to the Ephesians. We will resume our studies, Mr Feeder, in half an hour."

Dombey and Son

THE coach was in the yard, shining very much all over, but without any horses to it as yet; and it looked in that state as if nothing was more unlikely than its ever going to London. I was thinking this, and wondering what would ultimately become of my box, which Mr Barkis had put down on the yard-pavement by the pole (he having driven up the yard to turn his cart), and also what would ultimately become of me, when a lady looked out of a bow-window where some fowls and joints of meat were hanging up, and said—

"Is that the little gentleman from Blunderstone?"

"Yes, ma'am," I said.

"What name?" inquired the lady.

"Copperfield, ma'am," I said.

"That won't do," returned the lady. "Nobody's dinner is paid for here, in that name."

"Is it Murdstone, ma'am?" I said.

"If you're Master Murdstone," said the lady, "why do you go and give another name first?"

I explained to the lady how it was, who then rang a bell, and called out, "William! show the coffee-room!" upon which a waiter came running out of a kitchen on the opposite side of the yard to show it, and seemed a good deal surprised when he found he was only to show it to me.

It was a large, long room with some large maps in it. I doubt if I could have felt much stranger if the maps had been real foreign countries, and I cast away in the middle of them. I felt it was taking a liberty to sit down, with my cap in my hand, on the corner of the chair nearest the door; and when the waiter laid a cloth on purpose for me, and put a set of castors on it, I think I must have turned red all over with modesty.

He brought me some chops, and vegetables, and took the covers off in such a bouncing manner that I was afraid I must have given him some offence. But he greatly relieved my mind by putting a chair for me at the table, and saying, very affably, "Now, six-foot! come on!"

I thanked him, and took my seat at the board: but found it extremely difficult to handle my knife and fork with anything like dexterity, or to avoid splashing myself with the gravy, while he was standing opposite, staring so hard, and making me blush in the most dreadful manner every time I caught his eye. After watching me into the second chop, he said—

"There's half a pint of ale for you. Will you have it now?"

I thanked him, and said "Yes". Upon which he poured it out of a jug into a large tumbler, and held it up against the light, and made it look beautiful.

"My eye!" he said. "It seems a good deal, don't it?"

"It does seem a good deal," I answered with a smile. For it was quite delightful to me, to find him so pleasant. He was a twinkling-eyed, pimple-faced man, with his hair standing upright all over his head; and as he stood with one arm akimbo, holding up the glass to the light with the other hand, he looked quite friendly.

"There was a gentleman here, yesterday," he said, "a stout gentleman, by the name of Topsawyer—perhaps you know him!"

"No," I said, "I don't think——"

"In breeches and gaiters, broad-brimmed hat, gray coat, speckled choker," said the waiter.

"No," I said bashfully, "I haven't the pleasure——"

"He came in here," said the waiter, looking at the light through the tumbler, "ordered a glass of this ale—*would* order it—I told him not—drink it, and fell dead. It was too old for him. It oughtn't to be drawn; that's the fact."

I was very much shocked to hear of this melancholy accident, and said I thought I had better have some water.

"Why, you see," said the waiter, still looking at the light through the tumbler, with one of his eyes shut up, "our people don't like things being ordered and left. It offends 'em. But *I'll* drink it, if you like. I'm used to it, and use is everything. I don't think it'll hurt me, if I throw my head back, and take it off quick. Shall I?"

I replied that he would much oblige me by drinking it, if he thought he could do it safely, but by no means otherwise. When he did throw his head back, and take it off quick, I had a horrible fear, I confess, of seeing him meet the fate of the lamented Mr Topsawyer, and fall lifeless on the carpet. But it didn't hurt him. On the contrary, I thought he seemed the fresher for it.

"What have we got here?" he said, putting a fork into my dish. "Not chops?"

"Chops," I said.

"Lord bless my soul!" he exclaimed, "I didn't know they were chops. Why, a chop's the very thing to take off the bad effects of that beer! Ain't it lucky?"

So he took a chop by the bone in one hand, and a potato in the other, and ate away with a very good appetite, to my extreme satisfaction. He afterwards took another chop, and another potato; and after that, another chop and another potato. When we had done, he brought me a pudding, and having set it before me, seemed to ruminate, and to become absent in his mind for some moments.

"How's the pie?" he said, rousing himself.

"It's a pudding," I made answer.

"Pudding!" he exclaimed. "Why, bless me, so it is! What!" looking at it nearer. "You don't mean to say it's a batter-pudding!"

"Yes, it is indeed."

"Why, a batter-pudding," he said, taking up a tablespoon, "is my favourite pudding! Ain't that lucky? Come on, little 'un, and let's see who'll get most."

The waiter certainly got most. He entreated me more than once to come in and win, but what with his tablespoon to my tea-spoon, his despatch to my despatch, and his appetite to my appetite, I was left far behind at the first mouthful, and had no chance with him. I never saw anyone enjoy a pudding so much, I think; and he laughed, when it was all gone, as if his enjoyment of it lasted still.

David Copperfield

The Tender Passion

AND O what a bright old song it is, that O 'tis love, 'tis love, 'tis love, that makes the world go round!

Our Mutual Friend

"FINE girl, sir" (to Mr Tracy Tupman, who had been bestowing sundry anti-Pickwickian glances on a young lady by the roadside).

"Very!" said Mr Tupman.

"English girls not so fine as Spanish—noble creatures—jet hair—black eyes—lovely forms—sweet creatures—beautiful."

"You have been in Spain, sir?" said Mr Tracy Tupman.

"Lived there—ages."

"Many conquests, sir?" inquired Mr Tupman.

"Conquests! Thousands. Don Bolaro Fizzgig—Grandee—only daughter—Donna Christina—splendid creature—loved me to distraction—jealous father—high-souled daughter—handsome Englishman—Donna Christina in despair—prussic acid—stomach pump in my portmanteau—operation performed—old Bolaro in ecstasies—consent to our union—join hands and floods of tears—romantic story—very."

"Is the lady in England now, sir?" inquired Mr Tupman, on whom the description of her charms had produced a powerful impression.

"Dead, sir—dead," said the stranger, applying to his right eye the brief remnant of a very old cambric handkerchief. "Never recovered the stomach pump—undermined constitution—fell a victim."

"And her father?" inquired the poetic Snodgrass.

"Remorse and misery," replied the stranger. "Sudden disappearance—talk of the whole city—search made everywhere—without success—public fountain in the great square suddenly ceased playing—weeks elapsed—still a stoppage—workmen employed to clean it—water drawn off—father-in-law discovered sticking head first in the main pipe, with a full confession in his right boot—took him out, and the fountain played away again, as well as ever."

"Will you allow me to note that little romance down, sir?" said Mr Snodgrass, deeply affected.

"Certainly, sir, certainly,—fifty more if you like to hear 'em—strange life mine—rather curious history—not extraordinary, but singular."

Pickwick Papers

I HAD not been walking long, when I turned a corner, and met her. I tingle again from head to foot as my recollection turns that corner, and my pen shakes in my hand.

"You—are—out early, Miss Spenlow," said I.

"It's so stupid at home," she replied, "and Miss Murdstone

is so absurd! She talks such nonsense about its being necessary for the day to be aired, before I come out. Aired!" (She laughed, here, in the most melodious manner.) "On a Sunday morning when I don't practise, I must do something. So I told papa last night I *must* come out. Besides, it's the brightest time of the whole day. Don't you think so?"

I hazarded a bold flight, and said (not without stammering) that it was very bright to me then, though it had been very dark to me a minute before.

"Do you mean a compliment?" said Dora, "or that the weather has really changed?"

I stammered worse than before, in replying that I meant no compliment, but the plain truth; though I was not aware of any change having taken place in the weather. It was in the state of my own feelings, I added bashfully: to clench the explanation.

I never saw such curls—how could I, for there never were such curls!—as those she shook out to hide her blushes. As to the straw hat and blue ribbons which was on the top of the curls, if I could only have hung it up in my room in Buckingham Street, what a priceless possession it would have been!

"You have just come home from Paris," said I.

"Yes," said she. "Have you ever been there?"

"No."

"Oh! I hope you'll go soon. You would like it so much!"

Traces of deep-seated anguish appeared on my countenance. That she should hope I would go, that she should think it possible I *could* go, was insupportable. I depreciated Paris; I depreciated France. I said I wouldn't leave England, under existing circumstances for any earthly consideration. Nothing should induce me. In short, she was shaking the curls again, when the little dog came running along the walk to our relief.

He was mortally jealous of me, and persisted in barking at me. She took him up in her arms—oh, my goodness!—and caressed him, but he insisted upon barking still. He wouldn't let me touch him, when I tried; and then she beat him. It increased my sufferings greatly to see the pats she gave him for punishment on the bridge of his blunt nose, while he winked his eyes, and licked her hand, and still growled within himself like a little double-bass. At length he was quiet—well he might be with her dimpled chin upon his head!—and we walked away to look at a greenhouse.

"You are not very intimate with Miss Murdstone, are you?" said Dora.—"My pet!"

(The two last words were to the dog. Oh, if they had only been to me!)

"No," I replied. "Not at all so."

"She is a tiresome creature," said Dora, pouting. "I can't think what papa can have been about, when he chose such a vexatious thing to be my companion. Who wants a protector? I am sure *I* don't want a protector. Jip can protect me a great deal better than Miss Murdstone—can't you, Jip, dear?"

He only winked lazily, when she kissed his ball of a head.

"Papa calls her my confidential friend, but I am sure she is no such thing—is she, Jip? We are not going to confide in any such cross people, Jip and I. We mean to bestow our confidence where we like, and to find out our own friends, instead of having them found out for us—don't we, Jip?"

Jip made a comfortable noise, in answer, a little like a tea-kettle when it sings. As for me, every word was a new heap of fetters, rivetted above the last.

"It is very hard, because we have not a kind mama, that we are to have, instead, a sulky, gloomy old thing like Miss Murdstone, always following us about—isn't it, Jip? Never mind, Jip. We won't be confidential, and we'll make ourselves as happy as we can in spite of her, and we'll tease her, and not please her—won't we, Jip?"

If it had lasted any longer, I think I must have gone down on my knees on the gravel, with the probability before me of grazing them, and of being presently ejected from the premises besides. But, by good fortune, the greenhouse was not far off, and these words brought us to it.

It contained quite a show of beautiful geraniums. We loitered along in front of them, and Dora often stopped to admire this one or that one, and I stopped to admire the same one, and Dora laughing, held the dog up childishly, to smell the flowers; and if we were not all three in Fairyland, certainly *I* was. The scent of a geranium leaf, at this day, strikes me with a half-comical, half-serious wonder as to what change has come over me in a moment; and then I see a straw hat and blue ribbons, and a quantity of curls, and a little black dog being held up, in two slender arms, against a bank of blossoms and bright leaves.

Miss Murdstone had been looking for us. She found us here; and presented her uncongenial cheek, the little wrinkles in it filled with hair-powder, to Dora to be kissed. Then she took Dora's arm in hers, and marched us in to breakfast as if it were a soldier's funeral.

How many cups of tea I drank, because Dora made it, I don't know. But I perfectly remember that I sat swilling tea until my whole nervous system, if I had had any in those days, must have gone by the board. By and by we went to church. Miss Murdstone was between Dora and me in the pew; but I heard her sing, and the congregation vanished. A sermon was delivered—about Dora, of course—and I am afraid that is all I know of the service.

We had a quiet day. No company, a walk, a family dinner of four, and an evening of looking over books and pictures; Miss Murdstone with a homily before her, and her eye upon us, keeping guard vigilantly. Ah! little did Mr Spenlow imagine, when he sat opposite to me after dinner that day, with his pocket-handkerchief over his head, how fervently I was embracing him, in my fancy, as his son-in-law! Little did he think, when I took leave of him at night, that he had just given his full consent to my being engaged to Dora, and that I was invoking blessings on his head!

We departed early in the morning, for we had a Salvage case coming on in the Admiralty Court, requiring a rather accurate knowledge of the whole science of navigation, in which (as we couldn't be expected to know much about those matters in the Commons) the judge had entreated two old Trinity Masters, for charity's sake, to come and help him out. Dora was at the breakfast-table to make the tea again, however; and I had the melancholy pleasure of taking off my hat to her in the phaeton, as she stood on the door-step with Jip in her arms.

What the Admiralty was to me that day; what nonsense I made of our case in my mind, as I listened to it; how I saw "DORA" engraved upon the blade of the silver oar which they lay upon the table, as the emblem of that high jurisdiction; and how I felt, when Mr Spenlow went home without me (I had had an insane hope that he might take me back again), as if I were a mariner myself, and the ship to which I belonged had sailed away and left me on a desert island; I shall make no fruitless effort to describe. If that sleepy old court could rouse itself, and present in any visible form the day-dreams I have had in it about Dora it would reveal my truth.

I don't mean the dreams that I dreamed on that day alone, but day after day, from week to week, and term to term. I went there, not to attend to what was going on, but to think about Dora. If I ever bestowed a thought upon the cases, as they dragged their slow length before me, it was only to wonder, in the matrimonial cases (remembering Dora), how it was that married people could ever be otherwise than happy; and in the prerogative cases, to consider, if the money in question had been left to me, what were the foremost steps I should immediately have taken in regard to Dora. Within the first week of my passion, I bought four sumptuous waistcoats—not for myself; *I* had no pride in them; for Dora—and took to wearing straw-coloured kid gloves in the streets and laid the foundations of all the corns I have ever had. If the boots I wore at that period could only be produced and compared with the natural size of my feet, they would show what the state of my heart was, in a most affecting manner.

David Copperfield

I SHALL breakfast at 11 *precisely*; and as your mama was kind enough to promise to go to Pimlico for us, she will perhaps call here first, and take lunch with you here at that hour. I shall feel greatly disappointed if I have to wait longer than that time before I see you—I have not seen you, you know dearest, since seven o'clock yesterday evening. It seems an age.

Letter to his fiancee—1835

THOUGH lovers are remarkable for leaving a great deal unsaid on all occasions, and very properly desiring to come back and say it, they are remarkable also for a wonderful power of condensation; and can, in one way or other give utterance to more language—eloquent language—in any given short space of time, than all the six hundred and fifty-eight members in the Commons House of Parliament of the United Kingdom of Great Britain and Ireland; who are strong lovers, no doubt, but of their country only, which makes all the difference; for in a passion of that kind (which is not always returned), it is the custom to use as many words as possible, and express nothing whatever.

Martin Chuzzlewit

DOWN they sat to breakfast, but it was evident, notwithstanding the boasting of Mr Peter Magnus, that he laboured under a very considerable degree of nervousness, of which loss of appetite, a propensity to upset the tea-things, a spectral attempt at drollery, and an irresistible inclination to look at the clock, every other second, were among the principal symptoms.

"He—he—he," tittered Mr Magnus, affecting cheerfulness, and gasping with agitation. "It only wants two minutes, Mr Pickwick. Am I pale, sir?"

"Not very," replied Mr Pickwick.

There was a brief pause.

"I beg your pardon, Mr Pickwick; but have you ever done this sort of thing in your time?" said Mr Magnus.

"You mean proposing?" said Mr Pickwick.

"Yes."

"Never," said Mr Pickwick, with great energy, "never."

"You have no idea, then, how it's best to begin?" said Mr Magnus.

"Why," said Mr Pickwick, "I may have formed some ideas upon the subject, but, as I have never submitted them to the test of experience, I should be sorry if you were induced to regulate your proceedings by them."

"I should feel very much obliged to you, for any advice, sir," said Mr Magnus, taking another look at the clock: the hand of which was verging on the five minutes past.

"Well, sir," said Mr Pickwick, with the profound solemnity with which that great man could, when he pleased, render his remarks so deeply impressive: "I should commence, sir, with a tribute to the lady's beauty and excellent qualities; from them, sir, I should diverge to my own unworthiness."

"Very good," said Mr Magnus.

"Unworthiness for *her* only, mind, sir," resumed Mr Pickwick; "for to show that I was not wholly unworthy, sir, I should take a brief review of my past life, and present condition. I should argue, by analogy, that to anybody else, I must be a very desirable object. I should then expatiate on the warmth of my love, and the depth of my devotion. Perhaps I might then be tempted to seize her hand."

"Yes, I see," said Mr Magnus; "that would be a very great point."

"I should then, sir," continued Mr Pickwick, growing warmer as the subject presented itself in more glowing colours before him: "I should then, sir, come to the plain and simple question, 'Will you have me?' I think I am justified in assuming that upon this, she would turn away her head."

"You think that may be taken for granted?" said Mr Magnus; "because if she did not do that at the right place, it would be embarrassing."

"I think she would," said Mr Pickwick. "Upon this, sir, I should squeeze her hand, and I think—I *think*, Mr Magnus—that after I had done that, supposing there was no refusal, I should gently draw away the handkerchief, which my slight knowledge of human nature leads me to suppose the lady would be applying to her eyes at the moment, and steal a respectful kiss. I think I should kiss her, Mr Magnus; and at this particular point, I am decidedly of opinion that if the lady were going to take me at all she would murmur into my ears a bashful acceptance."

Mr Magnus started; gazed on Mr Pickwick's intelligent face, for a short time in silence; and then (the dial pointing to the ten minutes past) shook him warmly by the hand, and rushed desperately from the room.

Pickwick Papers

DAWN, with its passionless blank face, steals shivering to the church beneath which lies the dust of little Paul and his mother, and looks in at the windows. It is cold and dark. Night crouches yet, upon the pavement, and broods, sombre and heavy, in nooks and corners of the building. The steeple-clock, perched up above the houses, emerging from beneath another of the countless ripples in the tide of time that regularly roll and break on the eternal shore, is greyly visible, like a stone beacon, recording how the sea flows on; but within doors, dawn, at first, can only peep at night, and see that it is there.

Hovering feebly round the church, and looking in, dawn moans and weeps for its short reign, and its tears trickle on the window-glass, and the trees against the church-wall bow their heads, and wring their many hands in sympathy. Night, growing pale before it, gradually fades out of the church, but lingers in the vaults below, and sits upon the coffins. And now comes bright day, burnishing the steeple-clock, and reddening the spire, and drying up the tears of dawn, and stifling its complaining; and the scared dawn, following the night, and chasing it from its last refuge, shrinks into the vaults itself and hides, with a frightened face, among the dead, until night returns, refreshed, to drive it out.

And now, the mice, who have been busier with the prayer-books than their proper owners, and with the hassocks, more worn by their little teeth than by human knees, hide their bright eyes in their holes, and gather close together in affright at the resounding clashing of the church door. For the Beadle, that man of power, comes early this morning with the sexton; and Mrs Miff, the wheezy little pew-opener—a mighty dry old lady, sparely dressed, with not an inch of fulness anywhere about her—is also here, and has been waiting at the church gate half an hour, as her place is, for the Beadle.

A vinegary face has Mrs Miff, and a mortified bonnet, and eke a thirsty soul for sixpences and shillings. Beckoning to stray people to come into pews, has given Mrs Miff an air of mystery; and there is reservation in the eye of Mrs Miff, as always knowing of a softer seat, but having her suspicions of the fee. There is no such fact as Mr Miff, nor has there been, these twenty years, and Mrs Miff would rather not allude to him. He held some bad opinions, it would seem, about free seats; and though Mrs Miff hopes he may be gone upwards, she couldn't possibly undertake to say so.

Busy is Mrs Miff this morning at the church door, beating and dusting the altar cloth, the carpet, and the cushions; and much has Mrs Miff to say, about the wedding they are going to have. Mrs Miff is told, that the new furniture and alterations in the house cost full five thousand pound if they cost a penny; and Mrs Miff has heard, upon the best authority, that the lady hasn't got a sixpence wherewithal to bless herself. Mrs Miff remembers, likewise, as if it had happened yesterday, the first wife's funeral, and then the christening, and then the other funeral; and Mrs Miff says, by the by she'll soap-and-water that 'ere tablet presently, against the company arrive. Mr Sownds, the Beadle, who is sitting in the sun upon the church steps all this time (and seldom does anything else, except, in cold weather, sitting by the fire), approves of Mrs Miff's discourse, and asks if Mrs Miff has heard it said, that the lady is uncommon handsome? The information Mrs Miff has received, being of this nature, Mr Sownds the Beadle, who, though orthodox and corpulent, is still an admirer of female beauty, observes, with unction, yes, he hears she is a spanker—an expression that seems somewhat forcible to Mrs Miff, or would, from any lips but those of Mr Sownds the Beadle.

In Mr Dombey's house, at this same time, there is great stir and bustle, more especially among the women: not one of whom has had a wink of sleep since four o'clock, and all of whom were full dressed before six. Mr Towlinson is an object of greater consideration than usual to the housemaid, and the cook says at breakfast-time that one wedding makes many, which the housemaid can't believe, and don't think true at all. Mr Towlinson reserves his sentiments on this question; being rendered something gloomy by the engagement of a foreigner with whiskers (Mr Towlinson is whiskerless himself), who had been hired to accompany the happy pair to Paris, and who is busy packing the new chariot. In respect of this personage, Mr Towlinson admits, presently, that he never knew of any good that ever come of foreigners; and being charged by the ladies with prejudice, says, look at Bonaparte who was at the head of 'em, and see what *he* was always up to! Which the housemaid says is very true.

The pastry-cook is hard at work in the funereal room in Brook Street, and the very tall young men are busy looking on. One of the very tall young men already smells of sherry, and his eyes have a tendency to become fixed in his head, and to stare at objects without seeing them. The very tall young man is conscious of this failing in himself; and informs his comrade that it's his "exciseman." The very tall young man would say excitement, but his speech is hazy.

The men who play the bells have got scent of the marriage; and the marrow-bones and cleavers too; and a brass band too. The first are practising in a back settlement near Battlebridge; the second put themselves in communication, through their chief, with Mr Towlinson, to whom they offer terms to be bought off; and the third, in the person of an artful trombone, lurks and dodges round the corner, waiting for some traitor tradesman to reveal the place and hour of breakfast, for a bribe. Expectation and excitement extend further yet, and take a wider range. From Balls Pond, Mr Perch brings Mrs Perch to spend the day with Mr Dombey's servants, and accompany them, surreptitiously, to see the wedding. In Mr Toots's lodgings, Mr Toots attires himself as if he were at least the Bridegroom: determined to behold the spectacle in splendour from a secret corner of the gallery, and thither to convey the Chicken: for it is Mr Toots's desperate intent to point out Florence to the Chicken, then and there, and openly to say, "Now, Chicken, I will not deceive you any longer; the friend I have sometimes mentioned to you is myself; Miss Dombey is the object of my passion; what are your opinions, Chicken, in this state of things, and what, on the spot, do you advise?" The so-much-to-be-astonished Chicken, in the meanwhile dips his beak into a tankard of strong beer, in Mr Toots's kitchen, and pecks up two pounds of beefsteaks. In Princess's Place, Miss Tox is up and doing; for she too, though in sore distress, is resolved to put a shilling in the hands of Mrs Miff, and see the ceremony which has a cruel fascination for her, from some lonely corner. The quarters of the Wooden Midshipman are all alive; for Captain Cuttle, in his ankle-jacks and with a huge shirt-collar, is seated at his breakfast, listening to Rob the Grinder as he reads the Marriage Service to him beforehand, under orders, to the end that the Captain may perfectly understand the solemnity he is about to witness: for which purpose, the Captain gravely lays injunctions on his chaplain, from time to time, to "put about," or to "overhaul that 'ere article again," or to stick to his own duty, and leave the Amens to him, the Captain; one of which he repeats, whenever a pause is made by Rob the Grinder, with sonorous satisfaction.

Besides all this, and much more, twenty nursery-maids in Mr Dombey's street alone, have promised twenty families of little women, whose instinctive interest in nuptials dates from their cradles, that they shall go and see the marriage. Truly, Mr Sownds the Beadle has good reason to feel himself in office, as he suns his portly figure on the church steps, waiting for the marriage hour. Truly, Mrs Miff has cause to pounce on an unlucky dwarf child, with a giant baby, who peeps in at the porch, and drive her forth with indignation!

Cousin Feenix has come over from abroad, expressly to attend the marriage. Cousin Feenix was a man about town, forty years ago; but he is still so juvenile in figure and in manner, and so well got up, that strangers are amazed when they discover latent wrinkles in his lordship's face, and crows' feet in his eyes; and first observe him, not exactly certain when he walks across a room, of going quite straight to where he wants to go. But Cousin Feenix, getting up at half-past seven o'clock or so, is quite another thing from Cousin Feenix got up; and very dim, indeed, he looks, while being shaved at Long's Hotel, in Bond Street.

Mr Dombey leaves his dressing-room, amidst a general whisking away of the women on the staircase, who disperse in all directions, with a great rustling of skirts, except Mrs Perch, who, being (but that she always is) in an interesting situation, is not nimble, and is obliged to face him, and is ready to sink with confusion as she curtseys;—may Heaven avert all evil consequences from the house of Perch! Mr Dombey walks up to the drawing-room, to bide his time. Gorgeous are Mr Dombey's new blue coat, fawn-coloured pantaloons, and lilac waistcoat; and a whisper goes about the house, that Mr Dombey's hair is curled.

Dombey and Son

IT was evening. Isabella and Emily had strolled out with Mr Trundle; the deaf old lady had fallen asleep in her chair; the snoring of the fat boy penetrated in a low and monotonous sound from the distant kitchen; the buxom servants were lounging at the side-door, enjoying the pleasantness of the hour, and the delights of a flirtation, on first principles, with certain unwieldy animals attached to the farm; and there sat the interesting pair, uncared for by all, caring for none, and dreaming only of themselves; there they sat, in short, like a pair of carefully-folded kid-gloves—bound up in each other.

"I have forgotten my flowers," said the spinster aunt.

"Water them now," said Mr Tupman in accents of persuasion.

"You will take cold in the evening air," urged the spinster aunt, affectionately.

"No, no," said Mr Tupman rising; "it will do me good. Let me accompany you."

The lady paused to adjust the sling in which the left arm of the youth was placed, and taking his right arm led him to the garden.

There was a bower at the further end, with honeysuckle, jessamine, and creeping plants—one of those sweet retreats which humane men erect for the accommodation of spiders.

The spinster aunt took up a large watering-pot which lay in one corner, and was about to leave the arbour. Mr Tupman detained her, and drew her to a seat beside him.

"Miss Wardle!" said he.

The spinster aunt trembled, till some pebbles which had accidentally found their way into the large watering-pot shook like an infant's rattle.

"Miss Wardle," said Mr Tupman, "you are an angel."

"Mr Tupman!" exclaimed Rachael, blushing as red as the watering-pot itself.

"Nay," said the eloquent Pickwickian—"I know it but too well."

"All women are angels, they say," murmured the lady, playfully.

"Then what can *you* be; or to what, without presumption, can I compare you?" replied Mr Tupman. "Where was the woman ever seen who resembled you? Where else could I hope to find so rare a combination of excellence and beauty? Where else could I seek to—Oh!" Here Mr Tupman paused, and pressed the hand which clasped the handle of the happy watering-pot.

The lady turned aside her head. "Men are such deceivers," she softly whispered.

"They are, they are," ejaculated Mr Tupman; "but not all men. There lives at least one being who can never change—one being who would be content to devote his whole existence to your happiness—who lives but in your eyes—who breathes but in your smiles—who bears the heavy burden of life itself only for you."

"Could such an individual be found," said the lady—

"But he *can* be found," said the ardent Mr Tupman, interposing. "He *is* found. He is here, Miss Wardle." And ere the lady was aware of his intention, Mr Tupman had sunk upon his knees at her feet.

"Mr Tupman, rise," said Rachael.

"Never!" was the valorous reply. "Oh, Rachael!"—He seized her passive hand, and the watering-pot fell to the ground as he pressed it to his lips.—"Oh, Rachael! say you love me."

"Mr Tupman," said the spinster aunt, with averted head—"I can hardly speak the words; but—but—you are not wholly indifferent to me."

Mr Tupman no sooner heard this avowal, than he proceeded to do what his enthusiastic emotions prompted, and what, for aught we know (for we are but little acquainted with such matters), people so circumstanced always do. He jumped up, and, throwing his arm round the neck of the spinster aunt, imprinted upon her lips numerous kisses, which after a due show of struggling and resistance, she received so passively, that there is no telling how many more Mr Tupman might have bestowed, if the lady had not given a very unaffected start and exclaimed in an affrighted tone—

"Mr Tupman, we are observed!—we are discovered!"

Mr Tupman looked round. There was the fat boy, perfectly motionless, with his large circular eyes staring into the arbour, but without the slightest expression on his face that the most expert physiognomist could have referred to astonishment, curiosity, or any other known passion that agitates the human breast. Mr Tupman gazed on the fat boy, and the fat boy stared at him; and the longer Mr Tupman observed the utter vacancy of the fat boy's countenance, the more convinced he became that he either did not know, or did not understand anything that had been going forward. Under this impression, he said with great firmness—

"What do you want here, sir?"

"Supper's ready, sir," was the prompt reply.

"Have you just come here, sir?" inquired Mr Tupman, with a piercing look.

"Just," replied the fat boy.

Mr Tupman looked at him very hard again; but there was not a wink in his eye, or a curve in his face.

Mr Tupman took the arm of the spinster aunt, and walked towards the house; the fat boy followed behind.

"He knows nothing of what has happened," he whispered.

"Nothing," said the spinster aunt.

There was a sound behind them, as of an imperfectly suppressed chuckle. Mr Tupman turned sharply round. No; it could not have been the fat boy; there was not a gleam of mirth, or anything but feeding in his whole visage.

Pickwick Papers

"AH!" said Mr Gabriel Parsons, "I remember when I was a young man——Fill your glass, Timson."

"I have this moment emptied it."

"Then fill it again."

"I will," said Timson, suiting the action to the word.

"—I remember," resumed Mr Gabriel Parsons, "when I was a younger man, with what a strange compound of feelings I used to drink that toast, and how I used to think every woman was an angel."

"Was that before you were married?" mildly inquired Mr Watkins Tottle.

"Oh, certainly!" replied Mr Gabriel Parsons. "I have never thought so since; and a precious milksop I must have been, ever to have thought so at all. But, you know, I married Fanny under the oddest and most ridiculous circumstances possible."

"What were they, if one may inquire?" asked Timson, who had heard the story on an average, twice a week for the last six months. Mr Watkins Tottle listened attentively, in the hope of picking up some suggestion that might be useful to him in his new undertaking.

"I spent my wedding-night in a back kitchen chimney," said Parsons, by way of a beginning.

"In a back kitchen chimney!" ejaculated Watkins Tottle. "How dreadful!"

"Yes, it wasn't very pleasant," replied the small host. "The fact is, Fanny's father and mother liked me well enough as an individual, but had a decided objection to my becoming a husband. You see, I hadn't any money in those days, and they had; and so they wanted Fanny to pick up somebody else. However, we managed to discover the state of each other's affections somehow. I used to meet her at some mutual friends' parties; at first we danced together, and talked, and flirted, and all that sort of thing; then I used to like nothing so well as sitting by her side—we didn't talk so much then, but I remember I used to have a great notion of looking at her out of the extreme corner of my left eye—and then I got very miserable and sentimental, and began to write verses, and use Macassar oil. At last I couldn't bear it any longer, and after I had walked up and down the sunny side of Oxford Street in tight boots for a week—and a devilish hot summer it was, too—in the hope of meeting her, I sat down and wrote a letter, and begged her to manage to see me clandestinely, for I wanted to hear her decision from her own mouth. I said I had discovered, to my perfect satisfaction, that I couldn't live without her, and that, if she didn't have me, I had made up my mind to take prussic acid, or take to drinking, or emigrate, so as to take myself off in some way or other. Well, I borrowed a pound and bribed the housemaid to give her the note, which she did."

"And what was the reply?" inquired Timson, who had found before that to encourage the repetition of old stories is to get a general invitation.

"Oh, the usual one! Fanny expressed herself very miserable; hinted at the possibility of an early grave; said that nothing should induce her to swerve from the duty she owed her parents; implored me to forget her, and find out somebody more deserving; and all that sort of thing. She said she could, on no account, think of meeting me unknown to her pa and ma; and entreated me, as she should be in a particular part of Kensington Gardens at eleven o'clock next morning, not to attempt to meet her there."

"You didn't go, of course?" said Watkins Tottle.

"Didn't I? Of course I did. There she was, with the identical housemaid in perspective, in order that there might be no interruption. We walked about for a couple of hours; made ourselves delightfully miserable; and were regularly engaged. Then we began to 'correspond'—that is to say, we used to exchange about four letters a day; what we used to say in 'em I can't imagine. And I used to have an interview, in the kitchen, or the cellar, or some such place, every evening. Well, things went on in this way for some time; and we got fonder of each other every day. At last, as our love was raised to such a pitch, and as my salary had been raised too, shortly before, we determined on a secret marriage. Fanny arranged to sleep at a friend's on the previous night; we were to be married early in the morning; and then we were to return to her home and be pathetic. She was to fall at the old gentleman's feet, and bathe his boots with her tears; and I was to hug the old lady and call her 'mother,' and use my pocket-handkerchief as much as possible. Married we were the next morning; two girls—friends of Fanny's—acting as bridesmaids; and a man, who was hired for five shillings and a pint of porter, officiating as father. Now, the old lady unfortunately put off her return from Ramsgate, where she had been paying a visit, until the next morning: and, as we placed great reliance on her, we agreed to postpone our confession for four-and-twenty hours. My newly-made wife returned home, and I spent my wedding-day in strolling about Hampstead Heath and execrating my father-in-law. Of course, I went to comfort my dear little wife at night, as much as I could, with the assurance that our troubles would soon be over. I opened the garden-gate, of which I had a key, and was shown by the servant to our old place of meeting—a back kitchen, with a stone floor and a dresser; upon which, in the absence of chairs, we used to sit and make love."

"Make love upon a kitchen dresser?" interrupted Mr Watkins Tottle, whose ideas of decorum were greatly outraged.

"Ah! On a kitchen dresser!" replied Parsons. "And let me tell you, old fellow, that, if you were really over head and ears in love, and had no other place to make love in, you'd be devilish glad to avail yourself of such an opportunity. However, let me see; where was I?"

"On the dresser," suggested Timson.

"Oh—ah! Well, here I found poor Fanny, quite disconsolate and uncomfortable. The old boy had been very cross all day, which made her feel still more lonely; and she was quite out of spirits. So, I put a good face on the matter, and laughed it off, and said we should enjoy the pleasures of a matrimonial life more by contrast; and, at length, poor Fanny brightened up a little. I stopped there till about eleven o'clock, and, just as I was taking my leave for the fourteenth time, the girl came running down the stairs without her shoes, in a great fright, to tell us that the old villain—Heaven forgive me for calling him so, for he is dead and gone now!—prompted, I suppose, by the prince of darkness, was coming down, to draw his own beer for supper—a thing he had not done before for six months, to my certain knowledge; for the cask stood in that very back kitchen. If he discovered me there, explanation would have been out of the question; for he was so outrageously violent, when at all excited, that he never would have listened to me. There was only one thing to be done. The chimney was a very wide one; it had been originally built for an oven; went up perpendicularly for a few feet, and then shot backward and formed a sort of small cavern. My hopes and fortune—the means of our joint existence almost—were at stake. I scrambled in like a squirrel; coiled myself up in this recess; and, as Fanny and the girl replaced the deal chimney-board, I could see the light of the candle which my unconscious father-in-law carried in his hand. I heard him draw the beer; and I never heard beer run so slowly. He was just leaving the kitchen, and I was preparing to descend, when down came the infernal chimney-board with a tremendous crash. He stopped, and put down the candle and the jug of beer on the dresser; he was a nervous old fellow, and any unexpected noise annoyed him. He coolly observed that the fire-place was never used, and, sending the frightened servant into the next kitchen for a hammer and nails, actually nailed up the board, and locked the door on the outside. So, there was I, on my wedding-night, in the light kerseymere trousers, fancy waistcoat, and blue coat that I had been married in in the morning, in a back kitchen chimney, the bottom of which was nailed up, and the top of which had been formerly raised some fifteen feet, to prevent the smoke from annoying the neighbours. And there," added Mr Gabriel Parsons as he passed the bottle, "there I remained till half-past seven the next morning, when the housemaid's sweetheart, who was a carpenter, unshelled me. The old dog had nailed me up so securely that, to this very hour, I firmly believe that no one but a carpenter could ever have got me out."

"And what did Mrs Parson's father say when he found you were married?" inquired Watkins Tottle, who, although he never saw a joke, was not satisfied until he heard a story to the very end.

"Why, the affair of the chimney so tickled his fancy, that he pardoned us off-hand, and allowed us something to live on till he went the way of all flesh. I spent the next night in his second-floor front, much more comfortably than I had spent the preceding one; for, as you will probably guess—"

"Please, sir, missis has made tea," said a middle-aged female servant, bobbing into the room.

"That's the very housemaid that figures in my story," said Mr Gabriel Parsons. "She went into Fanny's service when we were first married, and has been with us ever since; but I don't think she has felt one atom of respect for me since the morning she saw me released, when she went into violent hysterics, to which she has been subject ever since. Now, shall we join the ladies?"

A Passage in the life of Mr Watkins Tottle

I HAVE set all this down, in my present blissful chapter, because here it comes into its natural place. Mr Spenlow and I falling into this conversation, prolonged it and our saunter to and fro, until we diverged into general topics. And so it came about, in the end, that Mr Spenlow told me this day week was Dora's birthday, and he would be glad if I would come down and join a little picnic on the occasion. I went out of my senses immediately; became a mere driveller next day, on receipt of a little lace-edged sheet of notepaper, "Favoured by papa. To remind"; and passed the intervening period in a state of dotage.

I think I committed every possible absurdity, in the way of preparation for this blessed event. I turn hot when I remember the cravat I bought. My boots might be placed in any collection of instruments of torture. I provided, and sent down by the Norwood coach the night before, a delicate little hamper, amounting in itself, I thought, almost to a declaration. There were crackers in it with the tenderest mottoes that could be got for money. At six in the morning, I was in Covent Garden Market, buying a bouquet for Dora. At ten I was on horseback (I hired a gallant gray, for the occasion), with the bouquet in my hat, to keep it fresh, trotting down to Norwood.

I suppose that when I saw Dora in the garden and pretended not to see her, and rode past the house pretending to be anxiously looking for it, I committed two small fooleries which other young gentlemen in my circumstances might have committed—because they came so very natural to me. But oh!

when I *did* find the house, and *did* dismount at the garden gate, and drag those stony-hearted boots across the lawn to Dora sitting on a garden seat under a lilac tree, what a spectacle she was, upon that beautiful morning, among the butterflies, in a white chip bonnet and a dress of celestial blue!

There was a young lady with her—comparatively stricken in years—almost twenty, I should say. Her name was Miss Mills, and Dora called her Julia. She was the bosom friend of Dora. Happy Miss Mills!

Jip was there, and Jip *would* bark at me again. When I presented my bouquet, he gnashed his teeth with jealousy. Well he might. If he had the least idea how I adored his mistress, well he might!

"Oh, thank you, Mr Copperfield! What dear flowers!" said Dora.

I had had an intention of saying (and had been studying the best form of words for three miles) that I thought them beautiful before I saw them so near *her*. But I couldn't manage it. She was too bewildering. To see her lay the flowers against her little dimpled chin, was to lose all presence of mind and power of language in a feeble ecstasy. I wonder I didn't say, "Kill me, if you have a heart, Miss Mills. Let me die here!"

Then Dora held my flowers to Jip to smell. Then Jip growled, and wouldn't smell them. Then Dora laughed, and held them a little closer to Jip, to make him. Then Jip laid hold of a bit of geranium with his teeth, and worried imaginary cats in it. Then Dora beat him, and pouted, and said, "My poor beautiful flowers!" as compassionately, I thought, as if Jip had laid hold of me. I wished he had!

"You'll be so glad to hear, Mr Copperfield," said Dora, "that that cross Miss Murdstone is not here. She has gone to her brother's marriage, and will be away at least three weeks. Isn't that delightful?"

I said I was sure it must be delightful to her, and all that was delightful to her was delightful to me. Miss Mills, with an air of superior wisdom and benevolence, smiled upon us.

"She is the most disagreeable thing I ever saw," said Dora.

"You can't believe how ill-tempered and shocking she is, Julia."

"Yes, I can, my dear!" said Julia.

"*You* can, perhaps, love," returned Dora, with her hand on Julia's. "Forgive my not excepting you, my dear, at first."

I learnt, from this, that Miss Mills had had her trials in the course of a chequered existence; and that to these, perhaps, I might refer that wise benignity of manner which I had already noticed. I found, in the course of the day, that this was the case: Miss Mills having been unhappy in a misplaced affection, and being understood to have retired from the world on her awful stock of experience, but still to take a calm interest in the unblighted hopes and loves of youth.

But now Mr Spenlow came out of the house, and Dora went to him, saying, "Look, papa, what beautiful flowers!" And Miss Mills smiled thoughtfully, as who should say, "Ye May-flies, enjoy your brief existence in the bright morning of life!" And we all walked from the lawn towards the carriage, which was getting ready.

I shall never have such a ride again. I have never had such another. There were only those three, their hamper, my hamper, and the guitar-case, in the phaeton; and, of course, the phaeton was open; and I rode behind it, and Dora sat with her back to the horses, looking towards me. She kept the bouquet close to her on the cushion, and wouldn't allow Jip to sit on that side of her at all, for fear he should crush it. She often carried it in her hand, often refreshed herself with its fragrance. Our eyes at those times often met; and my great astonishment is that I didn't go over the head of my gallant gray into the carriage.

There was dust, I believe. There was a good deal of dust, I believe. I have a faint impression that Mr Spenlow remonstrated with me for riding in it; but I knew of none. I was sensible of a mist of love and beauty about Dora, but of nothing else. He stood up sometimes, and asked me what I thought of the prospect. I said it was delightful, and I daresay it was; but it was all Dora to me. The sun shone Dora, and the birds sang Dora. The south wind blew Dora, and the wild-flowers in the hedges were all Doras, to a bud. My comfort is, Miss Mills understood me. Miss Mills alone could enter into my feelings thoroughly.

I don't know how long we were going, and to this hour I know as little where we went. Perhaps it was near Guildford. Perhaps some Arabian-night magician opened up the place for the day, and shut it for ever when we came away. It was a green spot, on a hill, carpeted with soft turf. There were shady trees, and heather, and, as far as the eye could see, a rich landscape.

It was a trying thing to find people here, waiting for us; and my jealousy, even of the ladies, knew no bounds. But all of my own sex—especially one imposter, three or four years my elder, with a red whisker, on which he established an amount of presumption not to be endured—were my mortal foes.

We all unpacked our baskets, and employed ourselves in getting dinner ready. Red Whisker pretended he could make a salad (which I don't believe), and obtruded himself on public notice. Some of the young ladies washed the lettuces for him, and sliced them under his directions. Dora was among these. I felt that fate had pitted me against this man, and one of us must fall.

Red Whisker made his salad (I wondered how they could eat it. Nothing should have induced *me* to touch it!) and voted himself into the charge of the wine-cellar, which he constructed, being an ingenious beast, in the hollow trunk of a tree. By and by I saw him, with the majority of a lobster on his plate, eating his dinner at the feet of Dora!

I have but an indistinct idea of what happened for some time after this baleful object presented itself to my view. I was very merry, I know; but it was hollow merriment. I attached myself to a young creature in pink, with little eyes, and flirted with her desperately. She received my attentions with favour; but whether on my account solely, or because she had any designs on Red Whisker, I can't say. Dora's health was drunk. When I drank it, I affected to interrupt my conversation for that purpose, and to resume it immediately afterwards. I caught Dora's eye as I bowed to her, and I thought it looked appealing. But it looked at me over the head of Red Whisker, and I was adamant.

The young creature in pink had a mother in green; and I rather think the latter separated us from motives of policy. Howbeit, there was a general breaking up of the party, while the remnants of the dinner were being put away; and I strolled off by myself among the trees, in a raging and remorseful state. I was debating whether I should pretend that I was not well, and fly—I don't know where—upon my gallant gray, when Dora and Miss Mills met me.

"Mr Copperfield," said Miss Mills, "you are dull."

I begged her pardon. Not at all.

"And, Dora," said Miss Mills, "*you* are dull."

Oh dear no! Not in the least.

"Mr Copperfield and Dora," said Miss Mills, with an almost venerable air. "Enough of this. Do not allow a trivial misunderstanding to wither the blossoms of spring, which once put forth and blighted, cannot be renewed. I speak," said Miss Mills, "from experience of the past—the remote, irrevocable past. The gushing fountains which sparkle in the sun, must not be stopped in mere caprice; the oasis in the desert of Sahara must not be plucked up idly."

I hardly knew what I did, I was burning all over to that extraordinary extent; but I took Dora's little hand and kissed it—and she let me! I kissed Miss Mills's hand; and we all seemed, to my thinking, to go straight up to the seventh heaven.

We did not come down again. We stayed up there all the evening. At first we strayed to and fro among the trees: I with Dora's shy arm drawn through mine: and Heaven knows, folly as it all was, it would have been a happy fate to have been struck immortal with those foolish feelings, and have strayed among the trees for ever!

But, much too soon, we heard the others laughing and talking and calling "where's Dora!" So we went back, and they wanted Dora to sing. Red Whisker would have got the guitar-case out of the carriage, but Dora told him nobody knew where it was, but I. So Red Whisker was done for in a moment; and *I* got it, and *I* unlocked it, and *I* took the guitar out, and *I* sat by her, and *I* held her handkerchief and gloves, and *I* drank in every note of her dear voice, and she sang to *me* who loved her, and all the others might applaud as much as they liked, but they had nothing to do with it!

I was intoxicated with joy. I was afraid it was too happy to be real, and that I should wake in Buckingham Street presently, and hear Mrs Crupp clinking the teacups in getting breakfast ready. But Dora sang, and others sang, and Miss Mills sang—about the slumbering echoes in the caverns of Memory; as if she were a hundred years old—and the evening came on; and we had tea, with a kettle boiling gipsy-fashion; and I was still as happy as ever.

I was happier than ever when the party broke up, and the other people, defeated Red Whisker and all, went their several ways, and we went ours through the still evening and the dying light, with sweet scents rising up around us. Mr Spenlow being a little drowsy after the champagne—honour to the soil that grew the grape, to the grape that made the wine, to the sun that ripened it, and to the merchant who adulterated it!—and being fast asleep in a corner of the carriage, I rode by the side, and talked to Dora. She admired my horse and patted him—oh, what a dear little hand it looked upon a horse!—and her shawl would not keep right, and now and then I drew it round her with my arm; and I even fancied that Jip began to see how it was, and to understand that he must make up his mind to be friends with me.

That sagacious Miss Mills, too; that amiable, though quite used up, recluse; that little patriarch of something less than twenty, who had done with the world, and mustn't on any account have the slumbering echoes in the caverns of Memory awakened; what a kind thing *she* did!

"Mr Copperfield," said Miss Mills, "come to this side of the carriage a moment—if you can spare a moment. I want to speak to you."

Behold me, on my gallant gray, bending at the side of Miss Mills, with my hand upon the carriage-door!

"Dora is coming to stay with me. She is coming home with me the day after tomorrow. If you would like to call, I am sure papa would be happy to see you."

What could I do but invoke a silent blessing on Miss Mills's head, and store Miss Mills's address in the securest corner of my memory! What could I do but tell Miss Mills, with grateful looks and fervent words, how much I appreciated her good offices, and what an inestimable value I set upon her friendship!

Then Miss Mills benignantly dismissed me, saying, "Go back to Dora!" and I went; and Dora leaned out of the carriage to talk to me, and we talked all the rest of the way; and I rode my gallant gray so close to the wheel that I grazed his near fore leg against it, and "took the bark off" as his owner told me, "to the tune of three pun' sivin"—which I paid, and thought extremely cheap for so much joy. What time Miss Mills sat looking at the moon, murmuring verses and recalling, I suppose, the ancient days when she and earth had anything in common.

Norwood was many miles too near, and we reached it many hours too soon; but Mr Spenlow came to himself a little short of it, and said, "You must come in, Copperfield, and rest!" and I consenting, we had sandwiches and wine-and-water. In the light room, Dora blushing looked so lovely, that I could not tear myself away, but sat there staring, in a dream, until the snoring of Mr Spenlow inspired me with sufficient consciousness to take my leave. So we parted; I riding all the way to London with the farewell touch of Dora's hand still light on mine, recalling every incident and word ten thousand times; lying down in my bed at last, as enraptured a young noodle as ever was carried out of his five wits by love.

David Copperfield

THE fat boy almost laughed again when he heard this suggestion. Mary, after a little more whispering, tripped forth from the group, and said:

"I am going to dine with you today, sir, if you have no objection."

"This way," said the fat boy, eagerly. "There is such a jolly meat pie!"

With these words, the fat boy led the way downstairs; his pretty companion captivating all the waiters and angering all the chambermaids as she followed him to the eating-room.

There was the meat pie of which the youth had spoken so feelingly, and there were, moreover, a steak, and a dish of potatoes, and a pot of porter.

"Sit down," said the fat boy. "Oh, my eye, how prime! I am *so* hungry."

Having apostrophised his eye, in a species of rapture, five or six times, the youth took the head of the little table, and Mary seated herself at the bottom.

"Will you have some of this?" said the fat boy, plunging into the pie up to the very ferules of the knife and fork.

"A little, if you please," replied Mary.

The fat boy assisted Mary to a little, and himself to a great deal, and was just going to begin eating when he suddenly laid down his knife and fork, leant forward in his chair, and letting his hands, with the knife and fork in them, fall on his knees, said, very slowly:

"I say! How nice you look!"

This was said in an admiring manner, and was, so far, gratifying; but still there was enough of the cannibal in the young gentleman's eyes to render the compliment a double one.

"Dear me, Joseph," said Mary, affecting to blush, "what do you mean?"

The fat boy gradually recovering his former position, replied with a heavy sigh, and remaining thoughtful for a few moments, drank a long draught of the porter. Having achieved this feat he sighed again, and applied himself assiduously to the pie.

"What a nice young lady Miss Emily is!" said Mary, after a long silence.

The fat boy had by this time finished the pie. He fixed his eyes on Mary, and replied:

"I knows a nicerer."

"Indeed!" said Mary.

"Yes, indeed!" replied the fat boy with unwonted vivacity.

"What's her name?" inquired Mary.

"What's yours?"

"Mary."

"So's hers," said the fat boy. "You're her." The boy grinned to add point to the compliment, and put his eyes into something between a squint and a cast, which there is reason to believe he intended for an ogle.

"You mustn't talk to me in that way," said Mary; "you don't mean it."

"Don't I though?" replied the fat boy; "I say!"

"Well."

"Are you going to come here regular?"

"No," rejoined Mary, shaking her head, "I'm going away again tonight. Why?"

"Oh!" said the fat boy in a tone of strong feeling; "how we should have enjoyed ourselves at meals, if you had been!"

"I might come here sometimes perhaps, to see you," said Mary, plaiting the table-cloth in assumed coyness, "if you would do me a favour."

The fat boy looked from the pie-dish to the steak, as if he thought a favour must be in a manner connected with something to eat; and then took out one of the half-crowns and glanced at it nervously.

"Don't you understand me?" said Mary, looking slyly in his fat face.

Again he looked at the half-crown, and said faintly, "No."

"The ladies want you not to say anything to the old gentleman about the young gentleman having been upstairs; and I want you too."

"Is that all?" said the fat boy, evidently very much relieved as he pocketed the half-crown again. "Of course I ain't a going to."

"You see," said Mary, "Mr Snodgrass is very fond of Miss Emily, and Miss Emily's very fond of him, and if you were to tell about it, the old gentleman would carry you all away miles into the country, where you'd see nobody."

"No, no, I won't tell," said the fat boy, stoutly.

"That's a dear," said Mary. "Now it's time I went upstairs, and got my lady ready for dinner."

"Don't go yet," urged the fat boy.

"I must," replied Mary. "Goodbye, for the present."

The fat boy, with elephantine playfulness, stretched out his arms to ravish a kiss; but as it required no great agility to elude him, his fair enslaver had vanished before he closed them again; upon which the apathetic youth ate a pound or so of steak with a sentimental countenance, and fell fast asleep.

Pickwick Papers

BY this time the good lady had been a long while upon one topic, so she fell at once into her daughter's little trap, if trap it were, and inquired what she had been going to say.

"About what, mama?" said Kate, who had apparently quite forgotten her diversion.

"Lor, Kate, my dear," returned her mother, "why, you're asleep or stupid! About the time before I was married."

"Oh yes!" said Kate, "I remember. I was going to ask, mama, before you were married, had you many suitors?"

"Suitors, my dear!" cried Mrs Nickleby, with a smile of wonderful complacency. "First and last, Kate, I must have had a dozen at least."

"Mama!" returned Kate, in a tone of remonstrance.

"I had indeed, my dear," said Mrs Nickleby; "not including your poor papa, or a young gentleman who used to go, at that time, to the same dancing-school, and who *would* send gold watches and bracelets to our house in gilt-edged paper (which were always returned), and who afterwards unfortunately went out to Botany Bay in a cadet ship—a convict ship I mean—and escaped into a bush and killed sheep (I don't know how they got there), and was going to be hung, only he accidentally choked himself, and the government pardoned him. Then there was young Lukin," said Mrs Nickleby, beginning with her left thumb and checking off the names on her fingers—"Mogley—Tipslark—Cabbery—Smifser—"

Having now reached her little finger, Mrs Nickleby was carrying the account over to the other hand, when a loud "Hem!" which appeared to come from the very foundation of the garden-wall, gave both herself and her daughter a violent start.

"Mama! what was that?" said Kate, in a low tone of voice.

"Upon my word, my dear," returned Mrs Nickleby, considerably startled, "unless it was the gentleman belonging to the next house, I don't know what it could possibly—"

"A—hem!" cried the same voice; and that, not in the tone of an ordinary clearing of the throat, but in a kind of bellow, which woke up all the echoes in the neighbourhood, and was prolonged to an extent which must have made the unseen bellower quite black in the face.

"I understand it now, my dear," said Mrs Nickleby, laying her hand on Kate's; "don't be alarmed, my love, it's not directed to you, and is not intended to frighten anybody. Let us give everybody their due, Kate; I am bound to say that."

So saying, Mrs Nickleby nodded her head, and patted the back of her daughter's hand, a great many times, and looked as if she could tell something vastly important if she chose, but had self-denial, thank Heaven; and wouldn't do it.

"What do you mean, mama?" demanded Kate, in evident surprise.

"Don't be flurried, my dear," replied Mrs Nickleby, looking towards the garden-wall, "for you see *I*'m not, and if it would be excusable in anybody to be flurried, it certainly would—under all the circumstances—be excusable in me, but I am not, Kate, not at all."

"It seems designed to attract our attention, mama," said Kate.

"It *is* designed to attract our attention, my dear; at least," rejoined Mrs Nickleby, drawing herself up, and patting her daughter's hand more blandly than before, "to attract the attention of one of us. Hem! you needn't be at all uneasy, my dear."

Kate looked very much perplexed, and was apparently about to ask for further explanation, when a shouting and scuffling noise, as of an elderly gentleman whooping, and kicking up his legs on loose gravel, with great violence, was heard to proceed from the same direction as the former sounds; and, before they had subsided, a large cucumber was seen to shoot up in the air with the velocity of a sky-rocket, whence it descended, tumbling over and over, until it fell at Mrs Nickleby's feet.

This remarkable appearance was succeeded by another of a precisely similar description; then a fine vegetable-marrow, of unusually large dimensions, was seen to whirl aloft, and come toppling down; then, several cucumbers shot up together; finally, the air was darkened by a shower of onions, turnip-radishes, and other small vegetables, which fell rolling and scattering, and bumping about, in all directions.

As Kate rose from her seat, in some alarm, and caught her mother's hand to run with her into the house, she felt herself rather retarded than assisted in her intention: and following the direction of Mrs Nickleby's eyes, was quite terrified by the apparition of an old black velvet cap, which, by slow degrees, as if its wearer were ascending a ladder or pair of steps, rose above the wall dividing their garden from that of the next cottage (which, like their own, was a detached building), and was gradually followed by a very large head, and an old face in which were a pair of most extraordinary grey eyes: very wild, very wide open, and rolling in their sockets, with a dull languishing leering look most ugly to behold.

"Mama!" cried Kate, really terrified for the moment, "why do you stop, why do you lose an instant? Mama, pray come in!"

"Kate, my dear," returned her mother, still holding back, "how can you be so foolish? I'm ashamed of you. How do you suppose you are ever to get through life, if you're such a coward as this! What do you want, sir?" said Mrs Nickleby, addressing the intruder with a sort of simpering displeasure. "How dare you look into this garden?"

"Queen of my soul," replied the stranger, folding his hands together, "this goblet sip!"

"Nonsense, sir," said Mrs Nickleby. "Kate, my love, pray be quiet."

"Won't you sip the goblet?" urged the stranger, with his head imploringly on one side, and his right hand on his breast. "Oh, do sip the goblet!"

"I shall not consent to do anything of the kind, sir," said Mrs Nickleby. "Pray, begone."

"Why is it," said the old gentleman, coming up a step higher, and leaning his elbows on the wall, with as much complacency as if he were looking out of a window, "why is it that beauty is always obdurate, even when admiration is as honourable and respectful as mine?" Here he smiled, kissed his hand, and made several low bows. "Is it owing to the bees, who, when the honey season is over, and they are supposed to have been killed with brimstone, in reality fly to Barbary and lull the captive Moors to sleep with their drowsy songs? Or is it," he added, dropping his voice almost to a whisper, "in consequence of the statue at Charing Cross having been lately seen, on the Stock Exchange at midnight, walking arm-in-arm with the Pump from Aldgate, in a riding-habit?"

"Mama," murmured Kate, "do you hear him?"

"Hush, my dear!" replied Mrs Nickleby, in the same tone of voice, "he is very polite, and I think that was a quotation from the poets. Pray don't worry me so—you'll pinch my arm black and blue. Go away, sir!"

"Quite away?" said the gentleman, with a languishing look. "Oh! quite away?"

"Yes," returned Mrs Nickleby, "certainly. You have no business here. This is private property, sir; you ought to know that."

"I do know," said the old gentleman, laying his finger on his nose, with an air of familiarity, most reprehensible, "that this is a sacred and enchanted spot, where the most divine charms"—here he kissed his hand and bowed again—"waft mellifluousness over the neighbours' gardens, and force the fruit and vegetables into premature existence. That fact I am acquainted with.

But will you permit me, fairest creature, to ask you one question, in the absence of the planet Venus, who has gone on business to the Horse Guards, and would otherwise—jealous of your superior charms—interpose between us?"

"Kate," observed Mrs Nickleby, turning to her daughter, "it's very awkward, positively. I really don't know what to say to this gentleman. One ought to be civil, you know."

"Dear mama," rejoined Kate, "don't say a word to him, but let us run away, as fast as we can, and shut ourselves up till Nicholas comes home."

Mrs Nickleby looked very grand, not to say contemptuous, at this humiliating proposal; and, turning to the old gentleman, who had watched them during these whispers with absorbing eagerness, said—

"If you will conduct yourself, sir, like the gentleman I should imagine you to be, from your language and—and—appearance (quite the counterpart of your grandpapa, Kate, my dear, in his best days), and will put your question to me in plain words, I will answer it."

If Mrs Nickleby's excellent papa had borne, in his best days, a resemblance to the neighbour now looking over the wall, he must have been, to say the least, a very queer-looking old gentleman in his prime. Perhaps Kate thought so, for she ventured to glance at his living portrait with some attention, as he took off his black velvet cap, and exhibiting a perfectly bald head, made a long series of bows, each accompanied with a fresh kiss of the hand. After exhausting himself, to all appearance, with this fatiguing performance, he covered his head once more, pulled the cap very carefully over the tips of his ears, and resuming his former attitude, said—

"The question is—"

Here he broke off to look round in every direction, and satisfy himself beyond all doubt that there were no listeners near. Assured that there were not, he tapped his nose several times, accompanying the action with a cunning look, as though congratulating himself on his caution; and stretching out his neck, said in a loud whisper—

"Are you a princess?"

"You are mocking me, sir," replied Mrs Nickleby, making a feint of retreating towards the house.

"No, but are you?" said the old gentleman.

"You know I am not, sir," replied Mrs Nickleby.

"Then are you any relation to the Archbishop of Canterbury?" inquired the old gentleman with great anxiety. "Or to the Pope of Rome? Or the Speaker of the House of Commons? Forgive me, if I am wrong, but I was told you were niece to the Commissioners of Paving, and daughter-in-law to the Lord Mayor and Court of Common Council, which would account for your relationship to all three."

"Whoever has spread such reports, sir," returned Mrs Nickleby with some warmth, "has taken great liberties with my name, and one which I am sure my son Nicholas, if he was aware of it, would not allow for an instant. The idea!" said Mrs Nickleby, drawing herself up. "Niece to the Commissioners of Paving!"

"Pray, mama, come away!" whispered Kate.

" 'Pray, mama!' Nonsense, Kate," said Mrs Nickleby, angrily, "but that's just the way. If they had said I was niece to a piping bullfinch, what would you care! But I have no sympathy," whimpered Mrs Nickleby. "I don't expect it, that's one thing."

"Tears!" cried the old gentleman, with such an energetic jump, that he fell down two or three steps and grated his chin against the wall. "Catch the crystal globules—catch 'em—bottle 'em up—cork 'em tight—put sealing-wax on the top—seal 'em with a cupid—label 'em 'Best quality'—and stow 'em away in the fourteen bin, with a bar of iron on the top to keep the thunder off!"

Issuing these commands, as if there were a dozen attendants all actively engaged in their execution, he turned his velvet cap inside out, put it on with great dignity so as to obscure his right eye and three-fourths of his nose, and sticking his arms akimbo, looked very fiercely at a sparrow hard by, till the bird flew away. He then put his cap in his pocket with an air of great satisfaction, and addressed himself with respectful demeanour to Mrs Nickleby.

"Beautiful madam," such were his words, "if I have made any mistake with regard to your family or connections, I humbly beseech you to pardon me. If I supposed you to be related to Foreign Powers or Native Boards, it is because you have a manner, a carriage, a dignity, which you will excuse my saying that none but yourself (with the single exception perhaps of the tragic muse, when playing extemporaneously on the barrel organ before the East India Company) can parallel. I am not a youth, ma'am, as you see; and although beings like you can never grow old, I venture to presume that we are fitted for each other."

"Really, Kate my love!" said Mrs Nickleby faintly, and looking another way.

"I have estates, ma'am," said the old gentleman, flourishing his right hand negligently, as if he made very light of such matters, and speaking very fast; "jewels, light-houses, fish-ponds, a whalery of my own in the North Sea, and several oyster-beds of great profit in the Pacific Ocean. If you will have the kindness to step down to the Royal Exchange and to take the cocked hat off the stoutest beadle's head, you will find my card in the lining of the crown, wrapped up in a piece of blue paper. My walking-stick is also to be seen on application to the chaplain of the House of Commons, who is strictly forbidden to take any money for showing it. I have enemies about me, ma'am," he looked towards his house and spoke very low, "who attack me on all occasions, and wish to secure my property. If you bless me with your hand and heart, you can apply to the Lord Chancellor or call out the military if necessary—sending my toothpick to the commander-in-chief will be sufficient—and so clear the house of them before the ceremony is performed. After that, love bliss and rapture; rapture love and bliss. Be mine, be mine?"

Repeating these last words with great rapture and enthusiasm, the old gentleman put on his black velvet cap again, and looking up into the sky in a hasty manner, said something that was not quite intelligible concerning a balloon he expected, and which was rather after its time.

"Be mine, be mine!" repeated the old gentleman.

"Kate, my dear," said Mrs Nickleby, "I have hardly the power to speak; but it is necessary for the happiness of all parties that this matter should be set at rest for ever."

"Surely there is no necessity for you to say one word, mama?" reasoned Kate.

"You will allow me, my dear, if you please, to judge for myself," said Mrs Nickleby.

"Be mine, be mine!" cried the old gentleman.

"It can scarcely be expected, sir," said Mrs Nickleby, fixing her eyes modestly on the ground, "that I should tell a stranger whether I feel flattered and obliged by such proposals, or not. They certainly are made under very singular circumstances; still at the same time, as far as it goes, and to a certain extent of course" (Mrs Nickleby's customary qualification), "they must be gratifying and agreeable to one's feelings."

"Be mine, be mine," cried the old gentleman. "Gog and Magog, Gog and Magog. Be mine, be mine!"

"It will be sufficient for me to say, sir," resumed Mrs Nickleby, with perfect seriousness—"and I'm sure you'll see the propriety of taking an answer and going away—that I have made up my mind to remain a widow, and to devote myself to my children. You may not suppose I am the mother of two children—indeed many people have doubted it, and said that nothing on earth could ever make 'em believe it possible—but it is the case, and they are both grown up. We shall be very glad to have you for a neighbour—very glad; delighted, I'm sure—but in any other character it's quite impossible, quite. As to my being young enough to marry again, that perhaps may be so, or it may not be; but I couldn't think of it for an instant, not on any account whatever. I said I never would, and I never will. It's a very painful thing to have to reject proposals, and I would much rather that none were made; at the same time this is the answer that I determined long ago to make, and this is the answer I shall always give."

These observations were partly addressed to the old gentleman, partly to Kate, and partly delivered in soliloquy. Towards their conclusion, the suitor evinced a very irreverent degree of inattention, and Mrs Nickleby had scarcely finished speaking when, to the great terror both of that lady and her daughter, he suddenly flung off his coat, and springing on the top of the wall, threw himself into an attitude which displayed his small clothes and grey worsteds to the fullest advantage, and concluded by standing on one leg, and repeating his favourite bellow with increased vehemence.

While he was still dwelling on the last note, and embellishing it with a prolonged flourish, a dirty hand was observed to glide stealthily and swiftly along the top of the wall, as if in pursuit of a fly, and then to clasp with the utmost dexterity one of the old gentleman's ankles. This done, the companion hand appeared, and clasped the other ankle.

Thus encumbered, the old gentleman lifted his legs awkwardly once or twice, as if they were very clumsy and imperfect pieces of machinery, and then looking down on his own side of the wall, burst into a loud laugh.

"It's you, is it?" said the old gentleman.

"Yes, it's me," replied a gruff voice.

"How's the Emperor of Tartary?" said the old gentleman.

"Oh! he's much the same as usual," was the reply. "No better and no worse."

"The young Prince of China," said the old gentleman, with much interest. "Is he reconciled to his father-in-law, the great potato salesman?"

"No," answered the gruff voice; "and he says he never will be, that's more."

"If that's the case," observed the old gentleman, "perhaps I'd better come down."

"Well," said the man on the other side, "I think you had, perhaps."

One of the hands being then cautiously unclasped, the old gentleman dropped into a sitting posture, and was looking round to smile and bow to Mrs Nickleby, when he disappeared with some precipitation, as if his legs had been pulled from below.

Very much relieved by his disappearance, Kate was turning to speak to her mama, when the dirty hands again became visible, and were immediately followed by the figure of a coarse squat man, who ascended by the steps which had been recently occupied by their singular neighbour.

"Beg your pardon, ladies," said this newcomer, grinning and touching his hat. "Has he been making love to either of you?"

"Yes," said Kate.

"Ah!" rejoined the man, taking his handkerchief out of his hat and wiping his face, "he always will, you know. Nothing will prevent his making love."

"I need not ask you if he is out of his mind, poor creature," said Kate.

"Why no," replied the man, looking into his hat, throwing his handkerchief in at one dab, and putting it on again. "That's pretty plain, that is."

"Has he been long so?" asked Kate.

"A long while."

"And is there no hope for him?" said Kate compassionately.

"Not a bit, and don't deserve to be," replied the keeper. "He's a deal pleasanter without his senses than with 'em. He was the cruellest, wickedest, out-and-outerest old flint that ever drawed breath."

"Indeed!" said Kate.

"By George!" replied the keeper, shaking his head so emphatically that he was obliged to frown to keep his hat on, "I never came across such a vagabond, and my mate says the same. Broke his poor wife's heart, turned his daughters out of doors, drove his sons into the streets; it was a blessing he went mad at last, through evil tempers, and covetousness, and selfishness, and guzzling, and drinking, or he'd have drove many others so. Hope for *him*, an old rip! There isn't too much hope going, but I'll bet a crown that what there is, is saved for more deserving chaps than him, anyhow."

With which confession of his faith, the keeper shook his head again, as much as to say that nothing short of this would do, if things were to go on at all; and touching his hat sulkily—not that he was in an ill-humour, but that his subject ruffled him—descended the ladder, and took it away.

During this conversation, Mrs Nickleby had regarded the man with a severe and steadfast look. She now heaved a profound sigh, and pursing up her lips, shook her head in a slow and doubtful manner.

"Poor creature!" said Kate.

"Ah! poor indeed!" rejoined Mrs Nickleby. "It's shameful that such things should be allowed. Shameful!"

"How can they be helped, mama?" said Kate, mournfully. "The infirmities of nature—"

"Nature!" said Mrs Nickleby. "What! Do *you* suppose this poor gentleman is out of his mind?"

"Can anybody who sees him entertain any other opinion, mama?"

"Why then, I just tell you this, Kate," returned Mrs Nickleby, "that he is nothing of the kind, and I am surprised you can be so imposed upon. It's some plot of these people to possess themselves of his property—didn't he say so himself? He may be a little odd and flighty, perhaps, many of us are that; but downright mad! and express himself as he does, respectfully, and in quite poetical language, and making offers with so much thought, and care, and prudence—not as if he ran into the streets, and went down upon his knees to the first chit of a girl he met, as a madman would! No, no, Kate, there's a great deal too much method in *his* madness; depend upon that, my dear."

Nicholas Nickleby

IT was a fine bright night, and for all her lowness of spirits Dolly kept looking up at the stars in a manner so bewitching (and *she* knew it!) that Joe was clean out of his senses, and plainly showed that if ever a man were—not to say over head and ears, but over the Monument and the top of St Paul's in love, that man was himself. The road was a very good one; not at all a jolting road, or an uneven one; and yet Dolly held the side of the chaise with one little hand, all the way. If there had been an executioner behind him with an uplifted axe ready to chop off his head if he touched that hand, Joe couldn't have helped doing it. From putting his own hand upon it as if by chance, and taking it away again after a minute or so, he got to riding along without taking it off at all; as if he, the escort, were bounded to do that as an important part of his duty, and had come out for the purpose. The most curious circumstance about this little incident was, that Dolly didn't seem to know of it. She looked so innocent and unconscious when she turned her eyes on Joe, that it was quite provoking.

Barnaby Rudge

A WONDERFUL fact to reflect upon, that every human creature is constituted to be that profound secret and mystery to every other. A solemn consideration, when I enter a great city by night, that every one of those darkly clustered houses encloses its own secret; that every room in every one of them encloses its own secret; that every beating heart in the hundreds of thousands of breasts there, is, in some of its imaginings, a secret to the heart nearest it!

A Tale of Two Cities

IT was not very long, you may be sure, before Joe Willet and Dolly Varden were made husband and wife, and with a handsome sum in bank (for the locksmith could afford to give his daughter a good dowry), reopened the Maypole.

It was not very long, you may be sure, before a red-faced little boy was seen staggering about the Maypole passage, and kicking up his heels on the green before the door. It was not very long, counting by years, before there was a red-faced little girl, another red-faced little boy, and a whole troop of girls and boys: so that, go to Chigwell when you would, there would surely be seen, either in the village street, or in the green, or frolicking in the farmyard—for it was a farm now, as well as a tavern—more small Joes and small Dollys than could be easily counted. It was not a very long time before these appearances ensued; but it *was* a *very* long time before Joe looked five years older, or Dolly either, or the locksmith either, or his wife either: for cheerfulness and content are great beautifiers, and are famous preservers of youthful looks, depend upon it.

Barnaby Rudge

Shakespearean Idyll (Mrs Joseph Porter)

MOST extensive were the preparations at Rose Villa, Clapham Rise, in the occupation of Mr Gattleton (a stockbroker in especially comfortable circumstances), and great was the anxiety of Mr Gattleton's interesting family, as the day fixed for the representation of the Private Play, which had been "many months in preparation," approached. The whole family was infected with the mania for Private Theatricals; the house, usually so clean and tidy, was, to use Mr Gattleton's expressive description, "regularly turned out o' windows"; the large dining-room, dismantled of its furniture and ornaments, presented a strange jumble of flats, flies, wings, lamps, bridges, clouds, thunder and lightning, festoons and flowers, daggers and foils, and various other messes in theatrical slang included under the comprehensive name of "properties." The bedrooms were crowded with scenery, the kitchen was occupied by carpenters. Rehearsals took place every other night in the drawing-room, and every sofa in the house was more or less damaged by the perseverance and spirit with which Mr Sempronius Gattleton and Miss Lucina rehearsed the smothering scene in *Othello*—it having been determined that the tragedy should form the first portion of the evening's entertainments.

"When we're a *leetle* more perfect, I think it will go admirably," said Mr Sempronius, addressing his *corps dramatique*, at the conclusion of the hundred and fiftieth rehearsal. In consideration of his sustaining the trifling inconvenience of bearing all the expenses of the play, Mr Sempronius had been, in the most handsome manner, unanimously elected stage manager. "Evans," continued Mr Gattleton the younger, addressing a tall, thin, pale young gentleman, with extensive whiskers; "Evans, you play *Roderigo* beautifully."

"Beautifully!" echoed the three Miss Gattletons; for Mr Evans was pronounced by all his lady friends to be "quite a dear." He looked so interesting, and had such lovely whiskers: to say nothing of his talent for writing verses in albums and playing the flute! *Roderigo* simpered and bowed.

"But I think," added the manager, "you are hardly perfect in the—fall—in the fencing scene, where you are—you understand?"

"It's very difficult," said Mr Evans thoughtfully; "I've fallen about a good deal in our counting-house lately, for practice, only I find it hurts one so. Being obliged to fall backwards, you see, it bruises one's head a good deal."

"But you must take care you don't knock a wing down," said Mr Gattleton the elder, who had been appointed prompter, and who took as much interest in the play as the youngest of the company, "The stage is very narrow, you know,"

"Oh! don't be afraid," said Mr Evans with a very self-satisfied air: "I shall fall with my head 'off,' and then I can't do any harm."

"But, egad!" said the manager, rubbing his hands, "we shall make a decided hit in *Masaniello*. Harleigh sings that music admirably."

Everybody echoed the sentiment. Mr Harleigh smiled, and looked foolish—not an unusual thing with him—hummed "Behold how brightly breaks the morning," and blushed as red as the fisherman's nightcap he was trying on.

"Let's see," resumed the manager, telling the number on his fingers; "we shall have three dancing female peasants, besides *Fenella*, and four fishermen. Then there's our man Tom; he can have a pair of ducks of mine, and a check shirt of Bob's, and a red nightcap, and he'll do for another—that's five. In the choruses, of course, we can sing at the sides; and in the market scene we can walk about in cloaks and things. When the revolt takes place, Tom must keep rushing in on one side and out on the other, with a pickaxe, as fast as he can. The effect will be electrical; it will look exactly as if there were an immense number of 'em. And in the eruption scene we must burn the red fire, and upset the tea-trays, and make all sorts of noises—and it's sure to do."

"Sure! sure!" cried all the performers *unâ voce*—and away hurried Mr Sempronius Gattleton to wash the burnt cork off his face, and superintend the "setting-up" of some of the amateur-painted, and never-sufficiently-to-be-admired, scenery.

Mrs Gattleton was a kind, good-tempered, vulgar soul, exceedingly fond of her husband and children, and entertaining only three dislikes. In the first place, she had a natural antipathy to anybody else's unmarried daughters; in the second, she was in bodily fear of anything in the shape of ridicule; lastly—almost a necessary consequence of this feeling—she regarded with feelings of the utmost horror one, Mrs Joseph Porter, over the way. However, the good folks of Clapham and its vicinity stood very much in awe of scandal and sarcasm; and thus Mrs Joseph Porter was courted, and flattered, and caressed, and invited, for much the same reason that induces a poor author, without a farthing in his pocket, to behave with extraordinary civility to a twopenny postman.

"Never mind, ma," said Miss Emma Porter in colloquy with her respected relative, and trying to look unconcerned; "if they had invited me, you know that neither you nor pa would have allowed me to take part in such an exhibition."

"Just what I should have thought from your high sense of propriety," returned the mother. "I am glad to see, Emma, you know how to designate the proceeding." Miss P., by-the-bye, had only the week before made "an exhibition" of herself for four days, behind a counter at a fancy fair, to all and every of her Majesty's liege subjects who were disposed to pay a shilling each for the privilege of seeing some four dozen girls flirting with strangers, and playing at shop.

"There!" said Mrs Porter, looking out of window; "there are two rounds of beef and a ham going in—clearly for sandwiches; and Thomas, the pastrycook, says there have been twelve dozen tarts ordered, besides blancmange and jellies. Upon my word! think of the Miss Gattletons in fancy dresses too!"

"Oh, it's too ridiculous!" said Miss Porter hysterically.

"I'll manage to put them a little out of conceit with the business, however," said Mrs Porter; and out she went on her charitable errand.

"Well, my dear Mrs Gattleton," said Mrs Joseph Porter after they had been closeted for some time, and when, by dint of indefatigable pumping she had managed to extract all the news about the play, "well, my dear, people may say what they please; indeed, we know they will, for some folks are so ill-natured. Ah, my dear Miss Lucina, how d'ye do? I was just telling your mama that I have heard it said that—"

"What?"

"Mrs Porter is alluding to the play, my dear," said Mrs Gattleton; "she was, I am sorry to say, just informing me that—"

"Oh, now, pray don't mention it!" interrupted Mrs Porter; "it's most absurd—quite as absurd as young What's-his-name saying he wondered how Miss Caroline, with such a foot and ankle, could have the vanity to play *Fenella*."

"Highly impertinent, whoever said it," said Mrs Gattleton, bridling up.

"Certainly, my dear," chimed in the delighted Mrs Porter; "most undoubtedly! Because, as I said, if Miss Caroline *does* play

Fenella, it doesn't follow, as a matter of course, that she should think she has a pretty foot, and then—such puppies as these young men are—he had the impudence to say that—"

How far the amiable Mrs Porter might have succeeded in her pleasant purpose, it is impossible to say, had not the entrance of Mr Thomas Balderstone, Mrs Gattleton's brother, familiarly called in the family "Uncle Tom," changed the course of conversation, and suggested to her mind an excellent plan of operation on the evening of the play.

Uncle Tom was very rich, and exceedingly fond of his nephews and nieces: as a matter of course, therefore, he was an object of great importance in his own family. He was one of the best-hearted men in existence; always in a good temper, and always talking. It was his boast that he wore top-boots on all occasions, and had never worn a black silk neckerchief; and it was his pride that he remembered all the principal plays of Shakespeare from beginning to end—and so he did. The result of this parrot-like accomplishment was, that he was not only perpetually quoting himself, but that he could never sit by and hear a misquotation from the "Swan of Avon" without setting the unfortunate delinquent right. He was also something of a wag; never missed an opportunity of saying what he considered a good thing, and invariably laughed until he cried at anything that appeared to him mirth-moving or ridiculous.

"Well, girls!" said Uncle Tom after the preparatory ceremony of kissing and how-d'ye-doing had been gone through—"how d'ye get on? Know your parts, eh?—Lucina, my dear, act ii., scene 1—place, left—cue—'Unknown fate'—What's next, eh?—Go on—'The heavens—'"

"Oh yes!" said Miss Lucina, "I recollect:

'The heavens forbid
But that our loves and comforts should increase
Even as our days do grow!'"

"Make a pause here and there," said the old gentleman, who was a great critic. "'But that our loves and comforts should increase'—emphasis on the last syllable, 'crease',—loud 'even', one, two, three, four; then loud again, 'as our days do grow;' emphasis on *days*. That's the way, my dear; trust to your uncle for emphasis. Ah! Sem, my boy, how are you?"

"Very well, thankee, uncle," returned Mr Sempronius, who had just appeared, looking something like a ring-dove, with a small circle round each eye: the result of his constant corking. "Of course we see you on Thursday."

"Of course, of course, my dear boy."

"What a pity it is your nephew didn't think of making you prompter, Mr Balderstone!" whispered Mrs Joseph Porter; "you would have been invaluable."

"Well, I flatter myself I *should* have been tolerably up to the thing," responded Uncle Tom.

"I must bespeak sitting next you on the night," resumed Mrs Porter; "and then, if our dear young friends here should be at all wrong, you will be able to enlighten me. I shall be so interested."

"I am sure I shall be most happy to give you any assistance in my power."

"Mind, it's a bargain."

"Certainly."

"I don't know how it is," said Mrs Gattleton to her daughters as they were sitting round the fire in the evening, looking over their parts, "but I really very much wish Mrs Joseph Porter wasn't coming on Thursday. I am sure she's scheming something."

"She can't make *us* ridiculous, however," observed Mr Sempronius Gattleton haughtily.

The long-looked for Thursday arrived in due course, and brought with it, as Mr Gattleton, senior, philosophically observed, "no disappointments to speak of." True, it was yet a matter of doubt whether *Cassio* would be enabled to get into the dress which had been sent for him from the masquerade warehouse. It was equally uncertain whether the principal female singer would be sufficiently recovered from the influenza to make her appearance; Mr Harleigh, the *Masaniello* of the night, was hoarse, and rather unwell, in consequence of the great quantity of lemon and sugar-candy he had eaten to improve his voice; and two flutes and a violoncello had pleaded severe colds. What of that? the audience were all coming. Everybody knew his part; the dresses were covered with tinsel and spangles; the white plumes looked beautiful; Mr Evans had practised falling until he was bruised from head to foot, and quite perfect; *Iago* was sure that in the stabbing scene he should make "a decided hit." A self-taught deaf gentleman, who had kindly offered to bring his flute would be a most valuable addition to the orchestra; Miss Jenkins's talent for the piano was too well known to be doubted for an instant; Mr Cape had practised the violin accompaniment with her frequently; and Mr Brown, who had kindly undertaken, at a few hours' notice, to bring his violoncello, would, no doubt, manage extremely well.

Seven o'clock came, and so did the audience; all the rank and fashion of Clapham and its vicinity was fast filling the theatre. There were the Smiths, the Gubbinses, the Nixons, the Dixons, the Hicksons, people with all sorts of names, two aldermen, a sheriff in perspective, Sir Thomas Glumper (who had been knighted in the last reign for carrying up an address on somebody's escaping from nothing); and last, not least, there were Mrs Joseph Porter and Uncle Tom, seated in the centre of the third row from the stage; Mrs P. amusing Uncle Tom with all sorts of stories, and Uncle Tom amusing everyone else by laughing most immoderately.

Ting, ting, ting! went the prompter's bell at eight o'clock precisely, and dash went the orchestra into the overture to *The Men of Prometheus*. The pianoforte player hammered away with laudable perseverance; and the violoncello, which struck in at intervals, "sounded very well, considering." The unfortunate individual, however, who had undertaken to play the flute accompaniment "at sight," found, from fatal experience, the perfect truth of the old adage, "Out of sight, out of mind"; for, being very near-sighted, and being placed at a considerable distance from his music-book, all he had the opportunity of doing was to play a bar now and then in the wrong place, and put the other performers out. It is, however, but justice to Mr Brown to say that he did this to admiration. The overture, in fact, was not unlike a race between the different instruments; the piano came in first by several bars, and the violoncello next, quite distancing the poor flute; for the deaf gentleman *too-too'd* away, quite unconscious that he was at all wrong, until apprised, by the applause of the audience, that the overture was concluded. A considerable bustle and shuffling of feet was then heard upon the stage accompanied by whispers of "Here's a pretty go!—what's to be done?" etc. The audience applauded again, by way of raising the spirits of the performers; and then Mr Sempronius desired the prompter, in a very audible voice, to "clear the stage, and ring up."

Ting, ting, ting! went the bell again. Everybody sat down; the curtain shook; rose sufficiently high to display several pairs of yellow boots paddling about; and there remained.

Ting, ting, ting! went the bell again. The curtain was violently convulsed, but rose no higher; the audience tittered; Mrs Porter looked at Uncle Tom; Uncle Tom looked at everybody, rubbing his hands, and laughing with perfect rapture. After as much ringing with the little bell as a muffin boy would make in going down a tolerably long street, and a vast deal of whispering, hammering, and calling for nails and cords, the curtain at length rose, and discovered Mr Sempronius Gattleton *solus*, and decked for *Othello*. After three distinct rounds of applause, during which Mr Sempronius applied his right hand to his left breast, and bowed in the most approved manner, the manager advanced, and said:

"Ladies and Gentlemen—I assure you it is with sincere regret, that I regret to be compelled to inform you, that *Iago* who was to have played Mr Wilson—I beg your pardon, Ladies and Gentlemen, but I am naturally somewhat agitated (applause)—I mean, Mr Wilson, who was to have played *Iago*, is—that is, has been—or, in other words, Ladies and Gentlemen, the fact is, that I have just received a note, in which I am informed that *Iago* is unavoidably detained at the Post Office this evening. Under these circumstances, I trust—a—a—

amateur performance—a—another gentleman undertaken to read the part—requests indulgence for a short time—courtesy and kindness of a British audience." Overwhelming applause. Exit Mr Sempronius Gattleton, and curtain falls.

The audience were, of course, exceedingly good-humoured; the whole business was a joke; and accordingly they waited for an hour with the utmost patience, being enlivened by an interlude of rout-cakes and lemonade. It appeared, by Mr Sempronius's subsequent explanation, that the delay would not have been so great, had it not so happened that when the substitute *Iago* had finished dressing, and just as the play was on the point of commencing, the original *Iago* unexpectedly arrived. The former was, therefore, compelled to undress, and the latter to dress for his part; which, as he found some difficulty in getting into his clothes, occupied no inconsiderable time. At last, the tragedy began in real earnest. It went off well enough, until the third scene of the first act, in which *Othello* addresses the Senate: the only remarkable circumstance being that, as *Iago* could not get on any of the stage boots, in consequence of his feet being violently swollen with the heat and excitement, he was under the necessity of playing the part in a pair of Wellingtons, which contrasted rather oddly with his richly-embroidered pantaloons. When *Othello* started with his address to the Senate (whose dignity was represented by the *Duke*, a carpenter, two men engaged on the recommendation of the gardener, and a boy), Mrs Porter found the opportunity she so anxiously sought.

Mr Sempronius proceeded:

> " 'Most potent, grave, and reverend signiors,
> My very noble and approv'd good masters,
> That I have ta'en away this old man's daughter.
> It is most true;—rude am I in my speech—' "

"Is that right?" whispered Mrs Porter to Uncle Tom.

"No."

"Tell him so, then."

"I will. Sem!" called out Uncle Tom, "that's wrong, my boy."

"What's wrong, uncle?" demanded *Othello*, quite forgetting the dignity of his situation.

"You've left out something. 'True I have married—' "

"Oh—ah!" said Mr Sempronius, endeavouring to hide his confusion as much and as ineffectually as the audience attempted to conceal their half-suppressed tittering, by coughing with extraordinary violence:

——" 'true I have married her:—
The very head and front of my offending.
Hath this extent; no more.' "

(*Aside*) "Why don't you prompt, father?"

"Because I've mislaid my spectacles," said poor Mr Gattleton, almost dead with the heat and bustle.

"There, now it's 'rude am I,' " said Uncle Tom.

"Yes, I know it is," returned the unfortunate manager, proceeding with his part.

It would be useless and tiresome to quote the number of instances in which Uncle Tom, now completely in his element, and instigated by the mischievous Mrs Porter, corrected the mistakes of the performers; suffice it to say that, having mounted his hobby, nothing could induce him to dismount; so during the whole remainder of the play, he performed a kind of running accompaniment, by muttering everybody's part as it was being delivered, in an undertone. The audience were highly amused, Mrs Porter delighted, the performers embarrassed; Uncle Tom never was better pleased in all his life; and Uncle Tom's nephews and nieces had never, although the declared heirs to his large property, so heartily wished him gathered to his fathers as on that memorable occasion.

Several other minor causes, too, united to damp the ardour of the *dramatis personae*. None of the performers could walk in their tights, or move their arms in their jackets; the pantaloons were too small, the boots too large, and the swords of all shapes and sizes. Mr Evans, naturally too tall for the scenery, wore a black velvet hat with immense white plumes, the glory of which was lost in the "flies"; and the only other inconvenience of which was, that when it was off his head he could not put it on, and when it was on he could not take it off. Notwithstanding all his practice, too, he fell with his head and shoulders as neatly through one of the side scenes as a harlequin would jump through a panel in a Christmas pantomime. The pianoforte player, overpowered by the extreme heat of the room, fainted away at the commencement of the entertainments, leaving the music of *Masaniello* to the flute and violoncello. The orchestra complained that Mr Harleigh put them out, and Mr Harleigh declared that the orchestra prevented his singing a note. The fishermen, who were hired for the occasion, revolted to the very life, positively refusing to play without an increased allowance of spirits; and, their demand being complied with, getting drunk in the eruption scene as naturally as possible. The red fire, which was burnt at the conclusion of the second act, not only nearly suffocated the audience, but nearly set the house on fire into the bargain; and, as it was, the remainder of the piece was acted in a thick fog.

In short, the whole affair was, as Mrs Joseph Porter triumphantly told everybody, "a complete failure." The audience went home at four o'clock in the morning, exhausted with laughter, suffering from severe headaches, and smelling terribly of brimstone and gunpowder. The Messrs Gattleton, senior and junior, retired to rest, with the vague idea of emigrating to Swan River early in the ensuing week.

Rose Villa has once again resumed its wonted appearance; the dining-room furniture has been replaced; the tables are as nicely polished as formerly; the horsehair chairs are ranged against the wall as regularly as ever; Venetian blinds have been fitted to every window in the house to intercept the prying gaze of Mrs Joseph Porter. The subject of theatricals is never mentioned in the Gattleton family, unless, indeed, by Uncle Tom, who cannot refrain from sometimes expressing his surprise and regret at finding that his nephews and nieces appear to have lost the relish they once possessed for the beauties of Shakespeare, and quotations from the works of that immortal bard.

The Happy Traveller

"IT is extraordinary what nonsense English people talk, write, and believe, about foreign countries."

Letter to John Forster

WE had a most miserable passage yesterday; the sea (very high) washing over us the whole way: nearly everybody ill (I among the number); and the boat so intolerably crowded that nobody had room to be ill in—but very few could get near the side—and the condition of things that resulted was most distressing. Collins, who was not ill and was raised aloft on a high pile of luggage, said that the after deck where the ladies were lying wet through, in all directions, looked like an immense picnic party with everybody intent upon a pigeon pie of her own—from the immense number of white basins. When these were all in use, the steward produced a slop-pail and two buckets, round each of which a prodigious family party assembled. I had a man, roaring like a lion with sickness, on each of my shoulders, and, as my place was a little corner of the leeward paddle box, every basin, pail, and bucket in the boat was emptied (at least twelve times each) over my head. We got to town at a quarter past seven.

Letter to his Wife, 1853

SEA-SICKNESS is like a belief in ghosts—every one entertains some misgivings on the subject, but few will acknowledge any.

The Steam Excursion

PARIS is very full, extraordinarily gay, and wonderfully improving. Thousands of houses must have been pulled down for the construction of an immense street now making for the dirty old end of the Rue de Rivoli, past the Palais Royal, away beyond the Hotel de Ville. It will be the finest thing in Europe. The quays by the riverside are Macadamized and as clean as Regent Street. Indeed the general improvement in the essential articles of what is to be seen and what is to be smelt, is highly remarkable.

Letter to his Wife from Paris, 1853

WE have had an amusingly absurd incident this afternoon. When we came home, I saw added to the hotel—our old hotel, and I am writing in the room where we once dined at the table d'hote—some baths, cold and hot, down on the margin of the torrent below. This induced us to order three hot baths. Therefore, the keys of the bathroom were found with immense difficulty, women ran backwards and forwards across the bridge, men bore in great quantities of wood, a horrible furnace was lighted, and a smoke was raised which filled the whole valley. This began at half-past three, and we congratulated each other on the distinction we should probably acquire by being the cause of the conflagration of the whole village. We sat by the fire until half-past five (dinner time) and still no baths. Then Edward came up to say that the water was as yet only "tippit"—which we supposed to be tepid—but that by half-past eight it would be in a noble state. Ever since, the smoke has poured forth in enormous volume, and the furnace has blazed, and the women have gone and come over the bridge and piles of wood have been carried in, but we observe a general avoidance of us by the establishment which still looks like failure. We have had a capital dinner, the dessert whereof is now on the table. Soup, beefsteak admirably cooked, boiled fowl and rice, roast leg of chamois, roast leg of mutton, and a pudding served in a blaze of rum. When we arrived, at nearly seven last night, all the linen in the house, newly washed, was piled in the sitting-room—all the curtains were taken down—and all the chairs piled bottom upwards. They cleared away as much as they could directly, and had even got the curtains up again at breakfast this morning.

Letter to his Wife from Chamonix, 1853

AVAILING ourselves of a part of the quiet interval between the termination of the Carnival and the beginning of the Holy Week: when everybody had run away from the one, and few people had yet begun to run back again for the other: we went conscientiously to work, to see Rome. And, by dint of going out early every morning, and coming back late every evening, and labouring hard all day, I believe we made acquaintance with every post and pillar in the city, and the country round; and, in particular, explored so many churches, that I abandoned that part of the enterprise at last, before it was half finished, lest I should never, of my own accord, go to church again, as long as I lived. But, I managed, almost every day, at one time or other, to get back to the Coliseum, and out upon the open Campagna, beyond the Tomb of Cecilia Metella.

We often encountered, in these expeditions, a company of English Tourists, with whom I had an ardent, but ungratified longing, to establish a speaking acquaintance. They were one Mr Davis, and a small circle of friends. It was impossible not to know Mrs Davis's name, from her being always in great request among her party, and her party being everywhere. During the Holy Week, they were in every part of every scene of every ceremony. For a fortnight or three weeks before it, they were in every tomb, and every church, and every ruin, and every Picture Gallery; and I hardly ever observed Mrs Davis to be silent for a moment. Deep underground, high up in St Peter's, out on the Campagna, and stifling in the Jews' quarter, Mrs Davis turned up, all the same. I don't think she ever saw anything, or ever looked at anything; and she had always lost something out of a straw hand-basket, and was trying to find it, with all her might and main, among an immense quantity of English halfpence, which lay, like sands upon the sea-shore, at the bottom of it. There was a professional Cicerone always attached to the party (which had been brought over from London, fifteen or twenty strong, by contract), and if he so much as looked at Mrs Davis, she invariably cut him short by saying, "There, God bless the man, don't worrit me! I don't understand a word you say, and shouldn't if you was to talk till you was black in the face!" Mr Davis always had a snuff-coloured great-coat on, and carried a great green umbrella in his hand, and had a slow curiosity constantly devouring him, which prompted him to do extraordinary things, such as taking the covers off urns in tombs, and looking in at the ashes as if they were pickles—and tracing out inscriptions with the ferrule of his umbrella, and saying, with intense thoughtfulness, "Here's a B you see, and there's a R, and this is the way we goes on in; is it!" His antiquarian habits occasioned his being frequently in the rear of the rest; and one of the agonies of Mrs

Davis, and the party in general, was an ever-present fear that Davis would be lost. This caused them to scream for him, in the strangest places, and at the most improper seasons. And when he came, slowly emerging out of some sepulchre or other, like a peaceful Ghoule, saying "Here I am!" Mrs Davis invariably replied, "You'll be buried alive in a foreign country, Davis, and it's no use trying to prevent you!"

Mr and Mrs Davis, and their party, had, probably, been brought from London in about nine or ten days. Eighteen hundred years ago, the Roman legions under Claudius, protested against being led into Mr and Mrs Davis's country, urging that it lay beyond the limits of the world.

Pictures from Italy

WE live in the same house that I lived in nine years ago, and have the same sitting-room—close to the Bridge of Sighs and the Palace of the Doges. The room is at the corner of the house, and there is a narrow street of water running round the side: so that we have the Grand Canal before the two front windows, and this wild little street at the corner window: into which, too, our three bedrooms look. We established a gondola as soon as we arrived, and we slide out of the hall on to the water twenty times a day. The gondoliers have queer old customs that belong to their class, and some are sufficiently disconcerting. . . . It is a point of honour with them, while they are engaged, to be always at your disposal. Hence it is no use telling them they may go home for an hour or two—for they won't go. They roll themselves in shaggy capuccins, great coats with hoods, and lie down on the stone or marble pavement until they are wanted again. So that when I come in or go out, on foot—which can be done from this house for some miles, over little bridges and by narrow ways—I usually walk over the principal of my vassals, whose custom it is to snore immediately across the doorway. Conceive the oddity of the most familiar things in this place, from one instance: Last night we go downstairs at half-past eight, step into the gondola, slide away on the black water, ripple and plash swiftly along for a mile or two, land at a broad flight of steps, and instantly walk into the most brilliant and beautiful theatre conceivable—all silver and blue, and precious little fringes made of glittering prisms of glass. There we sit until half-past eleven, come out again (gondolier asleep outside the box-door), and in a moment are on the black silent water, floating away as if there were no dry building in the world. It stops, and in a moment we are out again, upon the broad solid Piazza of St Mark, brilliantly lighted with gas, very like the Palais Royal at Paris, only far more handsome, and shining with no end of caffès. The two old pillars and the enormous bell-tower are as gruff and solid against the exquisite starlight as if they were a thousand miles from the sea or any undermining water; and the front of the cathedral, overlaid with golden mosaics and beautiful colours, is like a thousand rainbows even in the night.

Letter to John Forster, 1853

IN Genoa, and thereabouts, they train the vines on trellis-work, supported on square clumsy pillars, which, in themselves, are anything but picturesque. But, here, they twine them around trees, and let them trail among the hedges; and the vineyards are full of trees, regularly planted for this purpose, each with its own vine twining and clustering about it. Their leaves are now of the brightest gold and deepest red; and never was anything so enchantingly graceful and full of beauty. Through miles of these delightful forms and colours, the road winds its way. The wild festoons, the elegant wreaths, and crowns, and garlands of all shapes; the fairy nets flung over great trees, and making them prisoners in sport; the tumbled heaps and mounds of exquisite shapes upon the ground; how rich and beautiful they are! And every now and then, a long,

long line of trees, will be all bound and garlanded together: as if they had taken hold of one another, and were coming dancing down the field!

Pictures from Italy

WE left Genoa, as you know, soon after five on the evening of my departure; and in company with the lady whom you saw, and the Dog whom I don't think you did see—travelled all night *at the rate of Four Miles an Hour*, over bad roads, without the least refreshment, until daybreak, when the Brave and myself escaped into a miserable caffè while they were changing horses, and got a cup of that drink, hot. That same day a few hours afterwards—between ten and eleven, we came to (I hope) the damndest Inn in the world, where, in a vast chamber, rendered still more desolate by the presence of a most offensive specimen of what D'Israeli calls the Mosaic Arab (who had a beautiful girl with him) I regaled upon a breakfast, almost as cold and damp and cheerless as myself. Then, in another coach, much smaller than a small fly, I was packed up with an old Padre, a Young Jesuit, a provincial avvocato, a private gentleman with a very red nose and a very wet brown umbrella, and the Brave C; and so went on again, at the same pace through the same mud and rain, until four in the afternoon, when there was a place in the coupé (two indeed) which I took: holding that select compartment in company with a very ugly, but very agreeable Tuscan "Gent," who said "Sia" instead of "Si" and rung some other changes on this changing language, but with whom I got on very well: being extremely conversational. We were bound, as you know, perhaps, for Piacenza, but it was discovered that we couldn't get to Piacenza; and about ten o'clock at night we halted at a place called Stradella, where the Inn was a series of queer galleries open to the night, with a great courtyard full of waggons, and horses, and "velociferi" and what not, in the centre. It was bitter cold and very wet; and we all walked into a bare room (mine!) with two immensely broad beds on two deal dining tables—a third great empty table—the usual washing-stand tripod with a slop basin on it—and two chairs, and here we walked up and down for three-quarters of an hour or so, while dinner, or supper, or whatever it was, was getting ready. This was set forth (by way of variety) in the old Priest's bedroom, which had two more immensely broad beds on two more deal dining tables in it. The first dish was a cabbage boiled in a great quantity of rice and hot water: the whole flavoured with cheese. I was so cold that I thought it comfortable: and so hungry that a bit of cabbage, when I found such a thing floating my way, charmed me. After that, we had a dish of very little pieces of pork, fried: with pigs' kidneys. After that, a fowl. After that, something very red and stringy, which I think was veal; and after that two tiny little new-born-baby-looking turkeys, very red and very swollen. Fruit, of course, to wind up, and garlic in one shape or another with every course. I made three jokes at supper (to the immense delight of the company) and retired early.

Letter to his Wife, 1844

AS soon as we got our luggage from the Customs House, we packed complete changes in a bag, set off in a carriage for some warm baths, and had a most refreshing cleansing after our long journey. There was an odd Neopolitan attendant—a steady old man—who, bringing the linen into my bath, proposed to "soap me," upon which I called out to the other two that I intended to have everything done to me that could be done, and gave him directions accordingly. I was frothed all over with Naples soap, rubbed all down, scrubbed with a brush, had my nails cut, my corns cut, and all manner of extraordinary operations performed. He was as much disappointed (apparently) as surprised, not to find me dirty, and kept frequently ejaculating under his breath "O Heaven, how clean this Englishman is!" He also remarked that the Englishman was as fair as a beautiful woman—but there, he added, the resemblance ended.

Letter to his Wife from Naples, 1853

THE Alps appeared in sight, very soon after we left Milan—by eight or nine o'clock in the morning; and the Brave C was so far wrong in his calculations, that we began the ascent of the Simplon that same night. Most favourable state of circumstances for journeying up that tremendous pass! The brightest moon I ever saw, all night; and daybreak on the summit. The glory of which, making great wastes of snow a rosy red, exceeds all telling. We *sledged* through the snow on the summit, for two hours or so. The weather was perfectly fair and bright; and there was neither difficulty nor danger—except the danger that there always must be in such a place, of a horse stumbling on the brink of an immeasurable precipice. In which case, no piece of the unfortunate traveller would be left, large enough to tell his story in dumb-show. You may imagine something of the rugged grandeur of such a scene as this great passage of these great mountains; and indeed, Glencoe, well-sprinkled with snow, would be very like the ascent. But the top itself, so wild, and bleak, and lonely, is a thing by itself, and not to be likened to any other sight. The cold was piercing; the north-wind, high and boisterous; and when it came driving in our faces, bringing a sharp shower of little points of snow and piercing it into our very blood, it really was, what it is often said to be, "cutting"—with a very sharp edge too. There are houses of refuge here—bleak, solitary places—for travellers overtaken by the snow, to hurry to, as an escape from death; and one great house, called the Hospital, kept by monks, where wayfarers get supper and bed for nothing. We saw some coming out and pursuing their journey. If all monks devoted themselves to such uses, I should have little fault to find with them.

Letter to his Wife, 1844

THE insupportable solitude and dreariness of the white walls and towers, the sluggish moat and drawbridge, and the lonely ramparts, I never saw the like of. But there is a courtyard inside; surrounded by prisons, oubliettes, and old chambers of torture; so terrifically sad, that death itself is not more sorrowful. And oh! a wicked old Grand Duke's bed-chamber upstairs in the tower, with a secret staircase down into the chapel where the bats were wheeling about; and Bonnivard's dungeon; and a horrible trap whence prisoners were cast out into the lake; and a stake all burnt and crackled up, that still stands in the torture-ante-chamber to the saloon of justice(!) —what tremendous places! Good God, the greatest mystery in all the earth, to me, is how or why the world was tolerated by its Creator through the good old times, and wasn't dashed to fragments.

Letter to John Forster, 1846

THE weather obstinately clearing, we started off last Tuesday for the Great St Bernard, returning here on Friday afternoon. The party consisted of eleven people and two servants—Haldimand, Mr and Mrs Cerjat and one daughter, Mr and Mrs Watson, two Ladies Taylor, Kate, Georgy, and I. We were wonderfully unanimous and cheerful; went away from here by steamer; found at its destination a whole omnibus provided by the Brave (who went on in advance everywhere); rode therein to Bex; found two large carriages ready to take us to Martigny; slept there; and proceeded up the mountain on mules the next day. Although the St Bernard convent is, as I dare say you know, the highest inhabited spot but one in the world, the ascent is extremely gradual and uncommonly easy: really presenting no difficulties at all until within the last league, when the ascent, lying through a place called the valley of desolation, is very awful and tremendous, and the road is rendered toilsome by scattered rocks and melting snow. The convent is a most extraordinary place, full of great vaulted passages, divided from each other with iron gratings; and presenting a series of the most astonishing little dormitories, where the windows are so small (on account of the cold and snow) that it is as much as one can do to get one's head out of them. Here we slept: supping, thirty strong, in a rambling room with a great wood-fire in it set apart for that purpose; with a grim monk, in a high black sugar-loaf hat with a great knob at the top of it, carving the dishes. At five o'clock in the morning the chapel bell rang in the dismallest way for matins: and I, lying in bed close to the chapel, and being awakened by the solemn organ and the chaunting, thought for a moment I had died in the night and passed into the unknown world.

I wish to God you could see that place. A great hollow on the top of a range of dreadful mountains, fenced in by riven rocks of every shape and colour: and in the midst, a black lake, with phantom clouds perpetually stalking over it. Peaks, and points, and plains of eternal ice and snow, bounding the view, and shutting out the world on every side: the lake reflecting nothing: and no human figure in the scene. The air so fine, that it is difficult to breathe without feeling out of breath; and the cold so exquisitely thin and sharp that it is not to be described. Nothing of life or living interest in the picture, but the grey dull walls of the convent. No vegetation of any sort or kind. Nothing growing, nothing stirring. Everything iron-bound, and frozen up. Beside the convent, in a little outhouse with a grated iron door which you may unbolt for yourself, are the bodies of people found in the snow who have never been claimed and are withering away—not laid down, or stretched out, but standing up, in corners and against walls; some erect and, horribly human, with distinct expressions on the faces; some sunk down on their knees; some dropping over on one side; some tumbled down altogether, and presenting a heap of skulls and fibrous dust. There is no other decay in that atmosphere; and there they remain during the short days and the long nights, the only human company out of doors, withering away by grains, and holding ghastly possession of the mountain where they died.

It is the most distinct and individual place I have seen, even in this transcendent country. But, for the St Bernard holy fathers and convent in themselves, I am sorry to say that they are a piece of as sheer humbug as we ever learnt to believe in, in our young days. Trashy French sentiment and the dogs (of which, by the bye, there are only three remaining) have done it all. They are a lazy set of fellows; not over fond of going out themselves; employing servants to clear the road (which has not been important or much used as a pass these hundred years); rich; and driving a good trade in Innkeeping: the convent being a common tavern in everything but the sign. No charge is made for their hospitality, to be sure; but you are shown to a box in the chapel, where everybody puts in more than could, with any show of face, be charged for the entertainment; and from this the establishment derives a right good income. As to the self-sacrifice of living up there, they are obliged to go there young, it is true, to be inured to the climate: but it is an infinitely more exciting and various life than any other convent can offer; with constant change and company through the whole summer; with a hospital for invalids down in the valley, which affords another change; and with an annual begging-journey to Geneva and this place and all the places round for one brother or other, which affords farther change. The brother who carved at our supper could speak some English, and had just had *Pickwick* given him!—what a humbug he will think me when he tries to understand it! If I had had any other book of mine with me, I would have given it him that I might have had some chance of being intelligible. . . .

Letter to John Forster, 1846

IT is extraordinary that the only travellers we have encountered since we left Paris have been one horribly vapid Englishman and wife whom we dropped at Basle, one boring Englishman whom we found (and thank God we left) at

Geneva, and two English maiden ladies whom we found sitting on a rock (with parasols) the day before yesterday, in the most magnificent part of the Gorge of Gondo, the most awful portion of the Simplon—there awaiting their travelling chariot, in which, with their money, their parasols, and a perfect shop of Baskets, they were carefully *locked up* by an English servant in sky blue and silver buttons. We have been in the most extraordinary vehicles—like swings, like boats, like Noah's Arks, like barges and enormous bedsteads. After dark last night, a landlord where we changed horses, discovered that the baggage would certainly be stolen from questo porco d'uno carro—this pig of a cart—his complimentary description of our carriage—unless cords were attached to each of the trunks, which cords were to hang down so that we might hold them in our hands all the way, and feel any tug that might be made at our treasures. You will imagine the absurdity of our jolting along some twenty miles in this way, exactly as if we were in three shower-baths and were afraid to pull the strings.

Letter to his Wife from Milan, 1853

BY the way, whenever an Englishman would cry "All right!" an American cries "Go ahead!" which is somewhat expressive of the national character of the two countries.

I SHALL never forget the one-fourth serious and three-fourths comical astonishment with which, on the morning of the third of January eighteen-hundred-and-forty-two, I opened the door of, and put my head into a "state-room" on board the Britannia steam-packet, twelve hundred tons burthen per register, bound for Halifax and Boston, and carrying Her Majesty's mails.

That this state-room had been specially engaged for "Charles

Dickens, Esquire, and Lady," was rendered sufficiently clear even to my scared intellect by a very small manuscript, announcing the fact, which was pinned on a very flat quilt, covering a very thin mattress, spread like a surgical plaster on a most inaccessible shelf. But that this was the state-room concerning which Charles Dickens, Esquire, and Lady, had held daily and nightly conferences for at least four months preceding: that this could by any possibility be that small snug chamber of the imagination, which Charles Dickens, Esquire, with the spirit of prophecy strong upon him, had always foretold would contain at least one little sofa, and which his lady, with a modest yet most magnificent sense of its limited dimensions, had from the first opined would not hold more than two enormous portmanteaus in some odd corner out of sight (portmanteaus which could now no more be got in at the door, not to say stowed away, than a giraffe could be persuaded or forced into a flower-pot): that this utterly impracticable, thoroughly hopeless, and profoundly preposterous box had the remotest reference to, or connection with, those chaste and pretty, not to say gorgeous little bowers, sketched by a masterly hand, in the highly varnished lithographic plan hanging up in the agent's counting-house in the city of London: that this room of state, in short could be anything but a pleasant fiction and cheerful jest of the captain's, invented and put in practice for the better relish and enjoyment of the real state-room presently to be disclosed:—these were truths which I really could not, for the moment, bring my mind at all to bear upon or comprehend. And I sat down upon a kind of horsehair slab, or perch, of which there were two within, and looked, without any expression of countenance whatever, at some friends who had come on board with us, and who were crushing their faces into all manner of shapes by endeavouring to squeeze them through the small doorway.

We had experienced a pretty smart shock before coming below, which, but that we were the most sanguine people living, might have prepared us for the worst. The imaginative artist to whom I have already made allusion, has depicted in the same great work, a chamber of almost interminable perspective, furnished, as Mr Robins would say, in a style of more than Eastern splendour, and filled (but not inconveniently so) with groups of ladies and gentlemen, in the very highest state of enjoyment and vivacity. Before descending into the bowels of the ship, we had passed from the deck into a long narrow apartment, not unlike a gigantic hearse with windows in the sides; having at the upper end a melancholy stove, at which three or four chilly stewards were warming their hands; while on either side, extending down its whole dreary length, was a long, long table, over each of which a rack, fixed to the low roof, and stuck full of drinking-glasses and cruet-stands, hinted dismally at rolling seas and heavy weather. I had not at that time seen the ideal presentment of this chamber which has since gratified me so much, but I observed that one of our friends who had made the arrangements for our voyage, turned pale on entering, retreated on the friend behind him, smote his forehead involuntarily, and said below his breath, "Impossible! it cannot be!" or words to that effect. He recovered himself however by a great effort, and after a preparatory cough or two, cried, with a ghastly smile which is still before me, looking at the same time round the walls, "Ha! the breakfast-room, steward—eh?" We all foresaw what the answer must be: we knew the agony he suffered. He had often spoken of *the saloon*; had taken in and lived upon the pictorial idea; had usually given us to understand, at home, that to form a just conception of it, it would be necessary to multiply the size and furniture of an ordinary drawing-room by seven, and then fall short of the reality. When the man in reply avowed the truth; the blunt, remorseless, naked truth; "This is the saloon, sir"—he actually reeled beneath the blow.

In persons who were so soon to part, and interpose between their else daily communication the formidable barrier of many thousand miles of stormy space, and who were for that reason anxious to cast no other cloud, not even the passing shadow of a moment's disappointment or discomfiture, upon the short interval of happy companionship that yet remained to them—

in persons so situated, the natural transition from these first surprises was obviously into peals of hearty laughter, and I can report that I, for one, being still seated upon the slab or perch before-mentioned, roared outright until the vessel rang again. Thus, in less than two minutes after coming upon it for the first time, we all by common consent agreed that this state-room was the pleasantest and most facetious and capital contrivance possible; and that to have had it one inch larger, would have been quite a disagreeable and deplorable state of things. And with this; and with showing how,—by very nearly closing the door, and twining in and out like serpents, and by counting the little washing slab as standing-room—we could manage to insinuate four people into it, all at one time; and entreating each other to observe how very airy it was (in dock), and how there was a beautiful port-hole which could be kept open all day (weather permitting), and how there was quite a large bull's-eye just over the looking-glass which would render shaving a perfectly easy and delightful process (when the ship didn't roll too much); we arrived, at last, at the unanimous conclusion that it was rather spacious than otherwise: though I do verily believe that, deducting the two berths, one above the other, than which nothing smaller for sleeping in was ever made except coffins, it was no bigger than one of those hackney cabriolets which have the door behind, and shoot their fares out, like sacks of coals, upon the pavement.

Having settled this point to the perfect satisfaction of all parties, concerned and unconcerned, we sat down round the fire in the ladies' cabin—just to try the effect. It was rather dark, certainly; but somebody said, "of course, it would be light at sea," a proposition to which we all assented; echoing "of course, of course"; though it would be exceedingly difficult to say why we thought so. I remember, too, when we had discovered and exhausted another topic of consolation in the circumstance of this ladies' cabin adjoining our state-room, and the consequently immense feasibility of sitting there at all times and seasons, and had fallen into a momentary silence, leaning our faces on our hands and looking at the fire, one of our party said, with the solemn air of a man who had made a discovery, "What a relish mulled claret will have down here!" which appeared to strike us all most forcibly; as though there were something spicy and high-flavoured in cabins, which essentially improved that composition, and rendered it quite incapable of perfection anywhere else.

There was a stewardess, too, actively engaged in producing clean sheets and tablecloths from the very entrails of the sofas, and from unexpected lockers, of such artful mechanism, that it made one's head ache to see them opened one after another, and rendered it quite a distracting circumstance to follow her proceedings, and to find that every nook and corner and individual piece of furniture was something else besides what it pretended to be, and was a mere trap and deception and place of secret stowage, whose ostensible purpose was its least useful one.

God bless that stewardess for her piously fraudulent account of January voyages! God bless her for her clear recollection of the companion passage of last year, when nobody was ill, and everybody dancing from morning to night, and it was "a run" of twelve days, and a piece of the purest frolic, and delight, and jollity! All happiness be with her for her bright face and her pleasant Scotch tongue, which had sounds of old Home in it for my fellow traveller; and for her predictions of fair winds and fine weather (all wrong, or I shouldn't be half so fond of her); and for the ten thousand small fragments of genuine womanly tact, by which, without piecing them elaborately together, and patching them up into shape and form and case and pointed application, she nevertheless did plainly show that all young mothers on one side of the Atlantic were near and close at hand to their little children left upon the other; and that what seemed to the uninitiated a serious journey, was, to those who were in the secret, a mere frolic, to be sung about and whistled at! Light be her heart, and gay her merry eyes, for years!

The state-room had grown pretty fast; but by this time it had expanded into something quite bulky, and almost boasted a bay-window to view the sea from. So we went upon deck again in high spirits; and there, everything was in such a state of bustle and active preparation, that the blood quickened its pace, and whirled through one's veins on that clear frosty morning with involuntary mirthfulness. For every gallant ship was riding slowly up and down, and every little boat was splashing noisily in the water; and knots of people stood upon the wharf, gazing with a kind of "dread delight" on the far-famed fast American steamer; and one party of men were "taking in the milk," or, in other words, getting the cow on board; and another were filling the icehouses to the very throat with fresh provisions; with butchers'-meat and gardenstuff, pale sucking-pigs, calves' heads in scores, beef, veal, and pork, and poultry out of all proportion; and others were coiling ropes and busy with oakum yarns; and others were lowering heavy packages into the hold; and the purser's head was barely visible as it loomed in a state of exquisite perplexity from the midst of a vast pile of passengers' luggage; and there seemed to be nothing going on anywhere, or uppermost in the mind of anybody, but preparations for this mighty voyage. This, with the bright cold sun, the bracing air, the crisply-curling water, the thin white crust of morning ice upon the decks which crackled with a sharp and cheerful sound beneath the lightest tread, was irresistible. And when, again upon the shore, we turned and saw from the vessel's mast her name signalled in flags of joyous colours, and fluttering by their side the beautiful American banner with its stars and stripes,—the long three thousand miles and more, and, longer still, the six whole months of absence, so dwindled and faded, that the ship had gone out and come home again, and it was broad spring already in the Coburg Dock at Liverpool.

I have not inquired among my medical acquaintance, whether Turtle, and cold Punch, with Hock, Champagne, and Claret, and all the slight et cetera usually included in an unlimited order for a good dinner—especially when it is left to the liberal construction of my fautless friend, Mr Radley, of the Adelphi Hotel—are peculiarly calculated to suffer a sea-change; or whether a plain mutton-chop, and a glass or two of sherry, would be less likely of conversion into foreign and disconcerting material. My own opinion is, that whether one is discreet or indiscreet in these particulars, on the eve of a sea-voyage, is a matter of little consequence; and that, to use a common phrase, "it comes to very much the same thing in the end." Be this as it may, I know that the dinner of that day was undeniably perfect; that it comprehended all these items, and a great many more; and that we all did ample justice to it. And I know too, that, bating a certain tacit avoidance of any allusion to tomorrow; such as may be supposed to prevail between delicate-minded turnkeys, and a sensitive prisoner who is to be hanged next morning; we got on very well, and, all things considered, were merry enough.

When the morning—*the* morning—came, and we met at breakfast, it was curious to see how eager we all were to prevent a moment's pause in the conversation, and how astoundingly gay everybody was: the forced spirits of each member of the little party having as much likeness to his natural mirth, as hot-house peas at five guineas the quart, resemble in flavour the growth of the dews, and air, and rain of Heaven. But as one o'clock, the hour for going aboard, drew near, this volubility dwindled away by little and little, despite the most persevering efforts to the contrary, until at last, the matter being now quite desperate, we threw off all disguise; openly speculated upon where we should be this time tomorrow, this time the next day, and so forth; and entrusted a vast number of messages to those who intended returning to town that night, which were to be delivered at home and elsewhere without fail, within the very shortest possible space of time after the arrival of the railway train at Euston Square. And commissions and remembrances do so crowd upon one at such a time, that we were still busied with this employment when we found ourselves fused, as it were, into a dense conglomeration of passengers and passengers' friends and passengers' luggage, all jumbled together on the deck of a small steamboat, and panting and snorting off to the packet, which had worked out of dock yesterday afternoon and was now lying at her moorings in the river.

And there she is! all eyes are turned to where she lies, dimly discernible through the gathering fog of the early winter afternoon; every finger is pointed in the same direction; and murmurs of interest and admiration—as "How beautiful she looks!" "How trim she is!"—are heard on every side. Even the lazy gentleman with his hat on one side and his hands in his pockets, who has dispensed so much consolation by inquiring with a yawn of another gentleman whether he is "going across"—as if it were a ferry—even he condescends to look that way, and nod his head, as who should say, "No mistake about *that*": and not even the sage Lord Burleigh in his nod, included half so much as this lazy gentleman of might who has made the passage (as everybody on board has found out already; it's impossible to say how) thirteen times without a single accident! There is another passenger very much wrapped-up, who has been frowned down by the rest, and morally trampled upon and crushed, for presuming to inquire with a timid interest how long it is since the poor President went down. He is standing close to the lazy gentleman, and says with a faint smile that he believes She is a very strong Ship; to which the lazy gentleman, looking first in his questioner's eye and then very hard in the wind's, answers unexpectedly and ominously, that She need be. Upon this the lazy gentleman instantly falls very low in the popular estimation, and the passengers, with looks of defiance, whisper to each other that he is an ass, and an imposter, and clearly don't know anything at all about it.

But we are made fast alongside the packet, whose huge red funnel is smoking bravely, giving rich promise of serious intentions. Packing-cases, portmanteaus, carpet-bags, and boxes, are already passed from hand to hand, and hauled on board with breathless rapidity. The officers, smartly dressed, are at the gangway handing the passengers up the side, and hurrying the men. In five minutes' time, the little steamer is utterly deserted, and the packet is beset and over-run by its late freight, who instantly pervade the whole ship, and are to be met with by the dozen in every nook and corner: swarming down below with their own baggage, and stumbling over other people's; disposing themselves comfortably in wrong cabins, and creating a most horrible confusion by having to turn out again; madly bent upon opening locked doors, and on forcing a passage into all kinds of out-of-the-way places where there is no thoroughfare; sending wild stewards, with elfin hair, to and fro upon the breezy decks on unintelligible errands, impossible of execution: and in short, creating the most extraordinary and bewildering tumult. In the midst of all this, the lazy gentleman, who seems to have no luggage of any kind—not so much as a friend, even—lounges up and down the hurricane deck, coolly puffing a cigar; and, as this unconcerned demeanour again exalts him in the opinion of those who have leisure to observe his proceedings, every time he looks up at the masts, or down at the decks, or over the side, they look there too, as wondering whether he sees anything wrong anywhere, and hoping that, in case he should, he will have the goodness to mention it.

What have we here? The captain's boat! and yonder the captain himself. Now, by all our hopes and wishes, the very man he ought to be! A well-made, tight-built, dapper little fellow; with a ruddy face, which is a letter of invitation to shake him by both hands at once: and with a clear, blue honest eye, that it does one good to see one's sparkling image in. "Ring the bell!" "Ding, ding, ding!" the very bell is in a hurry. "Now for the shore—who's for the shore?"—"These gentlemen, I am sorry to say." They are away, and never said, "Good-bye." Ah! now they wave it from the little boat. "Good-bye! Good-bye!" Three cheers from them; three more from us; three more from them: and they are gone.

To and fro, to and fro, to and fro again a hundred times! This waiting for the latest mail-bags is worse than all. If we could have gone off in the midst of that last burst, we should have started triumphantly: but to lie here, two hours and more in the damp fog, neither staying at home nor going abroad, is letting one gradually down into the very depths of dullness and low spirits. A speck in the mist, at last! There's something. It is the boat we wait for! That's more to the purpose. The captain appears on the paddle-box with his speaking trumpet; the officers take their stations; all hands are on the alert; the flagging hopes of the passengers revive; the cooks pause in their savoury work, and look out with faces full of interest. The boat comes alongside; the bags are dragged in anyhow, and flung down for the moment anywhere. Three cheers more: and as the first one rings upon our ears, the vessel throbs like a strong giant that has just received the breath of life; the two great wheels turn fiercely round for the first time; and the noble ship, with wind and tide astern, breaks proudly through the lashed and foaming water.

American Notes

THE ladies of America are decidedly and unquestionably beautiful. Their complexions are not so good as those of Englishwomen; their beauty does not last so long; and their figures are very inferior. But they are most beautiful.

Letter to John Forster, 1842

THIS hotel is a trifle smaller than Finsbury-square; and is made so infernally hot (I use the expression advisedly) by means of a furnace with pipes running through the passages, that we can hardly bear it. There are no curtains to the beds, or to the bedroom windows. I am told there never are, hardly, all through America. The bedrooms are indeed very bare of furniture. Ours is nearly as large as your great room, and has a wardrobe in it of painted wood not larger (I appeal to K) than an English watch box. I slept in this room for two nights, quite satisfied with the belief that it was a shower bath.

Letter to John Forster, 1842

I MADE acquaintance with an American railroad, on this occasion, for the first time. As these works are pretty much alike all through the States, their general characteristics are easily described.

There are no first and second class carriages as with us: but there is a gentlemen's car and a ladies' car: the main distinction between which is that in the first everybody smokes; and in the second, nobody does. As a black man never travels with a white one, there is also a negro car; which is a great blundering clumsy chest, such as Gulliver put to sea in, from the kingdom of Brobdingnag. There is a great deal of jolting, a great deal of noise, a great deal of wall, not much window, a locomotive engine, a shriek, and a bell.

The cars are like shabby omnibuses, but larger: holding thirty, forty, fifty people. The seats, instead of stretching from end to end are placed crosswise. Each seat holds two persons. There is a long row of them on each side of the caravan, a narrow passage up the middle, and a door at both ends. In the centre of the carriage there is usually a stove, fed with charcoal or anthracite coal; which is for the most part red-hot. It is insufferably close; and you see the hot air fluttering between yourself and any other object you may happen to look at, like the ghost of smoke.

In the ladies' car, there are a great many gentlemen who have ladies with them. There are also a great many ladies who have nobody with them: for any lady may travel alone, from one end of the United States to the other, and be certain of the most courteous and considerate treatment everywhere. The conductor or check-taker or guard, or whatever he may be, wears no uniform. He walks up and down the car, and in and out of it, as his fancy dictates; leans against the door with his hands in his pockets and stares at you, if you chance to be a stranger; or enters into conversation with the passengers about him. A great many newspapers are pulled out, and a few of them are read. Everybody talks to you, or to anybody else who hits his fancy. If you are an Englishman, he expects that that railroad is pretty much like an English railroad. If you say

"No," he says "Yes?" (interrogatively), and asks in what respect they differ. You enumerate the heads of difference, one by one, and he says "Yes?" (still interrogatively) to each. Then he guesses that you don't travel faster in England; and on your replying that you do, says "Yes?" again (still interrogatively), and it is quite evident, don't believe it. After a long pause, he remarks, partly to you, and partly to the knob on the top of his stick, that "Yankees are reckoned to be considerable of a go-ahead people too"; upon which *you* say "Yes," and then *he* says "Yes" again (affirmatively this time); and upon your looking out of the window, tells you that behind that hill, and some three miles from the next station, there is a clever town in a smart lo-ca-tion, where he expects you have con-cluded to stop. Your answer in the negative naturally leads to more questions in reference to your intended route (always pronounced rout); and wherever you are going, you invariably learn that you can't get there without immense difficulty and danger, and that all the great sights are somewhere else.

If a lady take a fancy to any male passenger's seat, the gentleman who accompanies her gives him notice of the fact, and he immediately vacates it with great politeness. Politics are much discussed, so are banks, so is cotton. Quiet people avoid the question of the Presidency, for there will be a new election in three years and a half, and party feeling runs very high: the great constitutional feature of this institution being, that directly the acrimony of the last election is over, the acrimony of the next one begins; which is an unspeakable comfort to all strong politicians and true lovers of their country: that is to say, to ninety-seven men and boys out of every ninety-nine and a quarter.

Except when a branch road joins the main one, there is seldom more than one track of rails; so that the road is very narrow, and the view, where there is a deep cutting, by no means extensive. When there is not, the character of the scenery is always the same. Mile after mile of stunted trees: some hewn down by the axe, some blown down by the wind, some half hidden in the swamp, others mouldered away to spongy chips.

The very soil of the earth is made up of minute fragments such as these; each pool of stagnant water has its crust of vegetable rottenness; on every side there are the boughs, and trunks, and stumps of trees, in every possible stage of decay, decomposition, and neglect. Now you emerge for a few brief minutes on an open country, glittering with some bright lake or pool, broad as many an English river, but so small here that it scarcely has a name; now catch hasty glimpses of a distant town, with its clean white houses and their cool piazzas, its prim New England church and school-house; when whir-r-r-r! almost before you have seen them, comes the same dark screen: the stunted trees, the stumps, the logs, the stagnant water—all so like the last that you seem to have been transported back again by magic.

The train calls at stations in the woods, where the wild impossibility of anybody having the smallest reason to get out, is only to be equalled by the apparently desperate hopelessness of there being anybody to get in. It rushes across the turnpike road, where there is no gate, no policeman, no signal: nothing but a rough wooden arch, on which is painted "WHEN THE BELL RINGS, LOOK OUT FOR THE LOCOMOTIVE." On it whirls headlong, dives through the woods again, emerges in the light, clatters over frail arches, rumbles upon the heavy ground, shoots beneath a wooden bridge which intercepts the light for a second like a wink, suddenly awakens all the slumbering echoes in the main street of a large town, and dashes on haphazard, pell-mell, neck-or-nothing, down the middle of the road. There—with mechanics working at their trades, and people leaning from their doors and windows, and boys flying kites and playing marbles, and men smoking, and women talking, and children crawling, and pigs burrowing, and unaccustomed horses plunging and rearing, close to the very rails—there—on, on, on—tears the mad dragon of an engine with its train of cars; scattering in all directions a shower of burning sparks from its wood fire; screeching, hissing, yelling, panting; until at last the thirsty monster stops beneath a covered way to drink, the people cluster round, and you have time to breathe again.

American Notes

THE beautiful metropolis of America is by no means so clean a city as Boston, but many of its streets have the same characteristics; except that the houses are not quite so fresh-coloured, the sign-boards are not quite so gaudy, the gilded letters not quite so golden, the bricks not quite so red, the stone not quite so white, the blinds and area railings not quite so green, the knobs and plates upon the street doors not quite so bright and twinkling. There are many by-streets, almost as neutral in clean colours, and positive in dirty ones, as by-streets in London; and there is one quarter, commonly called the Five Points, which in respect of filth and wretchedness, may be safely backed against Seven Dials, or any other part of famed St Giles's.

The great promenade and thoroughfare, as most people know, is Broadway; a wide and bustling street, which, from the Battery Gardens to its opposite termination in a country road, may be four miles long. Shall we sit down in an upper floor of the Carlton House Hotel (situated in the best part of this main artery of New York), and when we are tired of looking down upon the life below, sally forth arm-in-arm, and mingle with the stream?

Warm weather! The sun strikes upon our heads at this open window, as though its rays were concentrated through a burning-glass; but the day is in its zenith, and the season an unusual one. Was there ever such a sunny street as this Broadway! The pavement stones are polished with the tread of feet until they shine again; the red bricks of the houses might be yet in the dry, hot kilns; and the roofs of those omnibuses look as though, if water were poured on them, they would hiss and smoke, and smell like half-quenched fires. No stint of omnibuses here! Half a dozen have gone by within as many minutes. Plenty of hackney cabs and coaches too; gigs, phaetons, large-wheeled tilburies, and private carriages—rather of a clumsy make, and not very different from the public vehicles, but built for the heavy roads beyond the city pavement. Negro coachmen and white; in straw hats, black hats, white hats, glazed caps, fur caps; in coats of drab, black, brown, green, blue, nankeen, striped jean and linen; and there, in that one instance (look while it passes, or it will be too late), in suits of livery. Some southern republican that, who puts his blacks in uniform, and swells with Sultan pomp and power. Yonder, where that phaeton with the well-clipped pair of greys has stopped—standing at their heads now—is a Yorkshire groom, who has not been very long in these parts, and looks sorrowfully round for a companion pair of top-boots, which he may traverse the city half a year without meeting. Heaven save the ladies, how they dress! We have seen more colours in these ten minutes, than we should have seen elsewhere, in as many days. What various parasols! what rainbow silks and satins! what pinking of thin stockings, and pinching of thin shoes, and fluttering of ribbons and silk tassels and display of rich cloaks with gaudy hoods and linings!

American Notes

WE called at the town of Erie, at eight o'clock that night, and lay there an hour. Between five and six next morning, we arrived at Buffalo, where we breakfasted; and being too near the Great Falls to wait patiently anywhere else, we set off by train, the same morning at nine o'clock, to Niagara.

It was a miserable day; chilly and raw; a damp mist falling; and the trees in that northern region quite bare and wintry. Whenever the train halted, I listened for the roar; and was constantly straining my eyes in the direction where I knew the Falls must be, from seeing the river rolling on towards them; every moment expecting to behold the spray. Within a few minutes of our stopping, not before, I saw two great white clouds rising up slowly and majestically from the depths of the earth. That was all. At length we alighted: and then for the first time, I heard the mighty rush of water, and felt the ground tremble underneath my feet.

The bank is very steep, and was slippery with rain, and half-melted ice. I hardly know how I got down, but I was soon at the bottom, and climbing, with two English officers who were crossing and had joined me, over some broken rocks, deafened by the noise, half-blinded by the spray, and wet to the skin. We were at the foot of the American Fall. I could see an immense torrent of water tearing headlong down from some great height, but had no idea of shape, or situation, or anything but vague immensity.

When we were seated in the little ferry-boat, and were crossing the swollen river immediately before both cataracts, I began to feel what it was: but I was in a manner stunned, and unable to comprehend the vastness of the scene. It was not until I came on Table Rock, and looked—Great Heaven, on what a fall of bright-green water!—that it came upon me in its full might and majesty.

Then, when I felt how near to my Creator I was standing, the first effect, and the enduring one—instant and lasting—of the tremendous spectacle, was Peace. Peace of Mind, tranquillity, calm recollections of the Dead, great thoughts of Eternal Rest and Happiness: nothing of gloom or terror. Niagara was at once stamped upon my heart, an Image of Beauty; to remain there, changeless and indelible, until its pulses cease to beat, for ever.

Oh, how the strife and trouble of daily life receded from my view, and lessened in the distance, during the ten memorable days we passed on that Enchanted Ground! What voices spoke from out the thundering water; what faces, faded from the earth, looked out upon me from its gleaming depths; what Heavenly promise glistened in those angels' tears, the drops of many hues, that showered around, and twined themselves about the gorgeous arches which the changing rainbows made!

I never stirred in all that time from the Canadian side, whither I had gone at first. I never crossed the river again; for I knew there were people on the other shore, and in such a place it is natural to shun strange company. To wander to and fro all day, and see the cataracts from all points of view; to stand upon the edge of the great Horse Shoe Fall, marking the hurried water gathering strength as it approached the verge, yet seeming, too, to pause before it shot into the gulf below; to gaze from the river's level up at the torrent as it came streaming down; to climb the neighbouring heights and watch it through the trees, and see the wreathing water in the rapids hurrying on to take its fearful plunge; to linger in the shadow of the solemn rocks three miles below; watching the river as, stirred by no visible cause, it heaved and eddied and awoke the echoes, being troubled yet, far down beneath the surface, by its giant leap; to have Niagara before me, lighted by the sun and by the moon, red in the day's decline, and grey as evening slowly fell upon it; to look upon it every day, and wake up in the night and hear its ceaseless voice: this was enough.

I think in every quiet season now, still do those waters roll and leap, and roar and tumble, all day long; still are the rainbows spanning them a hundred feet below. Still, when the sun is on them, do they shine and glow like molten gold. Still, when the day is gloomy, do they fall like snow, or seem to crumble away like the front of a great chalk cliff, or roll down the rock like dense white smoke. But always does the mighty stream appear to die as it comes down, and always from its unfathomable grave arises that tremendous ghost of spray and mist which is never laid: which has haunted this place with the same dread solemnity since Darkness brooded on the deep, and that first flood before the Deluge—Light—came rushing on Creation at the word of God.

American Notes

HOW can I tell you what has happened since that first day? How can I give you the faintest notion of my reception here; of the crowds that pour in and out the whole day; of the people that line the streets when I go out; of the cheering when I went to the theatre; of the copies of verses, letters of congratulation, welcomes of all kinds, balls, dinners, assemblies without end? There is to be a public dinner to me here in Boston, next Tuesday, and great dissatisfaction has been given to the many by the high price (three pounds sterling each) of the tickets. There is to be a ball next Monday week at New York, and 150 names appear on the list of the committee. There is to be a dinner in the same place, in the same week, to which I have had an invitation with every known name in America appended to it. But what can I tell you about any of these things which will give you the slightest notion of the enthusiastic greeting they give me, or the cry that runs through the whole country! I have had deputations from the Far West, who have come from more than two thousand miles distance: from the lakes, the rivers, the back-woods, the log-houses, the cities, factories, villages, and towns. Authorities from nearly all the States have written to me. I have heard from the universities, congress, senate, and bodies, public and private, of every sort and kind. "It is no nonsense, and no common feeling," wrote Dr Channing to me yesterday. "It is all heart. There never was, and never will be, such a triumph." And it is a good thing, is it not, . . . to find those fancies it has given me and you the greatest satisfaction to think of, at the core of it all? It makes my heart quieter, and me a more retiring, sober, tranquil man to watch the effect of those thoughts in all this noise and hurry, even than if I sat, pen in hand, to put them down for the first time. I feel, in the best aspects of this welcome, something of the presence and influence of that spirit which directs my life, and through a heavy sorrow has pointed upward with unchanging finger for more than four years past. And if I know my heart, not twenty times this praise would move me to an act of folly. . . .

Letter to John Forster, 1842

IN the ladies' car, there is no smoking of tobacco allowed. All gentlemen who have ladies with them sit in this car; and it is usually very full. Before it, is the gentlemen's car; which is something narrower. As I had a window close to me yesterday which commanded this gentlemen's car, I looked at it pretty often, perforce. The flashes of saliva flew so perpetually and incessantly out of the windows all the way, that it looked as though they were ripping open feather-beds inside, and letting the wind dispose of the feathers. But this spitting is universal. In the courts of law, the judge has his spittoon on the bench, the counsel have theirs, the witness has his, the prisoner his, and the crier his. The jury are accommodated at the rate of three men to a spittoon (or spit-box as they call it here); and the spectators in the gallery are provided for, as so many men who in the course of nature expectorate without cessation. There are spit-boxes in every steam-boat, bar-room, public dining-room, house of office, and place of general resort, no matter what it be. In the hospitals, the students are requested, by placard, to use the boxes provided for them, and not to spit upon the stairs. I have twice seen gentlemen, at evening parties in New York, turn aside when they were not engaged in conversation, and spit upon the drawing-room carpet. And in every bar-room and hotel passage the stone floor looks as if it were paved with open oysters from the quantity of this kind of deposit which tesselates it all over. . . .

Letters from America, 1842

ON looking back through these sheets, I am astonished to find how little I have told you, and how much I have, even now, in store which shall be yours by word of mouth. The American poor, the American factories, the institutions of all kinds—I have a book, already. There is no man in this town, or in this State of New England, who has not a blazing fire and a meat dinner every day of his life. A flaming sword in the air would not attract so much attention as a beggar in the streets. There are no charity uniforms, no wearisome repetition of the same dull ugly dress, in that blind school. All are attired after their own tastes, and every boy and girl has his or her individuality as distinct and unimpaired as you would find it in their own homes. At the theatres, all the ladies sit in the fronts of the boxes. The gallery are as quiet as the dress circle at dear Drury-lane. A man with seven heads would be no sight at all, compared with one who couldn't read and write.

Letter to John Forster, 1842

Britannia and Her Sons

"BUT you have not imparted to me," remarks Veneering, "what you think of my entering the House of Commons?"

"I think," rejoins Twemlow, feelingly, "that it is the best club in London."

Our Mutual Friend

AND let me linger in this place, for an instant, to remark that if ever household affections and loves are graceful things, they are graceful in the poor. The ties that bind the wealthy and the proud to home may be forged on earth, but those which link the poor man to his humble hearth are of the truer metal and bear the stamp of Heaven. The man of high descent may love the halls and lands of his inheritance as a part of himself: as trophies of his birth and power; his associations with them are associations of pride and wealth and triumph; the poor man's attachment to the tenements he holds, which strangers have held before, and may tomorrow occupy again, has a worthier root, struck deep into a purer soil. His household gods are of flesh and blood, with no alloy of silver, gold, or precious stone; he has no property but in the affections of his own heart; and when they endear bare floors and walls, despite of rags and toil and scanty fare, that man has his love of home from God, and his rude hut becomes a solemn place.

Oh! if those who rule the destinies of nations would but remember this—if they would but think how hard it is for the very poor to have engendered in their hearts, that love of home from which all domestic virtues spring, when they live in dense and squalid masses where social decency is lost, or rather never found,—if they would but turn aside from the wide thoroughfares and great houses, and strive to improve the wretched dwellings in bye-ways where only Poverty may walk,—many low roofs would point more truly to the sky, than the loftiest steeple that now rears proudly up from the midst of guilt, and crime, and horrible disease, to mock them by its contrast. In hollow voices from Workhouse, Hospital, and Jail, this truth is preached from day to day, and has been proclaimed for years. It is no light matter—no outcry from the working vulgar—no mere question of the people's health and comforts that may be whistled down on Wednesday nights. In love of home, the love of country has its rise; and who are the truer patriots or the better in time of need—those who venerate the land, owning its wood, and stream, and earth, and all that they produce? or those who love their country, boasting not a foot of ground in all its wide domain!

The Old Curiosity Shop

I WENT into the gallery of the House of Commons as a parliamentary reporter when I was a boy, and I left it—I can hardly believe the inexorable truth—nigh thirty years ago. I have pursued the calling of a reporter under circumstances of which many of my brethren here can form no adequate conception. I have often transcribed for the printer, from my shorthand notes, important public speeches in which the strictest accuracy was required, and a mistake in which would have been to a young man severely compromising, writing on the palm of my hand, by the light of a dark lantern, in a post-chaise and four, galloping through a wild country, and through the dead of night, at the then surprising rate of fifteen miles an hour. The very last time I was at Exeter, I strolled into the castle-yard there to identify, for the amusement of a friend, the spot on which I once "took," as we used to call it, an election speech of Lord John Russell at the Devon contest, in the midst of a lively fight maintained by all the vagabonds in that division of the county, and under such a pelting rain, that I remember two good-natured colleagues who chanced to be at leisure held a pocket-handkerchief over my note-book, after the manner of a state canopy in an ecclesiastical procession. I have worn my knees by writing on them on the old back-row of the old gallery of the House of Commons; and I have worn my feet by standing to write in a preposterous pen in the old House of Lords, where we used to be huddled together like so many sheep—kept in waiting, say, until the woolsack might want re-stuffing. Returning home from exciting political meetings in the country to the waiting press in London, I do verily believe I have been upset in almost every description of vehicle known in this country. I have been, in my time, belated on miry by-roads, towards the small hours, forty or fifty miles from London, in a wheelless carriage, with exhausted horses and drunken post-boys, and have got back in time for publication, to be received with never-forgotten compliments by the late Mr Black, coming in the broadest of Scotch from the broadest of hearts I ever knew. These trivial things I mention as an assurance to you that I never have forgotten the fascination of that old pursuit. The pleasure that I used to feel in the rapidity and dexterity of its exercise has never faded out of my breast. Whatever little cunning of hand or head I took to it, or acquired in it, I have so retained that I fully believe I could resume it tomorrow, very little the worse from long disuse. To this present year of my life, when I sit in this hall, or where not, hearing a dull speech (the phenomenon does occur), I sometimes beguile the tedium of the moment by mentally following the speaker in the old, old way; and sometimes, if you can believe me, I even find my hand going on the table-cloth, taking an imaginary note of it all.

From a Speech, 1865

YOU will see or hear by the Chronicle of yesterday, that we had a slight flare here yesterday morning, just stopping short of murder and a riot. Party feeling runs so high, and the contest is likely to be so sharp a one that I look forward to the probability of a scuffle before it is over. As the Tories are the principal party here, I am in no very good odour in the town, but I shall not spare them the more on that account in the descriptions of their behaviour I may forward to headquarters. Such a ruthless set of bloody-minded villains, I never set eyes on, in my life. In the convivial moments yesterday after the business of the day was over, they were perfect savages. If a foreigner were brought here on his first visit to an English town, to form his estimate of the national character, I am quite satisfied he would return forthwith to France and never set foot in England again. The remark will apply in greater or less degree to all agricultural places during the pendency of an election, but beastly as the electors usually are, these men are superlative blackguards. Would you believe that a large body of horsemen, mounted and armed, who galloped on a defenceless crowd yesterday, striking about them in all directions, and protecting a man who cocked a loaded pistol, were *led* by clergymen, and Magistrates? Or that I saw one of these fellows with my own eyes, unbuckle one of his stirrup-leathers, and cut about him in the crowd, with the iron part of it—communicating to the blows all the additional force that swinging it at the end of the leather could give them? Anything more sickening and disgusting, or anything that roused my indignation so much, I never beheld.

Letter to his fiancée from Kettering, 1835

WITHIN the precincts of the ancient city of Westminster, and within half a quarter of a mile of its ancient sanctuary, is a narrow and dirty region the sanctuary of the smaller members of Parliament in modern days. It is all comprised in one street of gloomy lodging-houses, from whose windows, in vacation-time, there frown long melancholy rows of bills, which say, as plainly as did the countenances of their occupiers, ranged on ministerial and opposition benches in the session which slumbers with its fathers, "To Let," "To Let." In busier periods of the year these bills disappear, and the houses swarm with legislators. There are legislators in the parlours, in the first floor, in the second, in the third, in the garrets; the small apartments reek with the breath of deputations and delegates. In damp weather, the place is rendered close by the steams of moist acts of Parliament and frowsy petitions; general postmen grow faint as they enter its infected limits, and shabby figures in quest of franks, flit restlessly to and fro like the troubled ghosts of Complete Letter-writers departed. This is Manchester Buildings; and here, at all hours of the night may be heard the rattling of latchkeys in their respective keyholes: with now and then—when a gust of wind sweeping across the water which washes the Buildings' feet, impels the sound towards its entrance—the weak, shrill voice of some young member practising tomorrow's speech. All the livelong day, there is a grinding of organs and clashing and clanging of little boxes of music; for Manchester Buildings is an eel-pot, which has no outlet but its awkward mouth—a case-bottle which has no thoroughfare and a short and narrow neck—and in this respect it may be typical of the fate of some few among its more adventurous residents, who, after wriggling themselves into Parliament by violent efforts and contortions, find that it, too, is no thoroughfare for them; that, like Manchester Buildings, it leads to nothing beyond itself; and that they are fain at last to back out, no wiser, no richer, not one whit more famous than they went in.

Into Manchester Buildings Nicholas turned, with the address of the great Mr Gregsbury in his hand. As there was a stream of people pouring into a shabby house not far from the entrance, he waited until they had made their way in, and then making up to the servant, ventured to inquire if he knew where Mr Gregsbury lived.

The servant was a very pale, shabby boy, who looked as if he had slept underground from his infancy, as very likely he had. "Mr Gregsbury?" said he, "Mr Gregsbury lodges here. It's all right. Come in!"

Nicholas thought he might as well get in while he could, so in he walked; and he had no sooner done so, than the boy shut the door, and made off.

This was odd enough; but what was more embarrassing was, that all along the passage, and all along the narrow stairs, blocking up the window, and making the dark entry darker still, was a confused crowd of persons with great importance depicted in their looks; who were, to all appearance, waiting in silent expectation of some coming event. From time to time, one man would whisper his neighbour, or a little group would whisper together, and then the whisperers would nod fiercely to each other, or give their heads a relentless shake, as if they were bent upon doing something very desperate, and were determined not be put off, whatever happened.

As a few minutes elapsed without anything occurring to explain this phenomenon, and as he felt his own position a peculiarly uncomfortable one, Nicholas was on the point of seeking some information from the man next him, when a sudden move was visible on the stairs, and a voice was heard to cry, "Now, gentlemen, have the goodness to walk up!"

So far from walking up, the gentlemen on the stairs began to walk down with great alacrity, and to entreat, with extraordinary politeness, that the gentlemen nearest the street would go first; the gentlemen nearest the street retorted, with equal courtesy, that they couldn't think of such a thing on any account; but they did it, without thinking of it, inasmuch as the other gentlemen pressing some half-dozen (among whom was Nicholas) forward, and closing up behind, pushed them, not merely up the stairs, but into the very sitting-room of Mr Gregsbury, which they were thus compelled to enter with most unseemly precipitation, and without the means of retreat; the press behind them, more than filling the apartment.

"Gentlemen," said Mr Gregsbury, "you are welcome. I am rejoiced to see you."

For a gentleman who was rejoiced to see a body of visitors, Mr Gregsbury looked as uncomfortable as might be; but perhaps this was occasioned by senatorial gravity, and a statesmanlike habit of keeping his feelings under control. He was a tough, burly, thick-headed gentleman, with a loud voice, a pompous manner, a tolerable command of sentences with no meaning in them, and, in short, every requisite for a very good member indeed.

"Now, gentlemen," said Mr Gregsbury, tossing a great bundle of papers into a wicker basket at his feet, and throwing himself back in his chair with his arms over the elbows, "you are dissatisfied with my conduct, I see by the newspapers."

"Yes, Mr Gregsbury, we are," said a plump old gentleman in a violent heat, bursting out of the throng, and planting himself in the front.

"Do my eyes deceive me," said Mr Gregsbury, looking towards the speaker, "or is that my old friend Pugstyles?"

"I am that man, and no other, sir," replied the plump old gentleman.

"Give me your hand, my worthy friend," said Mr Gregsbury. "Pugstyles, my dear friend, I am very sorry to see you here."

"I am very sorry to be here, sir," said Mr Pugstyles; "but your conduct, Mr Gregsbury, has rendered this deputation from your constituents, imperatively necessary."

"My conduct, Pugstyles," said Mr Gregsbury, looking round

upon the deputation with gracious magnanimity—"My conduct has been, and ever will be, regulated by a sincere regard for the true and real interests of this great and happy country. Whether I look at home or abroad; whether I behold the peaceful industrious communities of our island home: her rivers covered with steamboats, her roads with locomotives, her streets with cabs, her skies with balloons of a power and magnitude hitherto unknown in the history of aeronautics in this or any other nation—I say, whether I look merely at home, or, stretching my eyes farther, contemplate the boundless prospect of conquest and possession—achieved by British perseverance and British valour—which is outspread before me, I clasp my hands, and turning my eyes to the broad expanse above my head, exclaim, 'Thank Heaven, I am a Briton!' "

The time had been, when this burst of enthusiasm would have been cheered to the very echo; but now, the deputation received it with chilling coldness. The general impression seemed to be, that as an explanation of Mr Gregsbury's political conduct, it did not enter quite enough into detail; and one gentleman in the rear did not scruple to remark aloud, that, for his purpose, it savoured rather too much of a "gammon" tendency.

"The meaning of that term—gammon," said Mr Gregsbury, "is unknown to me. If it means that I grow a little too fervid, or perhaps even hyperbolical, in extolling my native land, I admit the full justice of the remark. I *am* proud of this free and happy country. My form dilates, my eye glistens, my breast heaves, my heart swells, my bosom burns, when I call to mind her greatness and her glory."

"We wish, sir," remarked Mr Pugstyles, calmly, "to ask you a few questions."

"If you please, gentlemen; my time is yours—and my country's—and my country's—" said Mr Gregsbury.

This permission being conceded, Mr Pugstyles put on his spectacles, and referred to a written paper which he drew from his pocket; whereupon nearly every other member of the deputation pulled a written paper from *his* pocket to check Mr

Pugstyles off, as he read the questions. This done, Mr Pugstyles proceeded to business.

"Question number one.—Whether, sir, you did not give a voluntary pledge previous to your election, that in event of your being returned, you would immediately put down the practice of coughing and groaning in the House of Commons? And whether you did not submit to be coughed and groaned down in the very first debate of the session, and have since made no effort to effect a reform in this respect? Whether you did not also pledge yourself to astonish the government, and make them shrink in their shoes? And whether you have astonished them, and made them shrink in their shoes, or not?"

"Go on to the next one, my dear Pugstyles," said Mr Gregsbury.

"Have you any explanation to offer with reference to that question, sir?" asked Mr Pugstyles.

"Certainly not," said Mr Gregsbury.

The members of the deputation looked fiercely at each other, and afterwards at the member. "Dear Pugstyles" having taken a very long stare at Mr Gregsbury over the tops of his spectacles, resumed his list of inquiries.

"Question number two.—Whether, sir, you did not likewise give a voluntary pledge that you would support your colleague on every occasion; and whether you did not, the night before last, desert him and vote upon the other side, because the wife of a leader on that other side had invited Mrs Gregsbury to an evening party?"

"Go on," said Mr Gregsbury.

"Nothing to say on that either, sir?" asked the spokesman.

"Nothing whatever," replied Mr Gregsbury. The deputation, who had only seen him at canvassing or election time, were struck dumb by his coolness. He didn't appear like the same man; then he was all milk and honey; now he was all starch and vinegar. But men *are* so different at different times!

"Question number three—and—last—" said Mr Pugstyles, emphatically. "Whether, sir, you did not state upon the hustings, that it was your firm and determined intention to oppose everything proposed; to divide the House upon every question, to move for returns on every subject, to place a motion on the books every day, and, in short, in your own memorable words, to play the very devil with everything and everybody?" With this comprehensive inquiry, Mr Pugstyles folded up his list of questions, as did all his backers.

Mr Gregsbury reflected, blew his nose, threw himself further back in his chair, came forward again, leaning his elbows on the table, made a triangle with his two thumbs and his two forefingers, and tapping his nose with the apex thereof, replied (smiling as he said it): "I deny everything."

At this unexpected answer, a hoarse murmur arose from the deputation; and the same gentleman who had expressed an opinion relative to the gammoning nature of the introductory speech, again made a monosyllabic demonstration, by growling out "Resign!" Which growl being taken up by his fellows, swelled into a very earnest and general remonstrance.

"I am requested, sir, to express a hope," said Mr Pugstyles, with a distant bow, "that on receiving a requisition to that effect from a great majority of your constituents, you will not object at once to resign your seat in favour of some candidate whom they think they can better trust."

To this, Mr Gregsbury read the following reply, which, anticipating the request, he had composed in the form of a letter, whereof copies had been made to send round to the newspapers.

"My dear Mr Pugstyles,

"Next to the welfare of our beloved island—this great and free and happy country, whose powers and resources are, I sincerely believe, illimitable—I value that noble independence which is an Englishman's proudest boast, and which I fondly hope to bequeath to my children, untarnished and unsullied. Actuated by no personal motives, but moved only by high and great constitutional considerations; which I will not attempt to explain, for they are really beneath the comprehension of those who have not made themselves masters, as I have, of the intricate and arduous study of politics; I would rather keep my seat, and intend doing so.

"Will you do me the favour to present my compliments to the constituent body, and acquaint them with this circumstance?

"With great esteem,

"My dear Mr Pugstyles,

"etc., etc."

"Then you will not resign, under any circumstances?" asked the spokesman.

Mr Gregsbury smiled, and shook his head.

"Then good morning, sir," said Pugstyles, angrily.

"Heaven bless you!" said Mr Gregsbury. And the deputation with many growls and scowls, filed off as quickly as the narrowness of the staircase would allow of their getting down.

The last man being gone, Mr Gregsbury rubbed his hands and chuckled, as merry fellows will, when they think they have said or done a more than commonly good thing; he was so engrossed in this self-congratulation, that he did not observe that Nicholas had been left behind in the shadow of the window-curtains, until that young gentleman, fearing he might otherwise overhear some soliloquy intended to have no listeners, coughed twice or thrice, to attract the member's notice.

"What's that?" said Mr Gregsbury, in sharp accents.

Nicholas stepped forward, and bowed.

"What do you do here, sir?" asked Mr Gregsbury; "a spy upon my privacy! A concealed voter! You have heard my answer, sir. Pray follow the deputation."

"I should have done so, if I had belonged to it, but I do not," said Nicholas.

"Then how came you here, sir?" was the natural inquiry of Mr Gregsbury, M.P. "And where the devil have you come from, sir?" was the question which followed it.

"I brought this card from the General Agency Office, Sir," said Nicholas, "wishing to offer myself as your secretary, and understanding that you stood in need of one."

"That's all you've come for, is it?" said Mr Gregsbury, eyeing him in some doubt.

Nicholas replied in the affirmative.

"You have no connection with any of those rascally papers, have you?" said Mr Gregsbury. "You didn't get into the room to hear what was going forward, and put it in print, eh?"

"I have no connection, I am sorry to say, with anything at present," rejoined Nicholas,—politely enough, but quite at his ease.

"Oh!" said Mr Gregsbury. "How did you find your way up here, then?"

Nicholas related how he had been forced up by the deputation.

"That was the way, was it?" said Mr Gregsbury. "Sit down."

Nicholas took a chair, and Mr Gregsbury stared at him for a long time, as if to make certain, before he asked any further questions, that there were no objections to his outward appearance.

"You want to be my secretary, do you?" he said at length.

"I wish to be employed in that capacity, sir," replied Nicholas.

"Well," said Mr Gregsbury; "now what can you do?"

"I suppose," replied Nicholas, smiling, "that I can do what usually falls to the lot of other secretaries."

"What's that?" inquired Mr Gregsbury.

"What is it?" replied Nicholas.

"Ah! What is it?" retorted the member, looking shrewdly at him, with his head on one side.

"A secretary's duties are rather difficult to define, perhaps," said Nicholas, considering. "They include, I presume correspondence?"

"Good," interposed Mr Gregsbury.

"The arrangement of papers and documents?"

"Very good."

"Occasionally, perhaps, the writing from your dictation; and possibly, sir,"—said Nicholas, with a half-smile, "the copying of your speech for some public journal, when you have made one of more than usual importance."

"Certainly," rejoined Mr Gregsbury. "What else?"

"Really," said Nicholas, after a moment's reflection, "I am not able, at this instant, to recapitulate any other duty of a secretary, beyond the general one of making himself as agreeable and useful to his employer as he can, consistently with his own respectability, and without overstepping that line of duties which he undertakes to perform, and which the designation of his office, is usually understood to imply."

Mr Gregsbury looked fixedly at Nicholas for a short time, and then glancing warily round the room, said in a suppressed voice—

"This is all very well, Mr—what is your name?"

"Nickleby."

"This is all very well, Mr Nickleby, and very proper, so far as it goes—so far as it goes, but it doesn't go far enough. There are other duties, Mr Nickleby, which a secretary to a parliamentary gentleman must never lose sight of. I should require to be crammed, sir."

"I beg your pardon," interposed Nicholas, doubtful whether he had heard aright.

"—To be crammed, sir," repeated Mr Gregsbury.

"May I beg your pardon again, if I inquire what you mean, sir?" said Nicholas.

"My meaning, sir, is perfectly plain," replied Mr Gregsbury, with a solemn aspect. "My secretary would have to make himself master of the foreign policy of the world, as it is mirrored in the newspapers; to run his eye over all accounts of public meetings, all leading articles, and accounts of the proceedings of public bodies; and to make notes of anything which it appeared to him might be made a point of, in any little speech upon the question of some petition lying on the table, or anything of that kind. Do you understand?"

"I think I do, sir," replied Nicholas.

"Then," said Mr Gregsbury, "it would be necessary for him to make himself acquainted, from day to day, with newspaper paragraphs on passing events; such as 'Mysterious disappearance, and supposed suicide of a pot-boy,' or anything of that sort, upon which I might found a question to the Secretary of

State for the Home Department. Then, he would have to copy the question, and as much as I remembered of the answer (including a little compliment about independence and good sense); and to send the manuscript in a frank to the local paper, with perhaps half a dozen lines of leader, to the effect, that I was always to be found in my place in Parliament, and never shrunk from the responsible and arduous duties, and so forth. You see?"

Nicholas bowed.

"Besides which," continued Mr Gregsbury, "I should expect him, now and then, to go through a few figures in the printed tables, and to pick out a few results, so that I might come out pretty well on timber duty questions, and finance questions, and so on; and I should like him to get up a few little arguments about the disastrous effects of a return to cash payments and a metallic currency, with a touch, now and then about the exportation of bullion, and the Emperor of Russia, and bank-notes, and all that kind of thing, which it's only necessary to talk fluently about, because nobody understands it. Do you take me?"

"I think I understand," said Nicholas.

"With regards to such questions as are not political," continued Mr Gregsbury, warming; "and which one can't be expected to care a curse about, beyond the natural care of not allowing inferior people to be as well off as ourselves else where are our privileges?—I should wish my secretary to get together a few little flourishing speeches, of a patriotic cast. For instance, if any preposterous bill were brought forward, for giving poor grubbing devils of authors a right to their own property, I should like to say, that I for one would never consent to opposing an insurmountable bar to the diffusion of literature among *the* people,—you understand?—that the creations of the pocket, being man's, might belong to one man, or one family; but that the creations of the brain, being God's, ought as a matter of course to belong to the people at large—and if I was pleasantly disposed, I should like to make a joke about posterity, and say that those who wrote for posterity should be content to be rewarded by the approbation *of* posterity; it might take with the House, and could never do me any harm, because posterity can't be expected to know anything about me or my jokes either—do you see?"

"I see that, sir," replied Nicholas.

"You must always bear in mind, in such cases as this, where our interests are not affected," said Mr Gregsbury, "to put it very strong about the people, because it comes out very well at election-time; and you could be as funny as you liked about the authors; because I believe the greater part of them live in lodgings, and are not voters. This is a hasty outline of the chief things you'd have to do, except waiting in the lobby every night, in case I forgot anything, and should want fresh cramming; and, now and then, during great debates, sitting in the front row of the gallery, and saying to the people about—'You see that gentleman, with his hand to his face, and his arm twisted round the pillar—that's Mr Gregsbury—the celebrated Mr Gregsbury'—with any other little eulogium that might strike you at the moment. And for salary," said Mr Gregsbury, winding up with great rapidity; for he was out of breath—"And for salary, I don't mind saying at once in round numbers, to prevent any dissatisfaction— though it's more than I've been accustomed to give—fifteen shillings a week, and find yourself. There!"

With this handsome offer, Mr Gregsbury once more threw himself back in his chair, and looked like a man who had been most profligately liberal, but is determined not to repent of it notwithstanding.

"Fifteen shillings a week is not much," said Nicholas mildly.

"Not much! Fifteen shillings a week not much, young man?" cried Mr Gregsbury. "Fifteen shillings a—"

"Pray do not suppose that I quarrel with the sum, sir," replied Nicholas; "for I am not ashamed to confess, that whatever it may be in itself, to me it is a great deal. But the duties and responsibilities make the recompense small, and they are so very heavy that I fear to undertake them."

"Do you decline to undertake them, sir?" inquired Mr Gregsbury, with his hand on the bell-rope.

"I fear they are too great for my powers, however good my will may be, sir," replied Nicholas.

"That is as much as to say that you had rather not accept the place and that you consider fifteen shillings a week too little," said Mr Gregsbury, ringing. "Do you decline it, sir?"

"I have no alternative but to do so," replied Nicholas.

"Door, Matthews!" said Mr Gregsbury, as the boy appeared.

"I am sorry I have troubled you unnecessarily, sir," said Nicholas.

"I am sorry you have," rejoined Mr Gregsbury, turning his back upon him. "Door, Matthews!"

"Good morning, sir," said Nicholas.

"Door, Matthews!" cried Mr Gregsbury.

The boy beckoned Nicholas, and tumbling lazily downstairs before him, opened the door, and ushered him into the street. With a sad and pensive air, he retraced his steps homeward.

Nicholas Nickleby

"I AM not fond of professions of humility," I returned, "or professions of anything else."

"There now!" said Uriah, looking flabby and lead-coloured in the moonlight. "Didn't I know it! But how little you think of the rightful umbleness of a person in my station, Master Copperfield! Father and me was both brought up at a foundation school for boys; and mother, she was likewise brought up at a public, sort of charitable, establishment. They taught us all a deal of umbleness—not much else that I know of, from morning to night. We was to be umble to this person, and umble to that; and to pull off our caps here, and to make bows there; and always to know our place, and abase ourselves before our betters. And we had such a lot of betters! Father got the monitor-medal by being umble. So did I. Father got made a sexton by being umble. He had the character, among the gentlefolks, of being such a well-behaved man, that they were determined to bring him in. 'Be umble, Uriah,' says father to me, 'and you'll get on. It was what was always being dinned into you and me at school; it's what goes down best. Be umble,' says father 'and you'll do!' And really it ain't done bad!"

David Copperfield

"THEN I'll commit him. I'll commit him as such," said Mr Nupkins.

"This is a wery impartial country for justice," said Sam. "There ain't a magistrate goin' as don't commit himself, twice as often as he commits other people."

Pickwick Papers

THERE was a great bustle in Bishopsgate Street Within, as they drew up, and (it being a windy day) half a dozen men were tacking across the road under a press of paper, bearing gigantic announcements that a Public Meeting would be holden at one o'clock precisely, to take into consideration the propriety of petitioning Parliament in favour of the United Metropolitan Improved Hot Muffin and Crumpet Baking and Punctual Delivery Company, capital five millions, in five hundred thousand shares of ten pounds each; which sums were duly set forth in fat black figures of considerable size. Mr Bonney elbowed his way briskly upstairs, receiving in his progress many low bows from the waiters who stood on the landings to show the way, and, followed by Mr Nickleby, dived into a suite of apartments behind the great public-room: in the second of which was a business-looking table, and several business-looking people.

"Hear!" cried a gentleman with a double chin, as Mr Bonney presented himself. "Chair, gentlemen, chair!"

The newcomers were received with universal approbation, and Mr Bonney bustled up to the top of the table, took off his hat, ran his fingers through his hair, and knocked a hackney-coachman's knock on the table with a little hammer: whereat several gentlemen cried "Hear!" and nodded slightly to each other, as much as to say what spirited conduct that was. Just at this moment, a waiter, feverish with agitation, tore into the room, and throwing the door open with a crash, shouted "Sir Matthew Pupker!"

The committee stood up and clapped their hands for joy; and while they were clapping them, in came Sir Matthew Pupker, attended by two live members of Parliament, one Irish and one Scotch, all smiling and bowing, and looking so pleasant that it seemed a perfect marvel how any man could have the heart to vote against them. Sir Matthew Pupker especially, who had a little round head with a flaxen wig on the top of it, fell into such a paroxysm of bows, that the wig threatened to be jerked off every instant. When these symptoms had in some degree subsided, the gentlemen who were on speaking terms with Sir Matthew Pupker, or the two other members, crowded round them in three little groups, near one or other of which the gentlemen who were *not* on speaking terms with Sir Matthew Pupker or the two other members, stood lingering, and smiling, and rubbing their hands, in the desperate hope of something turning up which might bring them into notice. All this time, Sir Matthew Pupker and the two other members were relating to their separate circles what the intentions of government were, about taking up the bill; with a full account of what the government had said in a whisper the last time they dined with it, and how the government had been observed to wink when it said so; from which premises they were at no loss to draw the conclusion, that if the government had one object more at heart than another, that one object was the welfare and advantage of the United Metropolitan Improved Hot Muffin and Crumpet Baking and Punctual Delivery Company.

Meanwhile, and pending the arrangements of the proceedings, and a fair division of the speechifying, the public in the large room were eyeing, by turns, the empty platform, and the ladies in the Music Gallery. In these amusements the greater portion of them had been occupied for a couple of hours before, and as the most agreeable diversions pall upon the taste on a too protracted enjoyment of them, the sterner spirits now began to hammer the floor with their boot-heels, and to express their dissatisfaction by various hoots and cries. These vocal exertions, emanating from the people who had been there longest, naturally proceeded from those who were nearest to the platform and furthest from the policemen in attendance, who having no great mind to fight their way through the crowd, but entertaining nevertheless a praiseworthy desire to do something to quell the disturbance, immediately began to drag forth, by the coat tails and collars, all the quiet people near the door; at the same time dealing out various smart and tingling blows with their truncheons, after the manner of that ingenious actor, Mr Punch: whose brilliant example, both in the fashion of his weapons and their use, this branch of the executive occasionally follows.

Several very exciting skirmishes were in progress, when a loud shout attracted the attention even of the belligerents, and then there poured on to the platform, from a door at the side, a long line of gentlemen with their hats off, all looking behind them, and uttering vociferous cheers; the cause whereof was sufficiently explained when Sir Matthew Pupker and the two other real members of Parliament came to the front, amidst deafening shouts, and testified to each other in dumb motions that they had never seen such a glorious sight as that, in the whole course of their public career.

At length, and at last, the assembly left off shouting, but Sir Matthew Pupker being voted into the chair, they underwent a relapse which lasted five minutes. This over, Sir Matthew Pupker went on to say what must be his feelings on that great occasion, and what must be that occasion in the eyes of the world, and what must be the intelligence of his fellow-countrymen before him, and what must be the wealth and respectability of his honourable friends behind him, and lastly, what must be the importance to the wealth, the happiness, the comfort, the liberty, the very existence of a free and great people, of such an Institution as the United Metropolitan Improved Hot Muffin and Crumpet Baking and Punctual Delivery Company!

Mr Bonney then presented himself to move the first resolution; and having run his right hand through his hair, and planted his left in an easy manner, in his ribs, he consigned his hat to the care of the gentleman with the double chin (who acted as a species of bottle-holder to the orators generally), and said he would read to them the first resolution—"That this meeting views with alarm and apprehension, the existing state of the Muffin Trade in the Metropolis and its neighbourhood; that it considers the Muffin Boys, as at present constituted, wholly undeserving the confidence of the public; and that it deems the whole Muffin system alike prejudicial to the health and morals of the people, and subversive of the best interests of a great commercial and mercantile community." The honourable gentleman made a speech which drew tears from the eyes of the ladies, and awakened the liveliest emotions in every individual present. He had visited the houses of the poor in the various districts of London, and had found them destitute of the slightest vestige of a muffin, which there appeared too much reason to believe some of these indigent persons did not taste from year's end to year's end. He had found that among the muffin-sellers there existed drunkenness, debauchery, and profligacy, which he attributed to the debasing nature of their employment as at present exercised; he had found the same vices among the poorer class of people who ought to be muffin consumers; and this he attributed to the despair engendered by their being placed beyond the reach of that nutritious article, which drove them to seek a false stimulant in intoxicating liquors. He would undertake to prove before a committee of the House of Commons, that there existed a combination to keep up the price of muffins, and to give the bellmen a monopoly; he would prove it by bellmen at the bar of that House; and he would also prove, that these men corresponded with each other by secret words and signs, as "Snooks," "Walker," "Ferguson," "Is Murphy right?" and many others. It was this melancholy state of things that the Company proposed to correct; firstly, by prohibiting, under heavy penalties, all private muffin trading of every description; secondly, by themselves supplying the public generally, and the poor at their own homes, with muffins of first quality at reduced prices. It was with this object that a bill had been introduced into Parliament by their patriotic chairman Sir Matthew Pupker; it was this bill that they had met to support; it was the supporters of this bill who would confer undying brightness and splendour upon England, under the name of the United Metropolitan Improved Hot Muffin and Crumpet Baking and Punctual Delivery Company; he would add, with a capital of Five Millions, in five hundred thousand shares of ten pounds each.

Mr Ralph Nickleby seconded the resolution, and another gentleman having moved that it be amended by the insertion of the words "and crumpet" after the word "muffin," whenever it occurred, it was carried triumphantly. Only one man in the crowd cried "No!" and he was promptly taken into custody, and straightaway borne off.

The second resolution, which recognised the expediency of immediately abolishing "all muffin (or crumpet) sellers, all traders in muffins (or crumpets) of whatsoever description, whether male or female, boys or men, ringing hand-bells or otherwise," was moved by a grevious gentleman of semi-clerical appearance, who went at once into such deep pathetics, that he knocked the first speaker clean out of the course in no time. You might have heard a pin fall—a pin! a feather—as he described the cruelties inflicted on muffin boys by their masters, which he very wisely urged were in themselves a sufficient reason for the establishment of that inestimable company. It seemed that the unhappy youths were nightly turned out into the wet streets at the most inclement periods of the year, to wander about, in darkness and rain—or it might be hail or snow—for hours together, without shelter, food, or warmth; and let the public never forget upon the latter point, that while the muffins were provided with warm clothing and blankets, the boys were wholly unprovided for, and left to their own miserable resources. (Shame!) The honourable gentleman related one case of a muffin boy, who having been exposed to this inhuman and barbarous system for no less than five years, at length fell a victim to a cold in the head, beneath which he gradually sunk until he fell into a perspiration and recovered; this he could vouch for, on his own authority, but he had heard (and he had no reason to doubt the fact) of a still more heart-rending and appalling circumstance. He had heard of the case of an orphan muffin boy, who, having been run over by a hackney carriage, had been removed to the hospital, had undergone the amputation of his leg below the knee, and was now actually pursuing his occupation on crutches. Fountain of justice, were these things to last!

This was the department of the subject that took the meeting, and this was the style of speaking to enlist their sympathies. The men shouted; the ladies wept into their pocket-handkerchiefs till they were moist, and waved them till they were dry; the excitement was tremendous; and Mr Nickleby whispered his friend that the shares were thenceforth at a premium of five-and-twenty per cent.

The resolution was, of course, carried with loud acclamations, every man holding up both hands in favour of it, as he would in his enthusiasm have held up both legs also, if he could have conveniently accomplished it. This done, the draft of the proposed petition was read at length; and the petition said, as all petitions *do* say, that the petitioners were very humble, and the petitioned very honourable, and the object very virtuous; therefore (said the petition) the bill ought to be passed into a law at once, to the everlasting honour and glory of that most honourable and glorious Commons of England in Parliament assembled.

Then, the gentleman who had been at Crockford's all night, and who looked something the worse about the eyes in consequence, came forward to tell his fellow-countrymen what a speech he meant to make in favour of that petition whenever it should be presented, and how desperately he meant to taunt the Parliament if they rejected the bill; and to inform them also, that he regretted his honourable friends had not inserted a clause rendering the purchase of muffins and crumpets compulsory upon all classes of the community, which he—opposing all half-measures, and preferring to go the extreme animal—

pledged himself to propose and divide upon, in committee. After announcing this determination, the honourable gentleman grew jocular; and as patent boots, lemon-coloured kid gloves, and a fur coat collar, assist jokes materially, there was immense laughter and much cheering, and moreover such a brilliant display of ladies' pocket-handkerchiefs, as threw the grevious gentleman quite into the shade.

And when the petition had been read and was about to be adopted, there came forward the Irish member (who was a young gentleman of ardent temperament), with such a speech as only an Irish member can make, breathing the true soul and and spirit of poetry, and poured forth with such fervour, that it made one warm to look at him; in the course whereof, he told them how he would demand the extension of that great boon to his native country; how he would claim for her equal rights in the muffin laws as in all other laws; and how he yet hoped to see the day when crumpets should be toasted in her lowly cabins, and muffin bells should ring in her rich green valleys. And, after him, came the Scotch member, with various pleasant allusions to the probable amount of profits, which increased the good humour that the poetry had awakened; and all the speeches put together did exactly what they were intended to do, and established in the hearers' minds that there was no speculation so promising, or at the same time so praiseworthy, as the United Metropolitan Improved Hot Muffin and Crumpet Baking and Punctual Delivery Company.

Nicholas Nickleby

"WHAT do you call law?"

"A joke," replied the Doctor.

"Did you ever go to law?" asked Mr Snitchey, looking out of the blue bag.

"Never," returned the Doctor.

"If you ever do," said Mr Snitchey, "perhaps you'll alter that opinion."

The Battle of Life

"IF the law supposes that," said Mr Bumble, squeezing his hat emphatically in both hands, "the law is a ass—a idiot."

Oliver Twist

THE Circumlocution Office was (as everybody knows without being told) the most important Department under Government. No public business of any kind could possibly be done at any time, without the acquiescence of the Circumlocution Office. It finger was in the largest public pie, and in the smallest public tart. It was equally impossible to do the plainest right and to undo the plainest wrong, without the express authority of the Circumlocution Office. If another Gunpowder Plot had been discovered half an hour before the lighting of the match, nobody would have been justified in saving the parliament until there had been half a score of boards, half a bushel of minutes, several sacks of official memoranda, and a family-vault full of ungrammatical correspondence, on the part of the Circumlocution Office.

This glorious establishment had been early in the field, when the one sublime principle involving the difficult art of governing a country, was first distinctly revealed to statesmen. It had been foremost to study that bright revelation, and to carry its shining influence through the whole of the official proceedings. Whatever was required to be done, the Circumlocution Office was beforehand with all the public departments in the art of perceiving—HOW NOT TO DO IT.

Through this delicate perception, through the tact with which it invariably seized it, and through the genius with which it always acted on it, the Circumlocution Office had risen to over-top all the public departments; and the public condition had risen to be—what it was.

It is true that How not to do it was the great study and object of all public departments and professional politicians all round the Circumlocution Office. It is true that every new premier and every new government, coming in because they had upheld a certain thing as necessary to be done, were no sooner come in than they applied their utmost faculties to discovering How not to do it. It is true that from the moment when a general election was over, every returned man who had been raving on hustings because it hadn't been done, and who had been asking the friends of the honourable gentleman in the opposite interest on pain of impeachment to tell him why it hadn't been done, and who had been asserting that it must be done, and who had been pledging himself that it should be done, began to devise, How it was not to be done. It is true that the debates of both Houses of Parliament the whole session through, uniformly tended to the protracted deliberation, How not to do it. It is true that the royal speech at the opening of such session virtually said, My lords and gentlemen, you have a considerable stroke of work to do, and you will please to retire to your respective chambers, and discuss, How not to do it. It is true that the royal speech, at the close of such session, virtually said, My lords and gentlemen, you have through several laborious months been considering with great loyalty and patriotism, How not to do it, and you have found out; and with the blessing of Providence upon the harvest (natural, not political), I now dismiss you. All this is true, but the Circumlocution Office went beyond it.

Because the Circumlocution Office went on mechanically, every day, keeping this wonderful, all-sufficient wheel of statesmanship, How not to do it, in motion. Because the Circumlocution Office was down upon any ill-advised public servant who was going to do it, or who appeared to be by any surprising accident in remote danger of doing it, with a minute, and a memorandum, and a letter of instructions, that extinguished him. It was this spirit of national efficiency in the Circumlocution Office that had gradually led to its having something to do with everything. Mechanicians, natural philosophers, soldiers, sailors, petitioners, memorialists, people with grievances, people who wanted to prevent grievances, people who wanted to redress grievances, jobbing people, jobbed people, people who couldn't get rewarded for merit, and people who couldn't get punished for demerit, were all indiscriminately tucked up under the foolscap paper of the Circumlocution Office.

Numbers of people were lost in the Circumlocution Office. Unfortunates with wrongs, or with projects for the general welfare (and they had better have had wrongs at first, than have taken that bitter English recipe for certainly getting them), who in slow lapse of time and agony had passed safely through other public departments; who, according to rule, had been bullied in this, over-reached by that, and evaded by the other; got referred at last to the Circumlocution Office, and never reappeared in the light of day. Boards sat upon them, secretaries minuted upon them, commissioners gabbled about them, clerks registered, entered, checked, and ticked them off, and they melted away. In short, all the business of the country went through the Circumlocution Office, except the business that never came out of it; and *its* name was Legion.

Sometimes, angry spirits attacked the Circumlocution Office. Sometimes, parliamentary questions were asked about it, and even parliamentary motions made or threatened about it, by demagogues so low and ignorant as to hold that the real recipe of government was, How to do it. Then would the noble lord, or right honourable gentleman, in whose department it was to defend the Circumlocution Office, put an orange in his pocket, and make a regular field-day of the occasion. Then would he come down to that house with a slap upon the table, and meet the honourable gentleman foot to foot. Then would he be there to tell that honourable gentleman that the Circumlocution Office not only was blameless in this matter, but was commendable in this matter, was extollable to the skies in this matter. Then would he be there to tell that honourable gentleman, that, although the Circumlocution Office was invariably right and wholly right, it never was so right as in this matter. Then would he be there to tell that honourable gentleman that it would have been more to his honour, more to his credit, more to his good taste, more to his good sense, more to half the dictionary of common-places, if he had left the Circumlocution Office alone, and never approached this matter. Then would he keep one eye upon a coach or crammer from the Circumlocution Office sitting below the bar, and smash the honourable gentleman with the Circumlocution Office account of this matter. And although one of two things always happened; namely, either that the Circumlocution Office had nothing to say and said it, or that it had something to say of which the noble lord, or right honourable gentleman, blundered one half and forgot the other; the Circumlocution Office was always voted immaculate, by an accommodating majority.

Such a nursery of statesmen had the Department become in virtue of a long career of this nature, that several solemn lords had attained the reputation of being quite unearthly prodigies of business, solely from having practised, How not to do it, at the head of the Circumlocution Office. As to the minor priests and acolytes of that temple, the result of all this was that they stood divided into two classes, and, down to the junior messenger, either believed in the Circumlocution Office as a heaven-born institution, that had an absolute right to do whatever it liked; or took refuge in total infidelity, and considered it a flagrant nuisance.

The Barnacle family had for some time helped to administer the Circumlocution Office. The Tite Barnacle Branch, indeed, considered themselves in a general way as having vested rights in that direction, and took it ill if any other family had much to say to it. The Barnacles were a very high family, and a very large family. They were dispersed all over the public offices, and held all sorts of public places. Either the nation was under a load of obligation to the Barnacles, or the Barnacles were under a load of obligation to the nation. It was not quite unanimously settled which; the Barnacles having their opinion, the nation theirs.

The Mr Tite Barnacle who at the period now in question usually coached or crammed the statesman at the head of the Circumlocution Office, when that noble or right honourable individual sat a little uneasily in his saddle, by reason of some vagabond making a tilt at him in a newspaper, was more flush of blood than money. As a Barnacle he had his place, which was a snug thing enough; and as a Barnacle he had of course put in his son Barnacle Junior, in the office. But he had intermarried with a branch of the Stiltstalkings, who were also better endowed in a sanguineous point of view than with real or personal property, and of this marriage there had been issue, Barnacle Junior, and three young ladies. What with the patrician requirements of Barnacle Junior, the three young ladies, Mrs Tite Barnacle nee Stiltstalking, and himself Mr Tite Barnacle found the intervals between quarter day and quarter day rather longer than he could have desired; a circumstance which he always attributed to the country's parsimony.

Little Dorrit

"WHAT else do you suppose I think I am made for? Nothing. Rattle me out of bed early, set me going, give me as short a time as you like to bolt my meals in, and keep me at it. Keep me always at it, and I'll keep you always at it, you keep somebody else always at it. There you are with the Whole Duty of Man in a commercial country."

Little Dorrit

TELLSON'S Bank by Temple Bar was an old-fashioned place, even in the year 1780. It was very small, very dark, very ugly, very incommodious. It was an old-fashioned place, moreover, in the moral attribute that the partners in the House were proud of its smallness, proud of its darkness, proud of its ugliness, proud of its incommodiousness. They were even boastful of its eminence in those particulars, and were fired by an express conviction that, if it were less objectionable, it would be less respectable. This was no passive belief, but an active weapon which they flashed at more convenient places of business. Tellson's (they said) wanted no elbow-room, Tellson's wanted no light, Tellson's wanted no embellishment. Noakes and Co.'s might, or Snooks Brothers' might; but Tellson's, thank Heaven!—

Any one of these partners would have disinherited his son on the question of rebuilding Tellson's. In this respect the House was much on a par with the Country; which did very often disinherit its sons for suggesting improvements in laws and customs that had long been highly objectionable, but were only the more respectable.

Thus it had come to pass, that Tellson's was the triumphant perfection of inconvenience. After bursting open a door of idiotic obstinacy with a weak rattle in its throat, you fell into Tellson's down two steps, and came to your senses in a miserable little shop, with two little counters, where the oldest of men made your cheque shake as if the wind rustled it, while they examined the signature by the dingiest of windows, which were always under a shower-bath of mud from Fleet-street, and which were made the dingier by their own iron bars proper, and the heavy shadow of Temple Bar. If your business necessitated your seeing "the House," you were put into a species of Condemned Hold at the back, where you meditated on a mis-spent life, until the House came with its hands in its pockets, and you could hardly blink at it in the dismal twilight. Your money came out of, or went into, wormy old wooden drawers, particles of which flew up your nose and down your throat when they were opened and shut. Your banknotes had a musty odour, as if they were fast decomposing into rags again. Your plate was stowed away among the neighbouring cesspools, and evil communications corrupted its good polish in a day or two. Your deeds got into extemporized strong-rooms made of kitchens and sculleries, and fretted all the fat out of their parchments into the banking-house air. Your lighter boxes of family papers went up-stairs into a Barmecide room, that always had a great dining-table in it and never had a dinner, and where, even in the year 1780, the first letters written to you by your old love, or by your little children, were but newly released from the horror of being ogled through the windows, by the heads exposed on Temple Bar with an insensate brutality and ferocity worthy of Abyssinia or Ashantee.

But indeed, at that time, putting to death was a recipe much in vogue with all trades and professions, and not least of all with Telson's. Death is Nature's remedy for all things, and why not Legislation's? Accordingly, the forger was put to Death; the utterer of a bad note was put to Death; the unlawful opener of a letter was put to Death; the purloiner of forty shillings and sixpence was put to Death; the holder of a horse at Tellson's door, who made off with it, was put to Death; the coiner of a bad shilling was put to Death; the sounders of three-fourths of the notes in the whole gamut of Crime, were put to Death. Not that it did the least good in the way of prevention—it might almost have been worth remarking that the fact was exactly the reverse—but, it cleared off (as to this world) the trouble of each particular case, and left nothing else connected with it to be looked after. Thus, Tellson's, in its day, like greater places of business, its contemporaries, had taken so many lives, that, if the heads laid low before it had been ranged on Temple Bar instead of being privately disposed of, they would probably have excluded what little light the ground floor had, in a rather significant manner.

Cramped in all kinds of dim cupboards and hutches at Tellson's, the oldest of men carried on the business gravely. When they took a young man into Tellson's London house, they hid him somewhere till he was old. They kept him in a dark place, like a cheese, until he had the full Tellson flavour and blue-mould upon him. Then only was he permitted to be seen, spectacularly poring over large books, and casting his breeches and gaiters into the general weight of the establishment.

A Tale of Two Cities

THE turnkey opening the door, disclosed in a wretched, ill-smelling little room, two hoarse, puffy, red-faced personages seated at a rickety table, playing at all-fours, smoking pipes, and drinking brandy.

"Doctor," said the turnkey, "here's a gentleman's wife in want of you without a minute's loss of time!"

The doctor's friend was in the positive degree of hoarseness, puffiness, red-facedness, all-fours, tobacco, dirt, and brandy; the doctor in the comparative—hoarser, puffier, more red-faced, more all-fourey, tobaccoer, dirtier, and brandier. The doctor was amazingly shabby, in a torn and darned rough-weather sea-jacket, out at elbows and eminently short of buttons (he had been in his time the experienced surgeon carried by a passenger ship), the dirtiest white trousers conceivable by mortal man, carpet slippers, and no visible linen. "Childbed?" said the doctor. "I'm the boy!" With that the doctor took a comb from the chimney-piece and stuck his hair upright—which appeared to be his way of washing himself—produced a professional chest or case, of most abject appearance, from the cupboard where his cup and saucer and coals were, settled his chin in the frowsy wrapper round his neck, and became a ghastly medical scarecrow.

The doctor and the debtor ran down-stairs, leaving the turnkey to return to the lock, and made for the debtor's room. All the ladies in the prison had got hold of the news, and were in the yard. Some of them had already taken possession of the two children, and were hospitably carrying them off; others were offering loans of little comforts from their own scanty store; others were sympathising with the greatest volubility. The gentlemen prisoners, feeling themselves at a disadvantage, had for the most part retired, not to say sneaked, to their rooms; from the open windows of which, some of them now complimented the doctor with whistles as he passed below, while others, with several stories between them, interchanged sarcastic references to the prevalent excitement.

It was a hot summer day, and the prison rooms were baking between the high walls. In the debtor's confined chamber, Mrs

Bangham, charwoman and messenger, who was not a prisoner (though she had been once), but was the popular medium of communication with the outer world, had volunteered her services as fly-catcher and general attendant. The walls and ceiling were blackened with flies. Mrs Bangham, expert in sudden device, with one hand fanned the patient with a cabbage leaf, and with the other set traps of vinegar and sugar in gallipots; at the same time enunciating sentiments of an encouraging and congratulatory nature, adapted to the occasion.

"The flies trouble you don't they, my dear?" said Mrs Bangham. "But p'raps they'll take your mind off it, and do you good. What between the buryin ground, the grocer's, the waggon-stables, and the paunch trade, the Marshalsea flies gets very large. P'raps they're sent as a consolation, if we only know'd it. How are you now, my dear? No better? No, my dear, it ain't to be expected; you'll be worse before you're better, and you know it, don't you? Yes. That's right! And to think of a sweet little cherub being born inside the lock! Now ain't it pretty, ain't *that* something to carry you through it pleasant? Why, we ain't had such a thing happen here, my dear, not for I couldn't name the time when. And you a crying too?" said Mrs Bangham, to rally the patient more and more. "You! Making yourself so famous! With the flies a falling into the gallipots by fifties! And everything a going on so well! And here if there ain't," said Mrs Bangham as the door opened, "if there ain't your dear gentleman along with Dr Haggage! And now indeed we *are* complete, I *think!*"

The doctor was scarcely the kind of apparition to inspire a patient with a sense of absolute completeness, but as he presently delivered the opinion, "We are as right as we can be, Mrs Bangham, and we shall come out of this like a house a fire;" and as he and Mrs Bangham took possession of the poor helpless pair as everybody else and anybody else had always done; the means at hand were as good on the whole as better would have been. The special feature in Dr Haggage's treatment of the case, was his determination to keep Mrs Bangham up to the mark. As thus:

"Mrs Bangham," said the doctor, before he had been there twenty minutes, "go outside and fetch a little brandy, or we shall have you giving in."

"Thank you, sir. But none on my accounts," said Mrs Bangham.

"Mrs Bangham," returned the doctor, "I am in professional attendance on this lady, and don't choose to allow any discussion on your part. Go outside and fetch a little brandy, or I foresee that you'll break down."

"You're to be obeyed, sir," said Mrs Bangham, rising. "If you was to put your own lips to it, I think you wouldn't be the worse, for you look but poorly, sir."

"Mrs Bangham," returned the doctor, "I am not your business, thank you, but you are mine. Never you mind *me*, if you please. What have you got to do, is, to do as you are told, and to go and get what I bid you."

Mrs Bangham submitted; and the doctor, having administered her potion, took his own. He repeated the treatment every hour, being very determined with Mrs Bangham. Three or four hours passed; the flies fell into the traps by hundreds; and at length one little life, hardly stronger than theirs, appeared among the multitude of lesser deaths.

"A very nice little girl indeed," said the doctor; "little, but well-formed. Halloa, Mrs Bangham! You're looking queer! You be off, ma'am, this minute, and fetch a little more brandy, or we shall have you in hysterics."

By this time, the rings had begun to fall from the debtor's irresolute hands, like leaves from a wintry tree. Not one was left upon them that night, when he put something that chinked into the doctor's greasy palm. In the meantime Mrs Bangham had been out an errand to a neighbouring establishment decorated with three golden balls, where she was very well known.

"Thank you," said the doctor, "thank you. Your good lady is quite composed. Doing charmingly."

"I am very happy and very thankful to know it," said the debtor, "though I little thought once, that—"

"That a child would be born to you in a place like this?" said the doctor. "Bah, bah, sir, what does it signify? A little more elbow-room is all we want here. We are quiet here; we don't get badgered here; there's no knocker here, sir, to be hammered at by creditors and bring a man's heart into his mouth. Nobody comes here to ask if a man's at home, and to say he'll stand on the door mat till he is. Nobody writes threatening letters about money to this place. It's freedom, sir, it's freedom! I have had to-day's practice at home and abroad, on a march, and aboard ship, and I'll tell you this: I don't know that I have ever pursued it under such quiet circumstances, as here this day. Elsewhere, people are restless, worried, hurried about, anxious respecting one thing, anxious respecting another. Nothing of the kind here, sir. We have done all that—we know the worst of it; we have got to the bottom, we can't fall, and what have we found? Peace. That's the word for it. Peace." With this profession of faith, the doctor, who was an old jail-bird, and was more sodden than usual, and had the additional and unusual stimulus of money in his pocket, returned to his associate and chum in hoarseness, puffiness, red-facedness, all-fours, tobacco, dirt, and brandy.

Little Dorrit

AT length they being among the trees, Mr Meagles stopped short, and said:

"Mr Clennam, will you do me the favour to look at this man? His name is Doyce, Daniel Doyce. You wouldn't suppose this man to be a notorious rascal; would you?"

"I certainly should not." It was really a disconcerting question, with the man there.

"No. You would not. I know you would not. You wouldn't suppose him to be a public offender; would you?"

"No."

"No. But he is. He is a public offender. What has he been

guilty of? Murder, manslaughter, arson, forgery, swindling, housebreaking, highway robbery, larceny, conspiracy, fraud? Which should you say, now?"

"I should say," returned Arthur Clennam, observing a faint smile in Daniel Doyce's face, "not one of them."

"You are right," said Mr Meagles. "But he has been ingenious and he has been trying to turn his ingenuity to his country's service. That makes him a public offender directly, sir."

Arthur looked at the man himself, who only shook his head.

"This Doyce," said Mr Meagles, "is a smith and engineer. He is not in a large way, but he is well known as a very ingenious man. A dozen years ago, he perfects an invention (involving a very curious secret process) of great importance to his country and his fellow-creatures. I won't say how much money it cost him, or how many years of his life he had been about it, but he brought it to perfection a dozen years ago. Wasn't it a dozen?" said Mr Meagles, addressing Doyce. "He is the most exasperating man in the world; he never complains!"

"Yes. Rather better than twelve years ago."

" Rather better?" said Mr Meagles, "you mean rather worse. Well, Mr Clennam. He addresses himself to the Government. The moment he addresses himself to the Government, he becomes a public offender! Sir," said Mr Meagles, in danger of making himself excessively hot again, "he ceases to be an innocent citizen, and becomes a culprit. He is treated from that instant as a man who has done some infernal action. He is a man to be shirked, put off, brow-beaten, sneered at, handed over by this highly-connected young or old gentleman, to that highly-connected young or old gentleman, and dodged back again; he is a man with no rights in his own time, or his own property; a mere outlaw, whom it is justifiable to get rid of anyhow; a man to be worn out by all possible means."

It was not so difficult to believe, after the morning's experience, as Mr Meagles supposed.

"Don't stand there, Doyce, turning your spectacle-case over

and over," cried Mr Meagles, "but tell Mr Clennam what you confessed to me."

"I undoubtedly was made to feel," said the inventor, "as if I had committed an offence. In dancing attendance at the various offices, I was always treated, more or less, as if it was a very bad offence. I have frequently found it necessary to reflect, for my own self-support, that I really had not done anything to bring myself into the Newgate Calendar, but only wanted to effect a great saving and a great improvement."

"There!" said Mr Meagles. "Judge whether I exaggerate. Now you'll be able to believe me when I tell you the rest of the case."

With this prelude, Mr Meagles went through the narrative; the established narrative, which has become tiresome; the matter-of-course narrative which we all know by heart. How, after interminable attendance and correspondence, after infinite impertinences, ignorances, and insults, my lords made a Minute, number 3,472, allowing the culprit to make certain trials of his invention at his own expense. How the trials were made in the presence of a board of six, of whom two ancient members were too blind to see it, two other ancient members were too deaf to hear it, one other ancient member was too lame to get near it, and the final ancient member was too pig-headed to look at it. How there were more years; more impertinences, ignorances, and insults. How my lords then made a Minute, number 5,103, whereby they resigned the business to the Circumlocution Office. How the Circumlocution Office, in course of time, took up the business as if it were a brand new thing of yesterday, which had never been heard of before; muddled the business, addled the business, tossed the business in a wet blanket. How the impertinences, ignorances, and insults went through the multiplication table. How there was a reference of the invention to three Barnacles and a Stiltstalking, who knew nothing about it; into whose heads nothing could be hammered about it; who got bored about it, and reported physical impossibilities about it. How the Circumlocution Office, in a Minute, number 8,740, "saw no reason to reverse the decision at which my lords had arrived." How the Circumlocution Office, being reminded that my lords had arrived at no decision, shelved the business. How there had been a final interview with the head of the Circumlocution Office that very morning, and how the Brazen Head had spoken, and had been, upon the whole, and under all the circumstances, and looking at it from the various points of view, of opinion that one of two courses was to be pursued in respect of the business: that was to say, either to leave it alone for evermore, or to begin it all over again.

"Upon which," said Mr Meagles, "as a practical man, I then and there, in that presence, took Doyce by the collar, and told him it was plain to me that he was an infamous rascal, and treasonable disturber of the government peace, and took him away. I brought him out of the office door by the collar, that the very porter might know I was a practical man who appreciated the official estimate of such characters; and here we are!"

If that airy young Barnacle had been there, he would have frankly told them perhaps that the Circumlocution Office had achieved its functions. That what the Barnacles had to do, was to stick on to the national ship as long as they could. That to trim the ship, lighten the ship, clean the ship, would be to knock them off; that they could but be knocked off once; and that if the ship went down with them yet sticking to it, that was the ship's look out, and not theirs.

Little Dorrit

I DID not allow my resolution, with respect to the Parliamentary Debates, to cool. It was one of the irons I began to heat immediately, and one of the irons I kept hot, and hammered at, with a perseverance I may honestly admire. I bought an approved scheme of the noble art and mystery of stenography (which cost me ten and sixpence); and plunged into a sea of perplexity that brought me, in a few weeks, to the confines of distraction. The changes that were rung upon dots, which in such a position meant such a thing, and in such another position something else, entirely different; the wonderful vagaries that were played by circles; the unaccountable consequences that resulted from marks like flies' legs; the tremendous effects of a curve in a wrong place; not only troubled my waking hours, but reappeared before me in my sleep. When I had groped my way, blindly, through these difficulties, and had mastered the alphabet, which was an Egyptian Temple in itself, there then appeared a procession of new horrors, called arbitrary characters; the most despotic characters I have ever known; who insisted, for instance, that a thing like the beginning of a cobweb, meant expectation, and that a pen-and-ink skyrocket stood for disadvantageous. When I had fixed these wretches in my mind, I found that they had driven everything else out of it; then, beginning again, I forgot them; while I was picking them up, I dropped the other fragments of the system; in short, it was almost heart-breaking.

It might have been quite heart-breaking, but for Dora, who was the stay and anchor of my tempest-driven bark. Every scratch in the scheme was a gnarled oak in the forest of difficulty, and I went on cutting them down, one after another, with such vigour, that in three or four months I was in a condition to make an experiment on one of our crack speakers in the Commons. Shall I ever forget how the crack speaker walked off from me before I began, and left my imbecile pencil staggering about the paper as if it were in a fit!

This would not do, it was quite clear. I was flying too high, and should never get on, so. I resorted to Traddles for advice; who suggested that he should dictate speeches to me, at a pace, and with occasional stoppages, adapted to my weakness. Very grateful for this friendly aid, I accepted the proposal; and night after night, almost every night, for a long time, we had a sort of private Parliament in Buckingham Street, after I came home from the Doctor's.

I should like to see such a Parliament anywhere else! My aunt and Mr Dick represented the Government or the Opposition (as the case might be), and Traddles, with the assistance of Enfield's Speaker or a volume of parliamentary orations, thundered astonishing invectives against them. Standing by the table, with his finger in the page to keep the place, and his right arm flourishing above his head, Traddles as Mr Pitt, Mr Fox, Mr Sheridan, Mr Burke, Lord Castlereagh, Viscount Sidmouth, or Mr Canning, would work himself into the most violent heats, and deliver the most withering denunciations of the profligacy and corruption of my aunt and Mr Dick; while I used to sit, at a little distance, with my note-book on my knee, lagging after him with all my might and main. The inconsistency and recklessness of Traddles were not to be exceeded by any real politician. He was for any description of policy, in the compass of a week; and nailed all sorts of colours to every denomination of mast. My aunt, looking very like an immovable Chancellor of the Exchequer, would occasionally throw in an interruption or two, as "Hear!" or "No!" or "Oh!" when the text seemed to require it: which was always a signal to Mr. Dick (a perfect country gentleman) to follow lustily with the same cry. But Mr Dick got taxed with such things in the course of his Parliamentary career, and was made responsible for such awful consequences, that he became uncomfortable in his mind sometimes. I believe he actually began to be afraid he really had been doing something, tending to the annihilation of the British constitution and the ruin of the country.

Often and often we pursued these debates until the clock pointed to midnight, and the candles were burning down. The result of so much good practice was, that by and by I began to keep pace with Traddles pretty well, and should have been quite triumphant if I had had the least idea what my notes were about. But, as to reading them after I had got them, I might as well have copied the Chinese inscriptions on an immense collection of tea-chests, or the golden characters on all the great red and green bottles in the chemists' shops!

David Copperfield

"WHY then, we'll all go back to the factory, or walk in that direction," returned Meagles cheerfully. "Mr Clennam won't be deterred by its being in Bleeding Heart Yard."

"Bleeding Heart Yard?" said Clennam. "I want to go there."

"So much the better," cried Mr Meagles. "Come along!"

As they went along, certainly one of the party, and probably more than one, thought that Bleeding Heart Yard was no inappropriate destination for a man who had been in official correspondence with my lords and the Barnacles—and perhaps had a misgiving also that Britannia herself might come to look for lodgings in Bleeding Heart Yard, some ugly day or other, if she over-did the Circumlocution Office.

Little Dorrit

THE foreigner, by name John Baptist Cavalletto—they called him Mr Baptist in the Yard—was such a chirping, easy, hopeful little fellow, that his attraction for Pancks was probably in the force of contrast. Solitary, weak, and scantily acquainted with the most necessary words of the only language in which he could communicate with the people about him, he went with the stream of his fortunes, in a brisk way that was new in those parts. With little to eat, and less to drink, and nothing to wear but what he wore upon him, or had brought tied up in one of the smallest bundles that ever were seen, he put as bright a face upon it as if he were in the most flourishing circumstances, when he first hobbled up and down the Yard, humbly propitiating the general good-will with his white teeth.

It was up-hill work for a foreigner, lame or sound, to make his way with the Bleeding Hearts. In the first place, they were vaguely persuaded that every foreigner had a knife about him; in the second, they held it to be a sound constitutional national axiom that he ought to go home to his own country. They never thought of inquiring how many of their own countrymen would be returned upon their hands from divers parts of the world, if the principle were generally recognized; they considered it practically and peculiarly British. In the third place, they had a notion that it was a sort of Divine visitation upon a foreigner that he was not an Englishman, and that all kinds of calamities happened to his country because it did things that England did not, and did not do things that England did. In this belief, to be sure, they had long been carefully trained by the Barnacles and Stiltstalkings, who were always proclaiming to them, officially and unofficially, that no country which failed to submit itself to those two large families could possibly hope to be under the protection of Providence; and who, when they believed it, disparaged them in private as the most prejudiced people under the sun.

This, therefore, might be called a political position of the Bleeding Hearts; but they entertained other objections to having foreigners in the Yard. They believed that foreigners were always badly off; and though they were as ill off themselves as they could desire to be, that did not diminish the force of the objection. They believed that foreigners were dragooned and bayoneted; and though they certainly got their own sculls promptly fractured if they showed any ill-humour, still it was with a blunt instrument, and that didn't count. They believed that foreigners were always immoral; and though they had an occasional assize at home, and now and then a divorce case or so, that had nothing to do with it. They believed that foreigners had no independent spirit, as never being escorted to the poll in droves by Lord Decimus Tite Barnacle, with colours flying and the tune of Rule Britannia playing. Not to be tedious, they had many other beliefs of a similar kind.

Little Dorrit

PEGGOTTY took me in her arms, and blessed and thanked me over and over again for being such a comfort to her (that was what she said) in her distress. She then entreated me to come upstairs, sobbing that Mr Barkis had always liked me and admired me; that he had often talked of me, before he fell into a stupor; and that she believed, in case of his coming to himself again, he would brighten up at sight of me, if he could brighten up at any earthly thing.

The probability of his ever doing so, appeared to me, when I saw him, to be very small. He was lying with his head and shoulders out of bed, in an uncomfortable attitude, half-resting on the box which had cost him so much pain and trouble. I learned, that, when he was past creeping out of bed to open it, and past assuring himself of its safety by means of the divining rod I had seen him use, he had required to have it placed on the chair at the bedside, where he had ever since embraced it, night and day. His arm lay on it now. Time and the world were slipping from beneath him, but the box was there; and the last words he had uttered were (in an explanatory tone) "Old clothes!"

"Barkis, my dear!" said Peggotty, almost cheerfully, bending over him, while her brother and I stood at the bed's foot. "Here's my dear boy—my dear boy, Master Davy, who brought us together, Barkis! That you sent messages by, you know! Won't you speak to Master Davy?"

He was as mute and senseless as the box, from which his form derived the only expression it had.

"He's a going out with the tide," said Mr Peggotty to me, behind his hand.

My eyes were dim, and so were Mr Peggotty's; but I repeated in a whisper, "With the tide?"

"People can't die, along the coast," said Mr Peggotty, "except when the tide's pretty nigh out. They can't be born, unless it's pretty nigh in—not properly born, till flood. He's a going out with the tide. It's ebb at half-arter three, slack water half an hour. If he lives 'till it turns, he'll hold his own till past the flood, and go out with the next tide."

We remained there, watching him, a long time—hours. What mysterious influence my presence had upon him in that state of his senses, I shall not pretend to say; but when he at last began to wander feebly, it is certain he was muttering about driving me to school.

"He's coming to himself," said Peggotty.

Mr Peggotty touched me, and whispered with much awe and reverence, "They are both a going out fast."

"Barkis, my dear!" said Peggotty.

"C. P. Barkis," he cried, faintly. "No better woman anywhere!"

"Look! Here's Master Davy!" said Peggotty. For he now opened his eyes.

I was on the point of asking him if he knew me, when he tried to stretch out his arm, and said to me, distinctly, with a pleasant smile—

"Barkis is willin'!"

And, it being low water, he went out with the tide.

David Copperfield

At the Seaside

(*The Tuggses at Ramsgate*)

ONCE upon a time there dwelt, in a narrow street on the Surrey side of the water, within three minutes' walk of old London Bridge, Mr Joseph Tuggs—a little dark-faced man, with shiny hair, twinkling eyes, short legs, and a body of very considerable thickness, measuring from the centre button of his waistcoat in front, to the ornamental buttons of his coat behind. The figure of the amiable Mrs Tuggs, if not perfectly symmetrical, was decidedly comfortable; and the form of her only daughter, the accomplished Miss Charlotte Tuggs, was fast ripening into that state of luxuriant plumpness which had enchanted the eyes, and captivated the heart, of Mr Joseph Tuggs in his earlier days. Mr Simon Tuggs, his only son, and Miss Charlotte Tuggs's only brother, was as differently formed in body, as he was differently constituted in mind, from the remainder of his family. There was that elongation in his thoughtful face, and that tendency to weakness in his interesting legs, which tell so forcibly of a great mind and romantic disposition. The slightest traits of character in such a being possess no mean interest to speculative minds. He usually appeared in public in capacious shoes with black cotton stockings; and was observed to be particularly attached to a black glazed stock, without tie or ornament of any description.

There is, perhaps, no profession, however useful; no pursuit, however meritorious; which can escape the petty attacks of vulgar minds. Mr Joseph Tuggs was a grocer. It might be supposed that a grocer was beyond the breath of calumny; but no—the neighbours stigmatized him as a chandler; and the poisonous voice of envy distinctly asserted that he dispensed tea and coffee by the quartern, retailed sugar by the ounce, cheese by the slice, tobacco by the screw, and butter by the pat. These taunts, however, were lost upon the Tuggses. Mr Tuggs attended to the grocery department; Mrs Tuggs to the cheesemongery; and Miss Tuggs to her education. Mr Simon Tuggs kept his father's books, and his own counsel.

One fine spring afternoon, the latter gentleman was seated on a tub of weekly Dorset, behind the little red desk with a wooden rail, which ornamented a corner of the counter, when a stranger dismounted from a cab, and hastily entered the shop. He was habited in black cloth, and bore with him a green umbrella and a blue bag.

"Mr Tuggs?" said the stranger inquiringly.

"My name is Tuggs," replied Mr Simon.

"It's the other Mr Tuggs," said the stranger, looking towards the glass door which led into the parlour behind the shop, and on the inside of which the round face of Mr Tuggs, senior, was distinctly visible, peeping over the curtain.

Mr Simon gracefully waved his pen, as if in intimation of his wish that his father would advance. Mr Joseph Tuggs, with considerable celerity, removed his face from the curtain, and placed it before the stranger.

"I come from the Temple," said the man with the bag.

"From the Temple!" said Mrs Tuggs, flinging open the door of the little parlour, and disclosing Miss Tuggs in perspective.

"From the Temple!" said Miss Tuggs and Mr Simon Tuggs at the same moment.

"From the Temple!" said Mr Joseph Tuggs, turning as pale as a Dutch cheese.

"From the Temple," repeated the man with the bag; "from Mr Cower's, the solicitor's. Mr Tuggs, I congratulate you, sir. Ladies, I wish you joy of your prosperity! We have been successful." And the man with the bag leisurely divested himself of his umbrella and glove, as a preliminary to shaking hands with Mr Joseph Tuggs.

Now, the words, "we have been successful," had no sooner issued from the mouth of the man with the bag than Mr Simon Tuggs rose from the tub of weekly Dorset, opened his eyes very wide, gasped for breath, made figures of eight in the air with his pen, and finally fell into the arms of his anxious mother, and fainted away, without the slightest ostensible cause or pretence.

"Water!" screamed Mrs Tuggs.

"Look up, my son!" exclaimed Mr Tuggs.

"Simon! dear Simon!" shrieked Miss Tuggs.

"I'm better now," said Mr Simon Tuggs. "What! successful!" And then, as corroborative evidence of his being better, he fainted away again, and was borne into the little parlour by the united efforts of the remainder of the family, and the man with the bag.

To a casual spectator, or to any one unacquainted with the position of the family, this fainting would have been unaccountable. To those who understood the mission of the man with the bag, and were, moreover, acquainted with the excitability of the nerves of Mr Simon Tuggs, it was quite comprehensible. A long-pending lawsuit respecting the validity of a will had been unexpectedly decided; and Mr Joseph Tuggs was the possessor of twenty thousand pounds.

A prolonged consultation took place that night in the little parlour—a consultation that was to settle the future destinies of the Tuggses. The shop was shut up at an unusually early hour; and many were the unavailing kicks bestowed upon the closed door by applicants for quarterns of sugar, or half-quarterns of bread, or penn'orths of pepper, which were to have been "left till Saturday," but which fortune had decreed were to be left alone altogether.

"We must certainly give up business," said Miss Tuggs.

"Oh, decidedly!" said Mrs Tuggs.

"Simon shall go to the bar," said Mr Joseph Tuggs.

"And I shall always sign myself 'Cymon' in future," said his son.

"And I shall call myself Charlotta," said Miss Tuggs.

"And you must always call *me* 'Ma,' and father 'Pa,'" said Mrs Tuggs.

"Yes, and pa must leave off all his vulgar habits," interposed Miss Tuggs.

"I'll take care of all that," responded Mr Joseph Tuggs complacently. He was, at that very moment, eating pickled salmon with a pocket-knife.

"We must leave town immediately," said Mr Cymon Tuggs.

Everybody concurred that this was an indispensable preliminary to being genteel. The question then arose, Where should they go?

"Gravesend?" mildly suggested Mr Joseph Tuggs. The idea was unanimously scouted. Gravesend was *low*.

"Margate?" insinuated Mrs Tuggs. Worse and worse—nobody there but tradespeople.

"Brighton?" Mr Cymon Tuggs opposed an insurmountable objection. All the coaches had been upset, in turn, within the last three weeks; each coach had averaged two passengers killed, and six wounded; and, in every case, the newspapers had distinctly understood that "no blame whatever was attributable to the coachman."

"Ramsgate?" ejaculated Mr Cymon thoughtfully. To be sure: how stupid they must have been, not to have thought of that before! Ramsgate was just the place of all others.

Two months after this conversation, the City of London

Ramsgate steamer was running gaily down the river. Her flag was flying, her band was playing, her passengers were conversing; everything about her seemed gay and lively.—No wonder—the Tuggses were on board.

"Charming, ain't it?" said Mr Joseph Tuggs, in a bottle-green greatcoat, with a velvet collar of the same, and a blue travelling cap with a gold band.

"Soul-inspiring!" replied Mr Cymon Tuggs—he was entered at the bar. "Soul-inspiring!"

"Delightful morning, sir!" said a stoutish, military-looking gentleman in a blue surtout buttoned up to his chin, and white trousers chained down to the soles of his boots.

Mr Cymon Tuggs took upon himself the responsibility of answering the observation. "Heavenly!" he replied.

"You are an enthusiastic admirer of the beauties of Nature, sir?" said the military gentleman.

"I am, sir," replied Mr Cymon Tuggs.

"Travelled much, sir?" inquired the military gentleman.

"Not much," replied Mr Cymon Tuggs.

"You've been on the continent, of course?" inquired the military gentleman.

"Not exactly," replied Mr Cymon Tuggs—in a qualified tone, as if he wished it to be implied that he had gone half-way, and come back again.

"You of course intend your son to make the grand tour, sir?" said the military gentleman, addressing Mr Joseph Tuggs.

As Mr Joseph Tuggs did not precisely understand what the grand tour was, or how such an article was manufactured, he replied, "Of course." Just as he said the word, there came tripping up, from her seat at the stern of the vessel, a young lady in a puce-coloured silk cloak, and boots of the same; with long black ringlets, large black eyes, brief petticoats, and unexceptionable ankles.

"Walter, my dear," said the young lady to the military gentleman.

"Yes, Belinda, my love," responded the military gentleman to the black-eyed young lady.

"What have you left me alone so long for?" said the young lady. "I have been stared out of countenance by those rude young men."

"What! stared at?" exclaimed the military gentleman with an emphasis which made Mr Cymon Tuggs withdraw his eyes from the young lady's face with inconceivable rapidity. "Which young men—where?" and the military gentleman clenched his fist, and glared fearfully on the cigar-smokers around.

"Be calm, Walter, I entreat," said the young lady.

"I won't," said the military gentleman.

"Do, sir," interposed Mr Cymon Tuggs. "They ain't worth your notice."

"No—no—they are not indeed," urged the young lady.

"I *will* be calm," said the military gentleman. "You speak truly sir. I thank you for a timely remonstrance, which may have spared me the guilt of manslaughter." Calming his wrath, the military gentleman wrung Mr Cymon Tuggs by the hand.

"My sister, sir!" said Mr Cymon Tuggs, seeing that the military gentleman was casting an admiring look towards Miss Charlotta.

"My wife, ma'am—Mrs Captain Waters," said the military gentleman, presenting the black-eyed young lady.

"My mother, ma'am—Mrs Tuggs," said Mr Cymon. The military gentleman and his wife murmured enchanting courtesies; and the Tuggses looked as unembarrassed as they could.

"Walter, my dear," said the black-eyed young lady, after they had sat chatting with the Tuggses some half-hour.

"Yes, my love," said the military gentleman.

"Don't you think this gentleman" (with an inclination of the head towards Mr Cymon Tuggs) "is very much like the Marquis Carriwini?"

"Lord bless me, very!" said the military gentleman.

"It struck me the moment I saw him," said the young lady, gazing intently, and with a melancholy air, on the scarlet countenance of Mr Cymon Tuggs. Mr Cymon Tuggs looked at everybody; and, finding that everybody was looking at him, appeared to feel some temporary difficulty in disposing of his eyesight.

"So exactly the air of the marquis," said the military gentleman.

"Quite extraordinary!" sighed the military gentleman's lady.

"You don't know the marquis, sir?" inquired the military gentleman.

Mr Cymon Tuggs stammered a negative.

"If you did," continued Captain Walter Waters, "you would feel how much reason you have to be proud of the resemblance—a most elegant man, with a most prepossessing appearance."

"He is—he is indeed!" exclaimed Belinda Waters energetically. As her eye caught that of Mr Cymon Tuggs, she withdrew it from his features in bashful confusion.

All this was highly gratifying to the feelings of the Tuggses; and when, in the course of farther conversation, it was discovered that Miss Charlotta Tuggs was the *fac-simile* of a titled relative of Mrs Belinda Waters, and that Mrs Tuggs herself was the very picture of the Dowager Duchess of Dobbleton, their delight in the acquisition of so genteel and friendly an acquaintance knew no bounds. Even the dignity of Captain Walter Waters relaxed to that degree, that he suffered himself to be prevailed upon by Mr Joseph Tuggs to partake of cold pigeon-pie and sherry on deck; and a most delightful conversation, aided by these agreeable stimulants, was prolonged, until they ran alongside Ramsgate Pier.

"Good-bye, dear!" said Mrs Captain Waters to Miss Charlotta Tuggs, just before the bustle of landing commenced; "we shall see you on the sands in the morning; and, as we are sure to have found lodgings before then, I hope we shall be inseparables for many weeks to come."

"Oh! I hope so," said Miss Charlotta Tuggs emphatically.

"Tickets, ladies and gen'l'm'n," said the man on the paddle-box.

"Want a porter, sir?" inquired a dozen men in smock-frocks.

"Now, my dear!" said Captain Waters.

"Good-bye!" said Mrs Captain Waters—"good-bye, Mr Cymon!" and, with a pressure of the hand which threw the amiable young man's nerves into a state of considerable derangement, Mrs Captain Waters disappeared among the crowd. A pair of puce-coloured boots were seen ascending the steps, a white handkerchief fluttered, a black eye gleamed. The Waterses were gone, and Mr Cymon Tuggs was alone in a heartless world.

Silently and abstractedly did that too sensitive youth follow his revered parents, and a train of smock-frocks and wheel-barrows, along the pier, until the bustle of the scene around recalled him to himself. The sun was shining brightly; the sea, dancing to its own music, rolled merrily in; crowds of people promenaded to and fro; young ladies tittered; old ladies talked; nursemaids displayed their charms to the greatest possible advantage; and their little charges ran up and down, and to and fro, and in and out, under the feet, and between the legs, of the assembled concourse, in the most playful and exhilarating manner. There were old gentlemen trying to make out objects through long telescopes: and young ones making objects of themselves in open shirt collars; ladies carrying about portable chairs, and portable chairs carrying about invalids; parties waiting on the pier for parties who had come by the steamboat; and nothing was to be heard but talking, laughing, welcoming, and merriment.

"Fly, sir?" exclaimed a chorus of fourteen men and six boys, the moment Mr Joseph Tuggs, at the head of his little party, set foot in the street.

"Here's the gen'l'm'n at last!" said one, touching his hat with mock politeness. "Wery glad to see you, sir,—been a waitin' for you these six weeks. Jump in, if you please, sir!"

"Nice light fly and a fast trotter, sir," said another: "fourteen mile a hour, and surroundin' objects rendered inwisible by ex-treme welocity!"

"Large fly for your luggage, sir?" cried a third. "Wery large fly here, sir—regular blue-bottle!"

"Here's *your* fly, sir!" shouted another aspiring charioteer, mounting the box, and inducing an old grey horse to indulge in some imperfect reminiscences of a canter. "Look at him, sir!—temper of a lamb and haction of a steam-ingein!"

Resisting even the temptation of securing the services of so valuable a quadruped as the last-named, Mr Joseph Tuggs beckoned to the proprietor of a dingy conveyance of a greenish hue, lined with faded striped calico; and, the luggage and the family having been deposited therein, the animal in the shafts, after describing circles in the road for a quarter of an hour, at last consented to depart in quest of lodgings.

"How many beds have you got?" screamed Mrs Tuggs out of the fly, to the woman who opened the door of the first house which displayed a bill intimating that apartments were to be let within.

"How many did you want, ma'am?" was, of course, the reply.

"Three."

"Will you step in, ma'am?" Down got Mrs Tuggs. The family were delighted. Splendid view of the sea from the front windows—charming! A short pause. Back came Mrs Tuggs again.—One parlour and a mattress.

"Why the devil didn't they say so at first?" inquired Mr Joseph Tuggs rather pettishly.

"Don't know," said Mrs Tuggs.

"Wretches!" exclaimed the nervous Cymon. Another bill—another stoppage. Same question—same answer—similar result.

"What do they mean by this?" inquired Mr Joseph Tuggs, thoroughly out of temper.

"Don't know," said the placid Mrs Tuggs.

"Orvis the vay here, sir," said the driver, by way of accounting for the circumstance in a satisfactory manner; and off they went again, to make fresh inquiries, and encounter fresh disappointments.

It had grown dusk when the "fly"—the rate of whose progress greatly belied its name—after climbing up four or five perpendicular hills, stopped before the door of a dusty house, with a bay-window, from which you could obtain a beautiful glimpse of the sea—if you thrust half your body out of it, at the imminent peril of falling into the area. Mrs Tuggs alighted. One ground-floor sitting-room, and three cells with beds in them upstairs. A double house. Family on the opposite side. Five children milk-and-watering in the parlour, and one little boy, expelled for bad behaviour, screaming on his back in the passage.

"What's the terms?" said Mrs Tuggs. The mistress of the house was considering the expediency of putting on an extra guinea; so, she coughed slightly, and affected not to hear the question.

"What's the terms?" said Mrs Tuggs in a louder key.

"Five guineas a week, ma'am, *with* attendance," replied the lodging-house keeper. (Attendance means the privilege of ringing the bell as often as you like for your own amusement.)

"Rather dear," said Mrs Tuggs.

"Oh dear no, ma'am!" replied the mistress of the house, with a benign smile of pity at the ignorance of manners and customs which the observation betrayed. "Very cheap!"

Such an authority was indisputable. Mrs Tuggs paid a week's rent in advance, and took the lodgings for a month. In an hour's time the family were seated at tea in their new abode.

"Capital srimps!" said Mr Joseph Tuggs.

Mr Cymon eyed his father with a rebellious scowl as he emphatically said "*Shrimps.*"

"Well, then, shrimps," said Mr Joseph Tuggs. "Srimps, or Shrimps, don't much matter."

There was pity, blended with malignity, in Mr Cymon's eye as he replied, "Don't matter, father! What would Captain Waters say if he heard such vulgarity?"

"Or what would dear Mrs Captain Waters say," added Charlotta, "if she saw mother—ma, I mean—eating them whole, heads and all?"

"It won't bear thinking of!" ejaculated Mr Cymon with a shudder. "How different," he thought, "from the Dowager Duchess of Dobbleton!"

"Very pretty woman, Mrs Captain Waters, is she not, Cymon?"

A glow of nervous excitement passed over the countenance

of Mr Cymon Tuggs as he replied, "An angel of beauty!"

"Hallo!" said Mr Joseph Tuggs. "Hallo, Cymon, my boy, take care. Married lady, you know;" and he winked one of his twinkling eyes knowingly.

"Why," exclaimed Cymon, starting up with an ebullition of fury as unexpected as alarming, "why am I to be reminded of that blight of my happiness, and ruin of my hopes? Why am I to be taunted with the miseries which are heaped upon my head? Is it not enough to—to—to—" and the orator paused; but whether for want of words, or lack of breath, was never distinctly ascertained.

There was an impressive solemnity in the tone of this address, and in the air with which the romantic Cymon, at its conclusion, rang the bell, and demanded a flat candlestick, which effectually forbade a reply. He stalked dramatically to bed, and the Tuggses went to bed too, half-an-hour afterwards, in a state of considerable mystification and perplexity.

If the pier had presented a scene of life and bustle to the Tuggses on their first landing at Ramsgate, it was far surpassed by the appearance of the sands on the morning after their arrival. It was a fine, bright, clear day, with a light breeze from the sea. There were the same ladies and gentlemen, the same children, the same nursemaids, the same telescopes, the same portable chairs. The ladies were employed in needlework, or watch-guard making, or knitting, or reading novels: the gentlemen were reading newspapers and magazines; the children were digging holes in the sands with wooden spades, and collecting water therein; the nursemaids, with their youngest charges in their arms, were running in after the waves, and then running back with the waves after them; and, now and then, a little sailing-boat either departed with a gay and talkative cargo of passengers, or returned with a very silent and particularly uncomfortable-looking one.

"Well, I never!" exclaimed Mrs Tuggs, as she and Mr Joseph Tuggs, and Miss Charlotta Tuggs, and Mr Cymon Tuggs, with their eight feet in a corresponding number of yellow shoes, seated themselves on four rush-bottomed chairs, which, being placed in a soft part of the sand, forthwith sunk down some two feet and a half. "Well, I never!"

Mr Cymon, by an exertion of great personal strength, uprooted the chairs, and removed them further back.

"Why, I'm blest if there ain't some ladies a-going in!" exclaimed Mr Joseph Tuggs with intense astonishment.

"Lor, pa!" exclaimed Miss Charlotta.

"There *is*, my dear," said Mr Joseph Tuggs. And, sure enough, four young ladies, each furnished with a towel, tripped up the steps of a bathing machine. In went the horse, floundering about in the water; round turned the machine; down sat the driver; and presently out burst the young ladies aforesaid, with four distinct splashes.

"Well, that's sing'ler too!" ejaculated Mr Joseph Tuggs after an awkward pause. Mr Cymon coughed slightly.

"Why, here's some gentlemen a-going in on this side," exclaimed Mrs Tuggs in a tone of horror.

Three machines—three horses—three flounderings—three turnings round—three splashes—three gentlemen disporting themselves in the water like so many dolphins.

"Well, *that's* sing'ler!" said Mr Joseph Tuggs again. Miss Charlotta coughed this time, and another pause ensued. It was agreeably broken.

"How d'ye do, dear? We have been looking for you all the morning," said a voice to Miss Charlotta Tuggs. Mrs Captain Waters was the owner of it.

"How d'ye do?" said Captain Walter Waters, all suavity; and a most cordial interchange of greetings ensued.

"Belinda, my love," said Captain Walter Waters, applying his glass to his eye, and looking in the direction of the sea.

"Yes, my dear," replied Mrs Captain Waters.

"There's Harry Thompson!"

"Where?" said Belinda, applying her glass to her eye.

"Bathing."

"Lor, so it is! He don't see us, does he?"

"No, I don't think he does," replied the captain. "Bless my soul, how very singular!"

"What?" inquired Belinda.

"There's Mary Golding too."

"Lor!—where?" (Up went the glass again.)

"There!" said the captain, pointing to one of the young ladies before noticed, who, in her bathing costume, looked as if she was enveloped in a patent mackintosh of scanty dimensions.

"So it is, I declare!" exclaimed Mrs Captain Waters. "How very curious we should see them both!"

"Very," said the captain with perfect coolness.

"It's the reg'lar thing here, you see," whispered Mr Cymon Tuggs to his father.

"I see it is," whispered Mr Joseph Tuggs in reply. "Queer, though—ain't it?" Mr Cymon Tuggs nodded assent.

"What do you think of doing with yourself this morning," inquired the captain. "Shall we lunch at Pegwell?"

"I should like that very much indeed," interposed Mrs Tuggs. She had never heard of Pegwell; but the word "lunch" had reached her ears, and it sounded very agreeable.

"How shall we go?" inquired the captain. "It's too warm to walk."

"A shay?" suggested Mr Joseph Tuggs.

"Chaise," whispered Mr Cymon.

"I should think one would be enough," said Mr Joseph Tuggs aloud, quite unconscious of the meaning of the correction. "However, two shays, if you like."

"I should like a donkey *so* much," said Belinda.

"Oh, so should I!" echoed Charlotta Tuggs.

"Well, we can have a fly," suggested the captain, "and you can have a couple of donkeys."

A fresh difficulty arose. Mrs Captain Waters declared it would be decidedly improper for two ladies to ride alone. The remedy was obvious. Perhaps young Mr Tuggs would be gallant enough to accompany them.

Mr Cymon Tuggs blushed, smiled, looked vacant, and faintly protested that he was no horseman. The objection was at once overruled. A fly was speedily found; and three donkeys—which the proprietor declared on his solemn asseveration to be "three parts blood, and the other corn"—were engaged in the service.

"Kim up!" shouted one of the two boys who followed behind to propel the donkeys, when Belinda Waters and Charlotta Tuggs had been hoisted, and pushed, and pulled into their respective saddles.

"Hi—hi—hi!" groaned the other body behind Mr Cymon Tuggs. Away went the donkey, with the stirrups jingling against the heels of Cymon's boots, and Cymon's boots nearly scraping the ground.

"Way—way! Wo—o—o—o—!" cried Mr Cymon Tuggs as well as he could in the midst of the jolting.

"Don't make it gallop!" screamed Mrs Captain Waters behind.

"My donkey *will* go into the public-house!" shrieked Miss Tuggs in the rear.

"Hi—hi—hi!" groaned both the boys together; and on went the donkeys as if nothing would ever stop them.

Everything has an end, however; even the galloping of donkeys will cease in time. The animal which Mr Cymon Tuggs bestrode, feeling sundry uncomfortable tugs at the bit, the intent of which he could by no means divine, abruptly sidled against a brick wall, and expressed his uneasiness by grinding Mr Cymon Tuggs's leg on the rough surface. Mrs Captain Water's donkey, apparently under the influence of some playfulness of spirit, rushed suddenly, head first, into a hedge, and declined to come out again: and the quadruped on which Miss Tuggs was mounted expressed his delight at this humorous proceeding by firmly planting his fore-feet against the ground, and kicking up his hind-legs in a very agile, but somewhat alarming manner.

This abrupt termination to the rapidity of the ride naturally occasioned some confusion. Both the ladies indulged in vehement screaming for several minutes; and Mr Cymon Tuggs, besides sustaining intense bodily pain, had the additional mental anguish of witnessing their distressing situation, without having the power to rescue them, by reason of his leg being firmly screwed in between the animal and the wall. The efforts of the boys, however, assisted by the ingenious expedient of twisting the tail of the most rebellious donkey, restored order in a much shorter time than could have reasonably been expected, and the little party jogged slowly on together.

"Now let 'em walk," said Mr Cymon Tuggs. "It's cruel to overdrive 'em."

"Wery well, sir," replied the boy, with a grin at his companion, as if he understood Mr Cymon to mean that the cruelty applied less to the animals than to their riders.

"What a lovely day, dear!" said Charlotta.

"Charming; enchanting, dear!" responded Mrs Captain Waters. "What a beautiful prospect, Mr Tuggs!"

Cymon looked full in Belinda's face as he responded—"Beautiful indeed!" The lady cast down her eyes, and suffered the animal she was riding to fall a little back. Cymon Tuggs instinctively did the same.

There was a brief silence, broken only by a sigh from Mr Cymon Tuggs.

"Mr Cymon," said the lady suddenly in a low tone, "Mr Cymon—I am another's."

Mr Cymon expressed his perfect concurrence in a statement which it was impossible to controvert.

"If I had not been——" resumed Belinda; and there she stopped.

"What—what?" said Mr Cymon earnestly. "Do not torture me. What would you say?"

"If I had not been"—continued Mrs Captain Waters—"if, in earlier life, it had been my fate to have known, and been beloved by, a noble youth—a kindred soul—a congenial spirit—one capable of feeling and appreciating the sentiments which——"

"Heavens! what do I hear?" exclaimed Mr Cymon Tuggs. "Is it possible? Can I believe my——Come up!" (This last unsentimental parenthesis was addressed to the donkey, who, with his head between his fore-legs, appeared to be examining the state of his shoes with great anxiety.)

"Hi—hi—hi!" said the boys behind. "Come up!" expostulated Cymon Truggs again. "Hi—hi—hi!" repeated the boys. And whether it was that the animal felt indignant at the tone of Mr Tuggs's command, or felt alarmed by the noise of the deputy proprietor's boots running behind him; or whether he burned with a noble emulation to outstrip the other donkeys; certain it is that he no sooner heard the second series of "Hi—hi's!" than he started away with a celerity of pace which jerked Mr Cymon's hat off instantaneously, and carried him to the Pegwell Bay hotel in no time, where he deposited his rider without giving him the trouble of dismounting, by sagaciously pitching him over his head, into the very doorway of the tavern.

Great was the confusion of Mr Cymon Tuggs when he was put right end uppermost by two waiters; considerable was the alarm of Mrs Tuggs in behalf of her son; agonising were the apprehensions of Mrs Captain Waters on his account. It was speedily discovered, however, that he had not sustained much more injury than the donkey—he was grazed and the animal was grazing—and then it *was* a delightful party to be sure! Mr and Mrs Tuggs, and the captain, had ordered lunch in the little garden behind: small saucers of large shrimps, dabs of butter, crusty loaves, and bottled ale. The sky was without a cloud; there were flower-pots and turf before them; the sea, from the foot of the cliff, stretching away as far as the eye could discern anything at all; vessels in the distance, with sails as white and as small as nicely-got-up cambric handkerchiefs. The shrimps were delightful, the ale better, and the captain even more pleasant than either. Mrs Captain Waters was in *such* spirits after lunch!—chasing, first the captain across the turf, and among the flower-pots; and then Mr Cymon Tuggs; and then Miss Tuggs; and laughing too, quite boisterously. But, as the captain said, it didn't matter; who knew what they were there? For all the people of the house knew, they might be common people. To which Mr Joseph Tuggs responded, "To be sure." And then they went down the steep wooden steps a little further on, which led to the bottom of the cliff; and looked at the crabs, and the seaweed, and the eels, till it was more than fully time to go back to Ramsgate again. Finally, Mr Cymon Tuggs ascended the steps last, and Mrs Captain Waters last but one; and Mr Cymon Tuggs discovered that the foot and ankle of Mrs Captain Waters were even more unexceptionable than he had at first supposed.

Taking a donkey towards his ordinary place of residence is a very different thing, and a feat much more easily to be accomplished, than taking him from it. It requires a great deal of foresight and presence of mind, in the one case, to anticipate the numerous flights of his discursive imagination, whereas, in the other, all you have to do is to hold on, and place a blind confidence in the animal. Mr Cymon Tuggs adopted the latter expedient on his return; and his nerves were so little discomposed by the journey, that he distinctly understood they were all to meet again at the library in the evening.

The library was crowded. There were the same ladies, and the same gentlemen, who had been on the sands in the morning, and on the pier the day before. There were young ladies, in maroon-coloured gowns and black velvet bracelets, dispensing fancy articles in the shop, and presiding over games of chance in the concert-room. There were marriageable daughters, and marriage-making mammas, gaming and promenading, and turning over music, and flirting. There were some male beaux doing the sentimental in whispers, and others doing the ferocious in moustache. There were Mrs Tuggs in amber, Miss Tuggs in sky-blue, Mrs Captain Waters in pink. There was Captain Waters in a braided surtout; there was Mr Cymon Tuggs in pumps and a gilt waistcoat; there was Mr Joseph Tuggs in a blue coat and a shirt-frill.

"Numbers three, eight, and eleven!" cried one of the young ladies in the maroon-coloured gowns.

"Numbers three, eight, and eleven!" echoed another young lady in the same uniform.

"Number three's gone," said the first young lady. "Numbers eight and eleven!"

"Numbers eight and eleven!" echoed the second young lady.

"Number eight's gone, Mary Ann," said the first young lady.

"Number eleven!" screamed the second.

"The numbers are all taken now, ladies, if you please," said the first. The representatives of numbers three, eight, and eleven, and the rest of the numbers, crowded round the table.

"Will you throw, ma'am?" said the presiding goddess, handing the dice-box to the eldest daughter of a stout lady with four girls.

There was a profound silence among the lookers-on.

"Throw, Jane, my dear," said the stout lady. An interesting display of bashfulness—a little blushing in a cambric handkerchief—a whispering to a younger sister.

"Amelia, my dear, throw for your sister," said the stout lady; and then she turned to a walking advertisement of Rowland's Macassar Oil, who stood next her, and said, "Jane is so *very* modest and retiring; but I can't be angry with her for it. An artless and unsophisticated girl is *so* truly amiable, that I often wish Amelia was more like her sister!"

The gentleman with the whiskers whispered his admiring approval.

"Now, my dear!" said the stout lady. Miss Amelia threw—eight for her sister, ten for herself.

"Nice figure, Amelia," whispered the stout lady to a thin youth beside her.

"Beautiful!"

"And *such* a spirit! I am like you in that respect. I can *not* help admiring that life and vivacity. Ah! (a sigh) I wish I could make poor Jane a little more like my dear Amelia!"

The young gentleman cordially acquiesced in the sentiment; both he, and the individual first addressed, were perfectly contented.

"Who's this?" inquired Mr Cymon Tuggs of Mrs Captain Waters, as a short female, in a blue velvet hat and feathers, was led into the orchestra by a fat man in black tights and cloudy Berlins.

"Mrs Tippin, of the London theatres," replied Belinda, referring to the programme of the concert.

The talented Tippin, having condescendingly acknowledged the clapping of hands and shouts of "Bravo!" which greeted her appearance, proceeded to sing the popular cavatina of "Bid me discourse," accompanied on the piano by Mr Tippin; after which, Mr Tippin sang a comic song, accompanied on the piano by Mrs Tippin: the applause consequent upon which was only to be exceeded by the enthusiastic approbation bestowed upon an air with variations on the guitar, by Miss Tippin, accompanied on the chin by Master Tippin.

Thus passed the evening; thus passed the days and evenings of the Tuggses and the Waterses for six weeks. Sands in the morning—donkeys at noon—pier in the afternoon—library at night—and the same people everywhere.

On that very night six weeks, the moon was shining brightly over the calm sea, which dashed against the feet of the tall gaunt cliffs, with just enough noise to lull the old fish to sleep, without disturbing the young ones, when two figures were discernible—or would have been, if anybody had looked for them—seated on one of the wooden benches which are stationed near the verge of the western cliff. The moon had climbed higher into the heavens, by two hours' journeying, since those figures first sat down—and yet they had moved not. The crowd of loungers had thinned and dispersed; the noise of itinerant musicians had died away; light after light had appeared in the windows of the different houses in the distance; blockade-man after blockade-man had passed the spot, wending his way towards his solitary post; and yet those figures had remained stationary. Some portions of the two forms were in deep shadow, but the light of the moon fell strongly on a puce-coloured boot and a glazed stock. Mr Cymon Tuggs and Mrs Captain Waters were seated on that bench. They spoke not, but were silently gazing on the sea.

"Walter will return to-morrow," said Mrs Captain Waters, mournfully breaking silence.

Mr Cymon Tuggs sighed like a gust of wind through a forest of gooseberry-bushes as he replied, "Alas, he will!"

"Oh, Cymon!" resumed Belinda, "the chaste delight, the

calm happiness, of this one week of Platonic love, is too much for me!"

Cymon was about to suggest that it was too little for him, but he stopped himself, and murmured unintelligibly.

"And to think that even this glimpse of happiness, innocent as it is," exclaimed Belinda, "is now to be lost for ever!"

"Oh, do not say for ever, Belinda!" exclaimed the excitable Cymon, as two strongly-defined tears chased each other down his pale face—it was so long that there was plenty of room for a chase. "Do not say for ever!"

"I must," replied Belinda.

"Why?" urged Cymon, "oh, why? Such Platonic acquaintance as ours is so harmless, that even your husband can never object to it."

"My husband!" exclaimed Belinda. "You little know him. Jealous and revengeful; ferocious in his revenge—a maniac in his jealousy! Would you be assassinated before my eyes?" Mr Cymon Tuggs, in a voice broken by emotion, expressed his disinclination to undergo the process of assassination before the eyes of anybody.

"Then leave me," said Mrs Captain Waters. "Leave me, this night, for ever. It is late; let us return."

Mr Cymon Tuggs sadly offered the lady his arm, and escorted her to her lodgings. He paused at the door—he felt a Platonic pressure of his hand. "Good night!" he said, hesitating.

"Good night!" sobbed the lady. Mr Cymon Tuggs paused again.

"Won't you walk in, sir?" said the servant. Mr Tuggs hesitated. Oh, that hesitation! He *did* walk in.

"Good night!" said Mr Cymon Tuggs again, when he reached the drawing-room.

"Good night!" replied Belinda; "and if, at any period of my life, I——Hush!" The lady paused and stared, with a steady gaze of horror, on the ashy countenance of Mr Cymon Tuggs. There was a double knock at the street-door.

"It is my husband!" said Belinda, as the captain's voice was heard below.

"And my family!" added Cymon Tuggs, as the voices of his relatives floated up the staircase.

"The curtain! the curtain!" gasped Mrs Captain Waters, pointing to the window, before which some chintz hangings were closely drawn.

"But I have done nothing wrong," said the hesitating Cymon.

"The curtain!" reiterated the frantic lady: "you will be murdered." This last appeal to his feelings was irresistible. The dismayed Cymon concealed himself behind the curtain with pantomime suddenness.

Enter the captain, Joseph Tuggs, Mrs Tuggs, and Charlotta.

"My dear," said the captain, "Lieutenant Slaughter." Two iron-shod boots and one gruff voice were heard by Mr Cymon to advance, and acknowledge the honour of the introduction. The sabre of the lieutenant rattled heavily upon the floor as he seated himself at the table. Mr Cymon's fears almost overcame his reason.

"The brandy, my dear!" said the captain. Here was a situation! They were going to make a night of it! And Mr Cymon Tuggs was pent up behind the curtain, and afraid to breathe!

"Slaughter," said the captain, "a cigar?"

Now, Mr Cymon Tuggs never could smoke without feeling it indispensably necessary to retire immediately, and never could smell smoke without a strong disposition to cough. The cigars were introduced; the captain was a professed smoker; so was the lieutenant; so was Joseph Tuggs. The apartment was small, the door was closed, the smoke powerful; it hung in heavy wreaths over the room, and at length found its way behind the curtain. Cymon Tuggs held his nose, his mouth, his breath. It was all of no use—out came the cough.

"Bless my soul!" said the captain, "I beg your pardon, Miss Tuggs. You dislike smoking?"

"Oh no; I don't indeed!" said Charlotta.

"It makes you cough."

"Oh dear no!"

"You coughed just now."

"Me, Captain Waters! Lor! how can you say so?"

"Somebody coughed," said the captain.

"I certainly thought so," said Slaughter. No; everybody denied it.

"Fancy," said the captain.

"Must be," echoed Slaughter.

Cigars resumed—more smoke—another cough—smothered, but violent.

"Damned odd!" said the captain, staring about him.

"Sing'ler!" ejaculated the unconscious Mr Joseph Tuggs.

Lieutenant Slaughter looked first at one person mysteriously, then at another; then, laid down his cigar; then, approached the window on tiptoe, and pointed with his right thumb over his shoulder, in the direction of the curtain.

"Slaughter!" ejaculated the captain, rising from table, "what do you mean?"

The lieutenant, in reply, drew back the curtain, and discovered Mr Cymon Tuggs behind it; pallid with apprehension, and blue with wanting to cough.

"Aha!" exclaimed the captain furiously. "What do I see? Slaughter, your sabre!"

"Cymon!" screamed the Tuggses.

"Mercy!" said Belinda.

"Platonic!" gasped Cymon.

"Your sabre!" roared the captain. "Slaughter—unhand me—the villain's life!"

"Murder!" screamed the Tuggses.

"Hold him fast, sir!" faintly articulated Cymon.

"Water!" exclaimed Joseph Tuggs—and Mr Cymon Tuggs and all the ladies forthwith fainted away, and formed a tableau.

Most willingly would we conceal the disastrous termination of the six weeks' acquaintance. A troublesome form and an arbitrary custom, however, prescribe that a story should have a conclusion, in addition to a commencement; we have therefore no alternative. Lieutenant Slaughter brought a message—the captain brought an action. Mr Joseph Tuggs interposed—the lieutenant negotiated. When Mr Cymon Tuggs recovered from the nervous disorder into which misplaced affection and exciting circumstances had plunged him, he found that his family had lost their pleasant acquaintance; that his father was minus fifteen hundred pounds; and the captain plus the precise sum. The money was paid to hush the matter up, but it got abroad notwithstanding; and there are not wanting some who affirm that three designing imposters never found more easy dupes than did Captain Waters, Mrs Waters, and Lieutenant Slaughter, in the Tuggses at Ramsgate.

Sketches by Boz

Pastimes and Pleasures

THE Six Jolly Fellowship-Porters, already mentioned as a tavern of a dropsical appearance, had long settled down into a state of hale infirmity. In its whole constitution it had not a straight floor, and hardly a straight line; but it had outlasted, and clearly would yet outlast, many a better-trimmed building, many a sprucer public-house. Externally, it was a narrow lopsided wooden jumble of corpulent windows heaped one upon another as you might heap as many toppling oranges, with a crazy wooden verandah impending over the water; indeed the whole house, inclusive of the complaining flag-staff on the roof, impended over the water, but seemed to have got into the condition of a faint-hearted diver who has paused so long on the brink that he will never go in at all.

This description applies to the river-frontage of the Six Jolly Fellowship-Porters. The back of the establishment, though the chief entrance was there, so contracted, that it merely represented, in its connection with the front, the handle of a flat-iron set upright on its broadest end. This handle stood at the bottom of a wilderness of court and alley; which wilderness pressed so hard and close upon the Six Jolly Fellowship-Porters as to leave the hostelry not an inch of ground beyond its door. For this reason, in combination with the fact that the house was all but afloat at high water, when the Porters had a family wash the linen subjected to that operation might usually be seen drying on lines stretched across the reception-rooms and bedchambers.

The wood forming the chimney-pieces, beams, partitions, floors and doors of the Six Jolly Fellowship-Porters, seemed in its old age fraught with confused memories of its youth. In many places it had become gnarled and riven, according to the manner of old trees; knots started out of it; and here and there it seemed to twist itself into some likeness of boughs. In this state of second childhood, it had an air of being in its own way garrulous about its early life. Not without reason was it often asserted by the regular frequenters of the Porters, that when the light shone full upon the grain of certain panels, and particularly upon an old corner cupboard of walnut-wood in the bar, you might trace little forests there, and tiny trees like the parent tree, in full umbrageous leaf.

The bar of the Six Jolly Fellowship-Porters was a bar to soften the human breast. The available space in it was not much larger than a hackney-coach; but no one could have wished the bar bigger, that space was so girt in by corpulent little casks, and by cordial-bottles radiant with fictitious grapes in bunches, and by lemons in nets, and by biscuits in baskets, and by the polite beer-pulls that made low bows when customers were served with beer, and by the cheese in a snug corner, and by the landlady's own small table in a snugger corner near the fire, with the cloth everlastingly laid. This haven was divided from the rough world by a glass partition and a half-door with a leaden sill upon it for the convenience of resting your liquor; but, over this half-door the bar's snugness so gushed forth, that, albeit customers drank there standing, in a dark and draughty passage where they were shouldered by other customers passing in and out, they always appeared to drink under an enchanting delusion that they were in the bar itself.

For the rest, both the tap and parlour of the Six Jolly Fellowship-Porters gave upon the river, and had red curtains matching the noses of the regular customers, and were provided with comfortable fireside tin utensils, like models of sugar-loaf hats, made in that shape that they might, with their pointed ends, seek out for themselves glowing nooks in the depths of the red coals, when they mulled your ale, or heated for you those delectable drinks, Purl, Flip, and Dog's Nose. The first of these humming compounds was a speciality of the Porters, which through an inscription on its door-posts, gently appealed to your feelings as, "The Early Purl House." For, it would seem that Purl must always be taken early; though whether for any more distinctly stomachic reason than that, as the early bird catches the worm, so the early purl catches the customer, cannot here be resolved. It only remains to add that in the handle of the flat-iron, and opposite the bar, was a very little room like a three-cornered hat, into which no direct ray of sun, moon, or star, ever penetrated, but which was superstitiously regarded as a sanctuary replete with comfort and retirement by gaslight, and on the door of which was therefore painted its alluring name: Cosy.

Our Mutual Friend

SUCH was the morning, when an open carriage, in which were three Pickwickians (Mr Snodgrass having preferred to remain at home), Mr Wardle, and Mr Trundle, with Sam Weller on the box beside the driver, pulled up by a gate at the road-side, before which stood a tall, raw-boned gamekeeper, and a half-booted, leather-legginged boy: each bearing a bag of capacious dimensions, and accompanied by a brace of pointers.

"I say," whispered Mr Winkle to Wardle, as the man let down the steps, "they don't suppose we're going to kill game enough to fill those bags, do they?"

"Fill them!" exclaimed old Wardle. "Bless you, yes! You shall fill one, and I the other; and when we've done with them, the pockets of our shooting-jackets will hold as much more."

Mr Winkle dismounted without saying anything in reply to this observation; but he thought within himself, that if the party remained in the open air, until he had filled one of the bags, they stood a considerable chance of catching colds in their heads.

"Hi, Juno, lass—hi, old girl; down, Daph, down," said Wardle, caressing the dogs. "Sir Geoffrey still in Scotland, of course, Martin?"

The tall gamekeeper replied in the affirmative, and looked with some surprise from Mr Winkle, who was holding his gun as if he wished his coat pocket to save him the trouble of pulling the trigger, to Mr Tupman, who was holding his as if he were afraid of it—as there is no earthly reason to doubt he really was.

"My friends are not much in the way of this sort of thing yet, Martin," said Wardle, noticing the look. "Live and learn you know. They'll be good shots one of these days. I beg my friend Winkle's pardon, though; he has had some practice."

Mr Winkle smiled feebly over his blue neckerchief in acknowledgment of the compliment, and got himself so mysteriously entangled with his gun, in his modest confusion, that if the piece had been loaded, he must inevitably have shot himself dead upon the spot.

"You mustn't handle your piece in that ere way, when you come to have the charge in it, sir," said the tall gamekeeper, gruffly, "or I'm damned if you won't make cold meat of some of us."

Mr Winkle, thus admonished, abruptly altered its position, and in so doing, contrived to bring the barrel into pretty sharp contact with Mr Weller's head.

"Hallo!" said Sam, picking up his hat, which had been knocked off, and rubbing his temple. "Hallo, sir! if you comes it this way, you'll fill one o' them bags, and something to spare, at one fire."

Here the leather-legginged boy laughed very heartily, and then tried to look as if it was somebody else, whereat Mr Winkle frowned majestically.

"Where did you tell the boy to meet us with the snack, Martin?" inquired Wardle.

"Side of One-tree Hill, at twelve o'clock, sir."

"That's not Sir Geoffrey's land is it?"

"No, sir; but it's close by it. It's Captain Boldwig's land; but there'll be nobody to interrupt us and there's a fine bit of turf there."

"Very well," said old Wardle. "Now the sooner we're off the better. Will you join us at twelve, then, Pickwick?"

Mr Pickwick was particularly desirous to view the sport, the more especially as he was rather anxious in respect of Mr Winkle's life and limbs. On so inviting a morning, too, it was very tantalising to turn back, and leave his friends to enjoy themselves. It was, therefore, with a very rueful air that he replied,

"Why, I suppose I must."

"An't the gentleman a shot, sir?" inquired the long gamekeeper.

"No," replied Wardle; "and he's lame besides."

"I should very much like to go," said Mr Pickwick, "very much."

There was a short pause of commiseration.

"There's a barrow t'other side the hedge," said the boy. "If the gentleman's servant would wheel along the paths, he could keep nigh us, and we could lift it over the stiles, and that."

"The wery thing," said Mr Weller, who was a party interested, inasmuch as he ardently longed to see the sport. "The wery thing. Well said, Smallcheck; I'll have it out in a minute."

But here a difficulty arose. The long gamekeeper resolutely protested against the introduction into a shooting party, of a gentleman in a barrow, as a gross violation of all established rules and precedents.

It was a great objection, but not an insurmountable one. The gamekeeper having been coaxed and feed, and having, moreover, eased his mind by "punching" the head of the inventive youth who had first suggested the use of the machine, Mr Pickwick was placed in it, and off the party set; Wardle and the long gamekeeper leading the way, and Mr Pickwick in the barrow, propelled by Sam, bringing up the rear.

"Stop, Sam," said Mr Pickwick, when they had got half across the first field.

"What's the matter now?" said Wardle.

"I won't suffer this barrow to be moved another step," said Mr Pickwick, resolutely, "unless Winkle carries that gun of his, in a different manner."

"How *am* I to carry it?" said the wretched Winkle.

"Carry it with the muzzle to the ground," replied Mr Pickwick.

"It's so unsportsman-like," reasoned Winkle.

"I don't care whether it's unsportsman-like or not," replied Mr Pickwick; "I am not going to be shot in a wheelbarrow, for the sake of appearances, to please anybody."

"I know the gentleman'll put that ere charge into somebody afore he's done," growled the long man.

"Well, well—I don't mind," said poor Winkle, turning his gun-stock uppermost;—"there."

"Anythin' for a quiet life," said Mr Weller; and on they went again.

"Stop!" said Mr Pickwick, after they had gone a few yards further.

"What now?" said Wardle.

"That gun of Tupman's is not safe: I know it isn't," said Mr Pickwick.

"Eh? What! not safe?" said Mr Tupman, in a tone of great alarm.

"Not as you are carrying it," said Mr Pickwick, "I am very sorry to make any further objection, but I cannot consent to go on, unless you carry it as Winkle does his."

"I think you had better, sir," said the long gamekeeper, "or you're quite as likely to lodge the charge in yourself as in anything else."

Mr Tupman, with the most obliging haste, placed his piece in the position required, and the party moved on again; the two amateurs marching with reversed arms, like a couple of privates at a royal funeral.

The dogs suddenly came to a dead stop, and the party advancing stealthily a single pace, stopped too.

"What's the matter with the dogs' legs?" whispered Mr Winkle. "How queer they're standing."

"Hush, can't you?" replied Wardle, softly. "Don't you see, they're making a point?"

"Making a point!" said Mr Winkle, staring about him, as if he expected to discover some particular beauty in the landscape, which the sagacious animals were calling special attention to. "Making a point! What are they pointing at?"

"Keep your eyes open," said Wardle, not heeding the question in the excitement of the moment. "Now then."

There was a sharp whirring noise, that made Mr Winkle start back as if he had been shot himself. Bang, bang, went a couple of guns;—the smoke swept quickly away over the field, and curled into the air.

"Where are they?" said Mr Winkle, in a state of the highest excitement, turning round and round in all directions. "Where are they? Tell me when to fire. Where are they—where are they?"

"Where are they?" said Wardle, taking up a brace of birds which the dogs had deposited at his feet. "Why, here they are."

"No, no; I mean the others," said the bewildered Winkle.

"Far enough off, by this time," replied Wardle, coolly reloading his gun.

"We shall very likely be up with another covey in five minutes," said the long gamekeeper. "If the gentleman begins to fire now, perhaps he'll just get the shot out of the barrel by the time they rise."

"Ha! ha! ha!" roared Mr Weller.

"Sam," said Mr Pickwick, compassionating his follower's confusion and embarrassment.

"Sir."

"Don't laugh."

"Certainly not, sir." So, by way of indemnification, Mr Weller contorted his features from behind the wheelbarrow, for the exclusive amusement of the boy with the leggings, who thereupon burst into a boisterous laugh, and was summarily cuffed by the long gamekeeper, who wanted a pretext for turning round, to hide his own merriment.

"Bravo, old fellow!" said Wardle to Mr Tupman; "you fired that time, at all events."

"Oh yes," replied Mr Tupman, with conscious pride. "I let it off."

"Well done. You'll hit something next time, if you look sharp. Very easy, ain't it?"

"Yes, it's very easy," said Mr Tupman. "How it hurts one's shoulder, though. It nearly knocked me backwards. I had no idea these small fire-arms kicked so."

"Ah," said the old gentleman, smiling; "you'll get used to it in time. Now then—all ready—all right with the barrow there?"

"All right, sir," replied Mr Weller.

"Come along then."

"Hold hard, sir," said Sam, raising the barrow.

"Aye, aye," replied Mr Pickwick, and on they went; as briskly as need be.

"Keep that barrow back now," cried Wardle when it had been hoisted over a stile into another field, and Mr Pickwick had been deposited in it once more.

"All right, sir," replied Mr Weller, pausing.

"Now, Winkle," said the old gentleman, "follow me softly, and don't be too late this time."

"Never fear," said Mr Winkle. "Are they pointing?"

"No, no; not now. Quietly now, quietly." On they crept,

and very quietly they would have advanced, if Mr Winkle, in the performance of some very intricate evolutions with his gun, had not accidently fired, at the most critical moment, over the boy's head, exactly in the very spot where the tall man's brain would have been, had he been there instead.

"Why, what on earth did you do that for?" said old Wardle, as the birds flew unharmed away.

"I never saw such a gun in my life," replied poor Mr Winkle, looking at the lock, as if that would do any good. "It goes off of its own accord. It *will* do it."

"Will do it!" echoed Wardle, with something of irritation in his manner. "I wish it would kill something of its own accord."

"It'll do that afore long, sir," observed the tall man, in a low, prophetic voice.

"What do you mean by that observation, sir?" inquired Mr Winkle, angrily.

"Never mind, sir, never mind," replied the long gamekeeper; "I've no family myself, sir; and this here boy's mother will get something handsome from Sir Geoffrey, if he's killed on his land. Load, again, sir, load again."

"Take away his gun," cried Mr Pickwick from the barrow, horror-stricken at the long man's dark insinuations. "Take away his gun, do you hear, somebody?"

Nobody, however, volunteered to obey the command; and Mr Winkle, after darting a rebellious glance at Mr Pickwick, reloaded his gun, and proceeded onwards with the rest.

We are bound, on the authority of Mr Pickwick, to state, that Mr Tupman's mode of proceeding evinced far more of prudence and deliberation, than that adopted by Mr Winkle. Still, this by no means detracts from the great authority of the latter gentleman, on all matters connected with the field; because, as Mr Pickwick beautifully observes, it has somehow or other happened from time immemorial, that many of the best and ablest philosophers, who have been perfect lights of science in matters of theory, have been wholly unable to reduce them to practice.

Mr Tupman's process, like many of our most sublime discoveries, was extremely simple. With the quickness and penetration of a man of genius, he had at once observed that the two great points to be attained were—first, to discharge his piece without injury to himself, and, secondly, to do so without danger to the by-standers;—obviously, the best thing to do, after surmounting the difficulty of firing at all, was to shut his eyes firmly, and fire into the air.

On one occasion, after performing this feat, Mr Tupman, on opening his eyes, beheld a plump partridge in the act of falling wounded to the ground. He was on the point of congratulating Mr Wardle on his invariable success, when that gentleman advanced towards him, and grasped him warmly by the hand.

"Tupman," said the old gentleman, "you singled out that particular bird?"

"No," said Mr Tupman—"no."

"You did," said Wardle. "I saw you do it—I observed you pick him out—I noticed you, as you raised your piece to take aim; and I will say this, that the best shot in existence could not have done it more beautifully. You are an older hand at this than I thought you, Tupman; you have been out before."

It was in vain for Mr Tupman to protest, with a smile of self-denial that he never had. The very smile was taken as evidence to the contrary; and from that time forth his reputation was established. It is not the only reputation that has been acquired as easily, nor are such fortunate circumstances confined to partridge-shooting.

Meanwhile, Mr Winkle flashed, and blazed, and smoked away, without producing any material results worthy of being noted down; sometimes expending his charge in mid-air, and at others sending it skimming along so near the surface of the ground as to place the lives of the two dogs on a rather uncertain and precarious tenure. As a display of fancy shooting, it was extremely varied and curious; as an exhibition of firing with any precise object, it was upon the whole, perhaps a failure. It is an established axiom, that "every bullet has its billet." If it apply in an equal degree to shot, those of Mr Winkle were unfortunate foundlings, deprived of their natural rights, cast loose upon the world, and billeted nowhere.

Pickwick Papers

BUSINESS disposed of, Mr Swiveller was inwardly reminded of its being nigh dinner-time, and to the intent that his health might not be endangered by longer abstinence, despatched a message to the nearest eating-house requiring an immediate supply of boiled beef and greens for two. With this demand, however, the eating-house (having experience of its customer) declined to comply, churlishly sending back for answer that if Mr Swiveller stood in need of beef perhaps he would be so obliging as to come there and eat it, bringing with him, as grace before meat, the amount of a certain small account which had been long outstanding. Not at all intimidated by this rebuff, but rather sharpened in wits and appetite, Mr Swiveller forwarded the same message to another and more distant eating-house, adding to it by way of rider that the gentleman was induced to send so far, not only by the great fame and popularity its beef had acquired, but in consequence of the extreme toughness of the beef retailed at the obdurate cook's shop, which rendered it quite unfit not merely for gentlemanly food, but for any human consumption. The good effect of this politic course was demonstrated by the speedy arrival of a small pewter pyramid, curiously constructed of platters and covers, whereof the boiled-beef-plates formed the base, and a foaming quart-pot the apex; the structure being resolved into its component parts afforded all things requisite and necessary for a hearty meal, to which Mr Swiveller and his friend applied themselves with great keenness and enjoyment.

"May the present moment," said Dick, sticking his fork into a large carbuncular potato, "be the worst of our lives! I like this plan of sending 'em with the peel on; there's a charm in drawing a potato from its native element (if I may so express it) to which the rich and powerful are strangers. Ah! 'Man wants but little here below, nor wants that little long!' How true that is!—after dinner."

"I hope the eating-house keeper will want but little and that *he* may not want that little long," returned his companion; "but I suspect you've no means of paying for this!"

"I shall be passing presently, and I'll call," said Dick, winking his eye significantly. "The waiter's quite helpless. The goods are gone, Fred and there's an end of it."

In point of fact, it would seem that the waiter felt this wholesome truth, for when he returned for the empty plates and dishes and was informed by Mr Swiveller with dignified carelessness that he would call and settle when he should be passing presently, he displayed some perturbation of spirit, and muttered a few remarks about "payment on delivery," and "no trust," and other unpleasant subjects, but was fain to content himself with inquiring at what hour it was likely the gentleman would call, in order that being personally responsible for the beef, greens, and sundries, he might take care to be in the way at the time. Mr Swiveller, after mentally calculating his engagements to a nicety, replied that he should look in at from two minutes before six to seven minutes past; and the man disappearing with this feeble consolation, Richard Swiveller took a greasy memorandum-book from his pocket and made an entry therein.

"Is that a reminder, in case you should forget to call?" said Trent with a sneer.

"Not exactly, Fred," replied the imperturbable Richard, continuing to write with a business-like air, "I enter in this little book the names of the streets that I can't go down while the shops are open. This dinner today closes Long Acre. I bought a pair of boots in Great Queen Street last week, and made that no thoroughfare too. There's only one avenue to the Strand left open now, and I shall have to stop up that to-night with a pair of gloves. The roads are closing so fast in every direction, that in about a month's time, unless my aunt sends me a remittance, I shall have to go three or four miles out of town to get over the way."

The Old Curiosity Shop

"HALLO!" said Mr Pickwick in his turn: seeing that his companion was armed with a gun, and that another lay ready on the grass. "What's going forward?"

"Why, your friend and I," replied the host, "are going out rook-shooting before breakfast. "He's a very good shot, an't he?"

"I've heard him say he's a capital one," replied Mr Pickwick; "but I never saw him aim at anything."

"Well," said the host, "I wish he'd come. Joe—Joe!"

The fat boy, who under the exciting influence of the morning did not appear to be more than three parts and a fraction asleep, emerged from the house.

"Go up, and call the gentleman, and tell him he'll find me and Mr Pickwick in the rookery. Show the gentleman the way there; d'ye hear?"

The boy departed to execute his commission; and the host, carrying both guns like a second Robinson Crusoe, led the way from the garden.

"This is the place," said the old gentleman, pausing after a few minutes walking, in an avenue of trees. The information was unnecessary; for the incessant cawing of the unconscious rooks sufficiently indicated their whereabout.

The old gentleman laid one gun on the ground, and loaded the other.

"Here they are," said Mr Pickwick; and as he spoke, the forms of Mr Tupman, Mr Snodgrass, and Mr Winkle appeared in the distance. The fat boy, not being quite certain which gentleman he was directed to call, had with peculiar sagacity, and to prevent the possibility of any mistake, called them all.

"Come along," shouted the old gentleman, addressing Mr

Winkle; "a keen hand like you ought to have been up long ago, even to such poor work as this."

Mr Winkle responded with a forced smile, and took up the spare gun with an expression of countenance which a metaphysical rook, impressed with a foreboding of his approaching death by violence, may be supposed to assume. It may have been keenness, but it looked remarkably like misery.

The old gentleman nodded; and two ragged boys who had been marshalled to the spot under the direction of the infant Lambert, forthwith commenced climbing up two of the trees.

"What are those lads for?" inquired Mr Pickwick abruptly. He was rather alarmed; for he was not quite certain but that the distress of the agricultural interest, about which he had often heard a great deal, might have compelled the small boys attached to the soil to earn a precarious and hazardous subsistence by making marks of themselves for inexperienced sportsmen.

"Only to start the game," replied Mr Wardle, laughing.

"To what?" inquired Mr Pickwick.

"Why, in plain English to frighten the rooks."

"Oh! is that all?"

"You are satisfied?"

"Quite."

"Very well. Shall I begin?"

"If you please," said Mr Winkle, glad of any respite.

"Stand aside, then. Now for it."

The boy shouted, and shook a branch with a nest on it. Half a dozen young rooks in violent conversation, flew out to ask what the matter was. The old gentleman fired by way of reply.

"Take him up, Joe," said the old gentleman.

There was a smile upon the youth's face as he advanced. Indistinct visions of rook-pie floated through his imagination. He laughed as he retired with the bird—it was a plump one.

"Now, Mr Winkle," said the host, reloading his own gun. "Fire away."

Mr Winkle advanced, and levelled his gun. Mr Pickwick and his friends cowered involuntarily to escape damage from the heavy fall of rooks, which they felt quite certain would be occasioned by the devastating barrel of their friend. There was a solemn pause—a shout—a flapping of wings—a faint click.

"Hallo!" said the old gentleman.

"Won't it go?" inquired Mr Pickwick.

"Missed fire," said Mr Winkle, who was very pale: probably from disappointment.

"Odd," said the old gentleman, taking the gun. "Never knew one of them miss fire before. Why, I don't see anything of the cap."

"Bless my soul," said Mr Winkle. "I declare I forgot the cap!"

The slight omission was rectified. Mr Pickwick crouched again. Mr Winkle stepped forward with an air of determination and resolution; and Mr Tupman looked out from behind a tree. The boy shouted; four birds flew out. Mr Winkle fired. There was a scream as of an individual—not a rook—in corporeal anguish. Mr Tupman had saved the lives of innumerable unoffending birds by receiving a portion of the charge in his left arm.

To describe the confusion that ensued would be impossible. To tell how Mr Pickwick in the first transports of his emotion called Mr Winkle "Wretch!" how Mr Tupman lay prostrate on the ground; and how Mr Winkle knelt horror-stricken beside him; how Mr Tupman called distractedly upon some feminine Christian name, and then opened first one eye, and then the other, and then fell back and shut them both;—all this would be as difficult to describe in detail, as it would be to depict the gradual recovering of the unfortunate individual, the binding up of his arm with pocket-handkerchiefs, and the conveying him back by slow degrees supported by the arms of his anxious friends.

Pickwick Papers

"I TAKES my determination on principle, sir," remarked Sam, "and you takes yours on the same ground; wich puts me in mind o' the man as killed his-self on principle, wich o' course you've heerd on, sir." Mr Weller paused when he arrived at this point, and cast a comical look at his master out of the corners of his eyes.

"There is no 'of course' in the case, Sam," said Mr Pickwick, gradually breaking into a smile, in spite of the uneasiness which Sam's obstinacy had given him. "The fame of the gentleman in question never reached my ears."

"No sir!" exclaimed Mr Weller. "You astonish me, sir; he wos a clerk in a gov'ment office, sir."

"Was he?" said Mr Pickwick.

"Yes, he wos, sir," rejoined Mr Weller; "and a wery pleasant gen'l'm'n too—one o' the precise and tidy sort, as puts their feet in little India-rubber fire-buckets wen its wet weather, and never has no other bosom friends but hare-skins; he saved up his money on principle, wore a clean shirt ev'ry day on principle; never spoke to none of his relations on principle, 'fear they shou'd want to borrow money of him; and wos altogether, in fact, an uncommon agreeable character. He had his hair cut on principle vunce a fortnight, and contracted for his clothes on the economic principle—three suits a year, and send back the old uns. Being a wery reg'lar gen'l'm'n, he din'd ev'ry day at the same place, were it wos one and nine to cut off the joint, and a wery good one and nine's worth he used to cut, as the landlord often said, with the tears a tricklin' down his face: let alone the way he used to poke the fire in the vinter time, which wos a dead loss o' four-pence ha'penny a day: to say nothin' at all o' the aggrawation o' seein' him do it. So uncommon grand with it too! 'Post arter the next gen'l'm'n,' he sings out ev'ry day ven he comes in. 'See arter the Times, Thomas; let me look at the Mornin' Herald, wen it's out o' hand; don't forget to bespeak the Chronicle; and just bring the 'Tizer, vill you': and then he'd set vith his eyes fixed on the clock, and rush out, just a quarter of a minit afore the time, to waylay the boy as wos a comin' in with the evenin' paper, wich he'd read with sich intense interest and persewerance as worked the other customers up to the wery confines o' desperation and insanity, 'specially one i-rascible old gen'l'm'n as the vaiter wos always obliged to keep a sharp eye on, at sich times, fear he should be tempted to commit some rash act with the carving knife. Vell, sir, here he'd stop, occupyin' the best place for three hours, and never takin' nothin' arter his dinner, but sleep, and then he'd go away to a coffee-house a few streets off, and have a small pot o' coffee and four crumpets, arter wich he'd walk home to Kensington and go to bed. One night he wos took very ill; sends for a doctor; doctor comes in a green fly, with a kind o' Robinson Crusoe set o' steps, as he could let down wen he got out, and pull up arter him wen he got in, to perwent the necessity o' the coachman's gettin' down, and thereby undeceivin' the public by lettin' 'em see that it wos only a livery coat as he'd got on, and not the trousers to match. 'Wot's the matter?' says the doctor. 'Wery ill,' says the patient. 'Wot have you been a eatin' on?' says the doctor. 'Roast weal,' says the patient. 'Wot's the last thing you dewoured?' says the doctor. 'Crumpets,' says the patient. 'That's it!' says the doctor. 'I'll send you a box of pills directly, and don't you never take no more of 'em,' he says. 'No more o' wot?' says the patient—'Pills?' 'No; crumpets,' says the doctor. 'Wy?' says the patient, starting up in bed; 'I've eat four crumpets, ev'ry night for fifteen year, on principle,' 'Well then, you'd better leave 'em off, on principle,' says the doctor. 'Crumpets is wholesome, sir,' says the patient. 'Crumpets is *not* wholesome, sir,' says the doctor, wery fierce. 'But they're so cheap,' says the patient, comin' down a little, 'and so wery filling at the price,' 'They'd be dear to you, at any price; dear if you wos paid to eat 'em,' says the doctor. 'Four crumpets a night,' he says, 'vill do your business in six months!' The patient looks him full in the face, and turns it over in his mind for a long time, and at last he says, 'Are you sure o' that 'ere, sir?' 'I'll stake my professional reputation on it,' says the doctor. 'How many crumpets, at a sittin' do you think 'ud kill me off at once?' says the patient. 'I don't know,' says the doctor. 'Do you think half a crown's wurth 'ud do it?' says the patient. 'I think it might,' says the doctor. 'Three shillins' wurth 'ud be sure to do it, I s'pose?' says the patient; 'Certainly,' says the doctor. 'Wery good', says the patient; 'good night.' Next mornin' he gets up, has a fire lit, orders in three shillins' wurth o' crumpets, toasts 'em all, eats 'em all, and blows his brains out."

"What did he do that for?" inquired Mr Pickwick abruptly; for he was considerably startled by this tragical termination of the narrative.

"Wot did he do it for, sir?" reiterated Sam. "Wy in support of his great principle that crumpets wos wholesome, and to show that he wouldn't be put out of his way for nobody!"

Pickwick Papers

MR PICKWICK found that his three companions had risen, and were waiting his arrival to commence breakfast, which was ready laid in tempting display. They sat down to the meal; and broiled ham, eggs, tea, coffee, and sundries, began to disappear with a rapidity which at once bore testimony to the excellence of the fare, and the appetites of its consumers.

"Now, about Manor Farm," said Mr Pickwick. "How shall we go?"

"We had better consult the waiter, perhaps," said Mr Tupman, and the waiter was summoned accordingly.

"Dingley Dell, gentlemen—fifteen miles, gentlemen—cross road—post-chaise, sir?"

"Post-chaise won't hold more than two," said Mr Pickwick.

"True, sir—beg your pardon, sir—Very nice four-wheeled chaise, sir—seat for two behind—one in front for the gentleman that drives—oh! beg your pardon, sir—that'll only hold three."

"What's to be done?" said Mr Snodgrass.

"Perhaps one of the gentlemen would like to ride, sir?" suggested the waiter, looking towards Mr Winkle; "very good saddle horses, sir—any of Mr Wardle's men coming to Rochester bring 'em back, sir."

"The very thing," said Mr Pickwick. "Winkle, will you go on horseback?"

Mr Winkle did entertain considerable misgivings in the very

lowest recesses of his own heart, relative to his equestrian skill; but, as he would not have them even suspected on any account, he at once replied with great hardihood, "Certainly. I should enjoy it, of all things."

Mr Winkle had rushed upon his fate; there was no resource. "Let them be at the door by eleven," said Mr Pickwick.

"Very well, sir," replied the waiter.

The waiter retired; the breakfast concluded; and the travellers ascended to their respective bed-rooms, to prepare a change of clothing, to take with them on their approaching expedition.

Mr Pickwick had made his preliminary arrangements, and was looking over the coffee-room blinds at the passengers in the street, when the waiter entered and announced that the chaise was ready—an announcement which the vehicle itself confirmed, by forthwith appearing before the coffee-room blinds aforesaid.

It was a curious little green box on four wheels, with a low place like a wine-bin for two behind, and an elevated perch for one in front, drawn by an immense brown horse, displaying great symmetry of bone. An hostler stood near, holding by the bridle another immense horse—apparently a near relative of the animal in the chaise—ready saddled for Mr Winkle.

"Bless my soul!" said Mr Pickwick, as they stood upon the pavement while the coats were being put in. "Bless my soul! who's to drive? I never thought of that."

"Oh! you, of course," said Mr Tupman.

"Of course," said Mr Snodgrass.

"I!" exclaimed Mr Pickwick.

"Not the slightest fear, sir," interposed the hostler. "Warrant him quiet, sir; a hinfant in arms might drive him."

"He don't shy, does he?" inquired Mr Pickwick.

"Shy, sir?—He wouldn't shy if he was to meet a vaggin-load of monkeys with their tails burnt off."

The last recommendation was indisputable. Mr Tupman and Mr Snodgrass got into the bin; Mr Pickwick ascended to his perch, and deposited his feet on a floor-clothed shelf, erected beneath it for that purpose.

"Now, shiny Villiam," said the hostler to the deputy hostler, "give the gen'lm'n the ribbins." "Shiny Villiam"—so called, probably, from his sleek hair and oily countenance—placed the reins in Mr Pickwick's left hand; and the upper hostler thrust a whip into his right.

"Wo—o!" cried Mr Pickwick, as the tall quadruped evinced a decided inclination to back into the coffee-room window.

"Wo—o!" echoed Mr Tupman and Mr Snodgrass, from the bin.

"Only his playfulness, gen'lm'n," said the head hostler encouragingly; "jist kitch hold on him, Villiam." The deputy restrained the animal's impetuosity, and the principal ran to assist Mr Winkle in mounting.

"T'other side, sir, if you please."

"Blowed if the gen'lm'n worn't a gettin' up on the wrong side," whispered a grinning post-boy to the inexpressibly gratified waiter.

Mr Winkle, thus instructed, climbed into his saddle, with about as much difficulty as he would have experienced in getting up the side of a first-rate man-of-war.

"All right?" inquired Mr Pickwick, with an inward presentiment that it was all wrong.

"All right," replied Mr Winkle faintly.

"Let 'em go," cried the hostler,—"Hold him in, sir," and away went the chaise, and the saddle-horse, with Mr Pickwick on the box of the one, and Mr Winkle on the back of the other, to the delight and gratification of the whole inn yard.

"What makes him go sideways?" said Mr Snodgrass in the bin, to Mr Winkle in the saddle.

"I can't imagine," replied Mr Winkle. His horse was drifting up the street in the most mysterious manner—side first, with his head towards one side of the way, and the tail towards the other.

Mr Pickwick had no leisure to observe either this or any other particular, the whole of his faculties being concentrated in the management of the animal attached to the chaise, who displayed various peculiarities, highly interesting to a by-stander, but by no means equally amusing to any one seated behind him.

Besides constantly jerking his head up, in a very unpleasant and uncomfortable manner, and tugging at the reins to an extent which rendered it a matter of great difficulty for Mr Pickwick to hold them, he had a singular propensity for darting suddenly every now and then to the side of the road, then stopping short, and then rushing forward for some minutes, at a speed which it was wholly impossible to control.

"What *can* he mean by this?" said Mr Snodgrass, when the horse had executed this manœuvre for the twentieth time.

"I don't know," replied Mr Tupman; "it *looks* very like shying, don't it?" Mr Snodgrass was about to reply, when he was interrupted by a shout from Mr Pickwick.

"Woo!" said that gentleman; "I have dropped my whip."

"Winkle," said Mr Snodgrass, as the equestrian came trotting up on the tall horse, with his hat over his ears, and shaking all over, as if he would shake to pieces, with the violence of the exercise, "pick up the whip, there's a good fellow." Mr Winkle pulled at the bridle of the tall horse till he was black in the face; and having at length succeeded in stopping him, dismounted, handed the whip to Mr Pickwick, and grasping the reins, prepared to remount.

Now whether the tall horse, in the natural playfulness of his disposition, was desirous of having a little innocent recreation with Mr Winkle, or whether it occurred to him that he could perform the journey as much to his own satisfaction without a rider as with one, are points upon which, of course, we can arrive at no definite and distinct conclusion. By whatever motives the animal was actuated, certain it is that Mr Winkle had no sooner touched the reins, than he slipped them over his head, and darted backwards to their full length.

"Poor fellow," said Mr Winkle, soothingly,—"poor fellow—good old horse." The "poor fellow" was proof against flattery: the more Mr Winkle tried to get nearer him, the more he sidled away; and, notwithstanding all kinds of coaxing and wheedling, there were Mr Winkle and the horse going round and round each other for ten minutes, at the end of which time each was at precisely the same distance from the other as when they first commenced—an unsatisfactory sort of thing under any circumstances, but particularly so in a lonely road, where no assistance can be procured.

"What am I to do?" shouted Mr Winkle, after the dodging had been prolonged for a considerable time. "What am I to do? I can't get on him."

"You had better lead him till we come to a turnpike," replied Mr Pickwick from the chaise.

"But he won't come!" roared Mr Winkle. "Do come, and hold him."

Mr Pickwick was the very personation of kindness and humanity: he threw the reins on the horse's back, and having descended from his seat, carefully drew the chaise into the hedge, lest anything should come along the road, and stepped back to the assistance of his distressed companion, leaving Mr Tupman and Mr Snodgrass in the vehicle.

The horse no sooner beheld Mr Pickwick advancing towards him with the chaise whip in his hand, than he exchanged the rotary motion in which he had previously indulged, for a retrograde movement of so very determined a character, that it at once drew Mr Winkle, who was still at the end of the bridle, at a rather quicker rate than fast walking, in the direction from which they had just come. Mr Pickwick ran to his assistance, but the faster Mr Pickwick ran forward, the faster the horse ran backward. There was a great scraping of feet, and kicking up of the dust; and at last Mr Winkle, his arms being nearly pulled out of their sockets, fairly let go his hold. The horse paused, stared, shook his head, turned round, and quietly trotted home to Rochester, leaving Mr Winkle and Mr Pickwick gazing on each other with countenances of blank dismay. A rattling noise at a little distance attracted their attention. They looked up.

"Bless my soul!" exclaimed the agonized Mr Pickwick, "there's the other horse running away!"

It was but too true. The animal was startled by the noise, and the reins were on his back. The result may be guessed. He tore off with the four-wheeled chaise behind him, and Mr Tupman and Mr Snodgrass in the four-wheeled chaise. The heat was a short one. Mr Tupman threw himself into the hedge, Mr Snodgrass followed his example, the horse dashed the four-wheeled chaise against a wooden bridge, separated the wheels from the body, and the bin from the perch; and finally stood stock still to gaze upon the ruin he had made.

Pickwick Papers

MR CODLIN followed with a willing mind and soon found that the landlord had not commended his preparations without good reason. A mighty fire was blazing on the hearth and roaring up the wide chimney with a cheerful sound, which a large iron cauldron, bubbling and simmering in the heat, lent its pleasant aid to swell. There was a deep red ruddy blush upon the room, and when the landlord stirred the fire, sending the flames skipping and leaping up—when he took off the lid of the iron pot and there rushed out a savoury smell, while the bubbling sound grew deeper and more rich, and an unctuous steam came floating out, hanging in a delicious mist above their heads—when he did this, Mr Codlin's heart was touched. He sat down in the chimney-corner and smiled.

Mr Codlin sat smiling in the chimney-corner, eyeing the landlord as with a roguish look he held the cover in his hand, and, feigning that his doing so was needful to the welfare of the cookery, suffered the delightful steam to tickle the nostrils of his guest. The glow of the fire was upon the landlord's bald head, and upon his twinkling eye, and upon his watering mouth, and upon his pimpled face, and upon his round fat figure. Mr Codlin drew his sleeve across his lips, and said in a murmuring voice, "What is it?"

"It is a stew of tripe," said the landlord smacking his lips, "and cow-heel," smacking them again, "and bacon," smacking them once more, "and steak," smacking them for the fourth time, "and peas, cauliflowers, new potatoes, and sparrow-grass, all working up together in one delicious gravy." Having come to the climax, he smacked his lips a great many times, and taking a long hearty sniff of the fragrance that was hovering about, put on the cover again with the air of one whose toils on earth were over.

The Old Curiosity Shop

THE wickets were pitched, and so were a couple of marquees for the rest and refreshment of the contending parties. The game had not yet commenced. Two or three Dingley Dellers, and All-Muggletonians, were amusing themselves with a majestic air by throwing the ball carelessly from hand to hand; and several other gentlemen dressed like them, in straw hats, flannel jackets, and white trousers—a costume in which they looked very much like amateur stone-masons—were sprinkled about the tents, towards one of which Mr Wardle conducted the party.

Several dozen of "How-are-you's?" hailed the old gentleman's arrival; and a general raising of the straw hats, and bending forward of the flannel jackets, followed his introduction of his guests as gentlemen from London, who were extremely anxious to witness the proceedings of the day, with which, he had no doubt, they would be greatly delighted.

"You had better step into the marquee, I think, sir," said one very stout gentleman, whose body and legs looked like half a gigantic roll of flannel, elevated on a couple of inflated pillow-cases.

"You'll find it much pleasanter, sir," urged another stout gentleman, who strongly resembled the other half of the roll of flannel aforesaid.

"You're very good," said Mr Pickwick.

"This way," said the first speaker; "they notch in here—it's the best place in the whole field"; and the cricketer, panting on before, preceded them to the tent.

"Capital game—smart sport—fine exercise—very," were the words which fell upon Mr Pickwick's ear as he entered the tent; and the first object that met his eyes was his green-coated friend of the Rochester coach, holding forth, to the no small delight and edification of a select circle of the chosen of All-Muggleton. His dress was slightly improved, and he wore boots; but there was no mistaking him.

The stranger recognised his friends immediately: and, darting forward and seizing Mr Pickwick by the hand, dragged him to a seat with his usual impetuosity, talking all the while as if the whole of the arrangements were under his especial patronage and direction.

"This way—this way—capital fun—lots of beer—hogs-heads; rounds of beef—bullocks; mustard—cart loads; glorious day—down with you—make yourself at home—glad to see you—very."

Mr Pickwick sat down as he was bid, and Mr Winkle and Mr Snodgrass also complied with the directions of their mysterious friend. Mr Wardle looked on, in silent wonder.

"Mr Wardle—a friend of mine," said Mr Pickwick.

"Friend of yours!—My dear sir, how are you?—Friend of *my* friend's—give me your hand, sir"—and the stranger grasped Mr Wardle's hand with all the fervour of a close intimacy of many years, and then stepped back a pace or two as if to take a full survey of his face and figure, and then shook hands with him again, if possible, more warmly than before.

"Well; and how came you here?" said Mr Pickwick, with a smile in which benevolence struggled with surprise.

"Come," replied the stranger—"stopping at Crown—Crown at Muggleton—met a party—flannel jackets—white trousers—anchovy sandwiches—devilled kidneys—splendid fellows—glorious."

Mr Pickwick was sufficiently versed in the stranger's system of stenography to infer from this rapid and disjointed communication that he had, somehow or other, contracted an acquaintance with the All-Muggletons, which he had converted, by a process peculiar to himself, into that extent of good fellowship on which a general invitation may be easily founded. His curiosity was therefore satisfied, and putting on his spectacles he prepared himself to watch the play which was just commencing.

All-Muggleton had the first innings; and the interest became intense when Mr Dumkins and Mr Podder, two of the most renowned members of that most distinguished club, walked, bat in hand, to their respective wickets. Mr Luffey, the highest ornament of Dingley Dell, was pitched to bowl against the redoubtable Dumkins, and Mr Struggles was selected to do the same kind of office for the hitherto unconquered Podder. Several players were stationed, to "look out," in different parts of the field, and each fixed himself into the proper attitude by placing one hand on each knee, and stooping very much as if he were "making a back" for some beginner at leap-frog. All the regular players do this sort of thing;—indeed it's generally supposed that it is quite impossible to look out properly in any other position.

The umpires were stationed behind the wickets; the scorers were prepared to notch the runs; a breathless silence ensued. Mr Luffey retired a few paces behind the wicket of the passive Podder, and applied the ball to his right eye for several seconds. Dunkins confidently awaited its coming with his eyes fixed on the motions of Luffey.

"Play!" suddenly cried the bowler. The ball flew from his hand straight and swift towards the centre stump of the wicket. The wary Dumkins was on the alert; it fell upon the tip of the bat, and bounded far away over the heads of the scouts, who had just stooped low enough to let it fly over them.

"Run—run—another.—Now, then, throw her up—up with her—stop there—another—no—yes—no—throw her up, throw her up!"—Such were the shouts which followed the stroke; and, at the conclusion of which All-Muggleton had scored two. Nor was Podder behindhand in earning laurels wherewith to garnish himself and Muggleton. He blocked the doubtful balls, missed the bad ones, took the good ones, and sent them flying to all parts of the field. The scouts were hot and tired; the bowlers were changed and bowled till their arms ached; but Dumkins and Podder remained unconquered. Did an elderly gentleman essay to stop the progress of the ball, it rolled between his legs or slipped between his fingers. Did a slim gentleman try to catch it, it struck him on the nose, and bounded pleasantly off with redoubled violence, while the slim gentleman's eyes filled with water, and his form writhed with anguish. Was it thrown straight up to the wicket, Dumkins had reached it before the ball. In short, when Dumkins was caught out, and Podder stumped out, All-Muggleton had notched some fifty-four, while the score of the Dingley Dellers was as blank as their faces. The advantage was too great to be recovered. In vain did the eager Luffey, and the enthusiastic Struggles, do all that skill and experience could suggest, to regain the ground Dingley Dell had lost in the contest;—it was of no avail; and in an early period of the winning game Dingley Dell gave in, and allowed the superior prowess of All-Muggleton.

The stranger, meanwhile, had been eating, drinking, and talking, without cessation. At every good stroke he expressed his satisfaction and approval of the player in a most condescending and patronising manner, which could not fail to have been highly gratifying to the party concerned; while at every bad attempt at a catch, and every failure to stop the ball, he launched his personal displeasure at the head of the devoted individual in such denunciations as—"Ah, ah!—stupid"—"Now, butterfingers"—"Muff"—"Humbug"—and so forth—ejaculations which seemed to establish him in the opinion of all around, as a most excellent and undeniable judge of the whole art and mystery of the noble game of cricket.

"Capital game—well played—some strokes admirable," said the stranger, as both sides crowded into the tent, at the conclusion of the game.

"You have played it, sir?" inquired Mr Wardle, who had been much amused by his loquacity.

"Played it! Think I have—thousands of times—not here—West Indies—exciting thing—hot work—very."

"It must be rather a warm pursuit in such a climate," observed Mr Pickwick.

"Warm!—red hot—scorching—glowing. Played a match once—single wicket—friend the Colonel—Sir Thomas Blazo—who should get the greatest number of runs.—Won the toss—

first innings—seven o'clock a.m.—six natives to look out—went in; kept in—heat intense—natives all fainted—taken away—fresh half-dozen ordered—fainted also—Blazo bowling—supported by two natives—couldn't bowl me out—fainted too—cleared away the Colonel—wouldn't give in—faithful attendant—Quanko Samba—last man left—sun so hot, bat in blisters, ball scorched brown—five hundred and seventy runs—rather exhausted—Quanko mustered up last remaining strength bowled me out—had a bath, and went out to dinner."

"And what became of what's-his-name, sir?" inquired an old gentleman.

"Blazo?"

"No—the other gentleman."

"Quanko Samba?"

"Yes, sir."

"Poor Quanko—never recovered it—bowled on, on my account—bowled off, on his own—died, sir." Here the stranger buried his countenance in a brown jug, but whether to hide his emotion or imbibe its contents, we cannot distinctly affirm. We only know that he paused suddenly, drew a long and deep breath, and looked anxiously on, as two of the principal members of the Dingley Dell club approached Mr Pickwick, and said—

"We are about to partake of a plain dinner at the Blue Lion, sir; we hope you and your friends will join us."

"Of course," said Mr Wardle, "among our friends we include Mr—;" and he looked towards the stranger.

"Jingle," said that versatile gentleman, taking the hint at once. "Jingle—Alfred Jingle, Esq., of No Hall, Nowhere."

"I shall be very happy, I am sure," said Mr Pickwick.

"So shall I," said Mr Alfred Jingle, drawing one arm through Mr Pickwick's, and another through Mr Wardle's, as he whispered confidentially in the ear of the former gentleman:—

"Devilish good dinner—cold, but capital—peeped into the room this morning—fowls and pies, and all that sort of thing—pleasant fellows these—well behaved, too—very."

There being no further preliminaries to arrange, the company straggled into the town in little knots of twos and threes; and within a quarter of an hour were all seated in the great room of the Blue Lion Inn, Muggleton—Mr Dumkins acting as chairman, and Mr Luffey officiating as vice.

There was a vast deal of talking and rattling of knives and forks, and plates: a great running about of three ponderous headed waiters, and a rapid disappearance of the substantial viands on the table; to each and every of which item of confusion, the facetious Mr Jingle lent the aid of half-a-dozen ordinary men at least. When everybody had eaten as much as possible, the cloth was removed, bottles, glasses, and dessert were placed on the table; and the waiters withdrew to "clear away," or in other words, to appropriate to their own private use and emolument whatever remnants of the eatables and drinkables they could contrive to lay their hands on.

Amidst the general hum of mirth and conversation that ensued, there was a little man with a puffy Say-nothing-to-me, -or-I'll-contradict-you sort of countenance, who remained very quiet; occasionally looking round him when the conversation slackened, as if he contemplated putting in something very weighty; and now and then bursting into a short cough of inexpressible grandeur. At length, during a moment of comparative silence, the little man called out in a very loud, solemn voice—

"Mr Luffey!"

Everybody was hushed into a profound stillness as the individual addressed, replied—

"Sir!"

"I wish to address a few words to you, sir, if you will entreat the gentlemen to fill their glasses."

Mr Jingle uttered a patronising "hear, hear," which was responded to by the remainder of the company: and the glasses having been filled the Vice-President assumed an air of wisdom in a state of profound attention; and said—

"Mr Staple."

"Sir," said the little man, rising, "I wish to address what I have to say to *you* and not to our worthy chairman, because our worthy chairman is in some measure—I may say in a great degree—the subject of what I have to say, or I may say to—to—"

"State," suggested Mr Jingle.

—"Yes, to state," said the little man, "I thank my honourable friend, if he will allow me to call him so—(four hears, and one certainly from Mr Jingle)—for the suggestion. Sir, I am a Deller—a Dingley Deller (cheers). I cannot lay claim to the honour of forming an item in the population of Muggleton; nor, sir, I will frankly admit, do I covet that honour: and I will tell you why, sir—(hear); to Muggleton I will readily concede all those honours and distinctions to which it can fairly lay claim—they are too numerous and too well known to require aid or recapitulation from me. But, sir, while we remember that Muggleton has given birth to a Dumkins and a Podder, let us never forget that Dingley Dell can boast a Luffey and a Struggles. (Vociferous cheering.) Let me not be considered as wishing to detract from the merits of the former gentlemen. Sir, I envy them the luxury of their own feelings on this occasion. (Cheers.) Every gentleman who hears me, is probably acquainted with the reply made by an individual, who—to use an ordinary figure of speech—'hung out' in a tub, to the emperor Alexander:—'If I were not Diogenes,' said he, 'I would be Alexander.' I can well imagine these gentlemen to say, 'If I were not Dumkins I would be Luffey; if I were not Podder I would be Struggles.' (Enthusiasm.) But, gentlemen of Muggleton, is it in cricket alone that your fellow-townsmen stand preeminent? Have you never heard of Dumkins and determination? Have you never been taught to associate Podder with property? (Great applause.) Have you never, when struggling for your rights, your liberties, and your privileges, been reduced, if only for an instant, to misgiving and despair? And when you have been thus depressed, has not the name of Dumkins laid afresh within your breast the fire which had just gone out; and has not a word from that man, lighted it again as brightly as if it had never expired? (Great cheering.) Gentlemen, I beg to surround with a rich halo of enthusiastic cheering the united names of 'Dumkins and Podder.' "

Here the little man ceased, and here the company commenced a raising of voices, and thumping of tables, which lasted with little intermission during the remainder of the evening. Other toasts were drunk. Mr Luffey and Mr Struggles, Mr Pickwick and Mr Jingle, were, each in his turn, the subject of unqualified eulogium; and each in due course returned thanks for the honour.

The Pickwick Papers

"HALLOA!" cried a hoarse voice in his ear. "Halloa, halloa, halloa! Bow wow wow. What's the matter here! Hal-loa!"

The speaker—who made the locksmith start, as if he had seen some supernatural agent—was a large raven; who had perched upon the top of the easy-chair, unseen by him and Edward, and listened with a polite attention and a most extraordinary appearance of comprehending every word, to all they had said up to this point; turning his head from one to the other, as if his office were to judge between them, and it were of the very last importance that he should not lose a word.

"Look at him!" said Varden, divided between admiration of the bird and a kind of fear of him. "Was there ever such a knowing imp as that! Oh he's a dreadful fellow!"

The raven, with his head very much on one side, and his bright eye shining like a diamond, preserved a thoughtful silence for a few seconds, and then replied in a voice so hoarse and distant, that it seemed to come through his thick feathers rather than out of his mouth.

"Halloa, halloa, halloa! What's the matter here! Keep up your spirits. Never say die. Bow wow wow. I'm a devil, I'm a devil, I'm a devil. Hurrah!"—And then, as if exulting in his infernal character, he began to whistle.

"I more than half believe he speaks the truth. Upon my word

I do," said Varden. "Do you see how he looks at me, as if he knew what I was saying?"

To which the bird, balancing himself on tiptoe, as it were, and moving his body up and down in a sort of grave dance, rejoined, "I'm a devil, I'm a devil, I'm a devil," and flapped his wings against his sides as if he were bursting with laughter. Barnaby clapped his hands, and fairly rolled upon the ground in an ecstasy of delight.

"Strange companions, sir," said the locksmith, shaking his head and looking from one to the other. "The bird has all the wit."

"Strange indeed!" said Edward, holding out his forefinger to the raven, who, in acknowledgment of the attention, made a dive at it immediately with his iron bill. "Is he old?"

"A mere boy, sir," replied the locksmith. "A hundred and twenty, or thereabouts. Call him down, Barnaby my man."

"Call him!" echoed Barnaby, sitting upright upon the floor, and staring vacantly at Gabriel, as he thrust his hair back from his face. "But who can make him come! He calls me, and makes me go where he will. He goes on before, and I follow. He's the master, and I'm the man. Is that the truth, Grip?"

The raven gave a short, comfortable, confidential kind of croak;—a most expressive croak, which seemed to say "You needn't let these fellows into our secrets. We understand each other. It's all right."

"I make *him* come!" cried Barnaby, pointing to the bird. "Him, who never goes to sleep, or so much as winks!—Why, any time of night, you may see his eyes in my dark room, shining like two sparks. And every night, and all night too, he's broad awake, talking to himself, thinking what he shall do to-morrow, where we shall go, and what he shall steal, and hide, and bury. I make *him* come! Ha, ha, ha!"

On second thoughts, the bird appeared disposed to come of himself. After a short survey of the ground, and a few sidelong looks at the ceiling and at everybody present in turn, he fluttered to the floor, and went to Barnaby—not in a hop, or walk, or run, but in a pace like that of a very particular gentleman with exceedingly tight boots on, trying to walk fast over loose pebbles. Then, stepping into his extended hand, and condescending to be held out at arm's length, he gave vent to a succession of sounds, not unlike the drawing of some eight or ten dozen of long corks, and again asserted his brimstone birth and parentage with great distinctness.

Barnaby Rudge

WE will endeavour to sketch the bar of a large gin-shop, and its ordinary customers, for the edification of such of our readers as may not have had opportunities of observing such scenes; and, on the chance of finding one well suited to our purpose, we will make for Drury Lane, through the narrow streets and dirty courts which divide it from Oxford Street, and that classical spot adjoining the brewery at the bottom of Tottenham Court Road, best known to the initiated as the "Rookery."

The filthy and miserable appearance of this part of London can hardly be imagined by those (and there are many such) who have not witnessed it. Wretched houses with broken windows patched with rags and paper; every room let out to a different family, and in many instances to two or even three—fruit and "sweetstuff" manufacturers in the cellars, barbers and red-herring vendors in the front parlours, cobblers in the back; a bird-fancier in the first floor, three families on the second, starvation in the attics, Irishmen in the passage, a "musician" in the front kitchen, and a charwoman and five hungry children in the back one—filth everywhere—a gutter before the houses, and a drain behind—clothes drying, and slops emptying, from the windows; girls of fourteen or fifteen with matted hair, walking about barefoot, and in white greatcoats, almost their only covering; boys of all ages, in coats of all sizes and no coats at all; men and women, in every variety of scanty and dirty apparel, lounging, scolding, drinking, smoking, squabbling, fighting, and swearing.

You turn the corner. What a change! All is light and brilliancy. The hum of many voices issues from that splendid gin-shop which forms the commencement of the two streets opposite; and the gay building with the fantastically-ornamented parapet, the illuminated clock, the plate-glass windows surrounded by stucco rosettes, and its profusion of gas-lights in richly-gilt burners, is perfectly dazzling when contrasted with the darkness and dirt we have just left. The interior is even gayer than the exterior. A bar of French-polished mahogany, elegantly carved, extends the whole width of the place; and there are two side-aisles of great casks, painted green and gold, enclosed within a light brass rail, and bearing such inscriptions as "Old Tom, 549"; "Young Tom, 360"; "Samson, 1421"—the figures agreeing, we presume, with "gallons," understood. Beyond the bar is a lofty and spacious saloon, full of the same enticing vessels, with a gallery running round it, equally well furnished. On the counter, in addition to the usual spirit apparatus, are two or three little baskets of cakes and biscuits, which are carefully secured at top with wicker-work, to prevent their contents being unlawfully abstracted. Behind it are two showily-dressed damsels with large necklaces, dispensing the spirits and "compounds." They are assisted by the ostensible proprietor of the concern, a stout coarse fellow in a fur cap, put on very much on one side to give him a knowing air, and to display his sandy whiskers to the best advantage.

The two old washerwomen, who are seated on a little bench to the left of the bar, are rather overcome by the head-dresses and haughty demeanour of the young ladies who officiate. They receive their half-quartern of gin and peppermint with considerable deference, prefacing a request for "one of them soft biscuits," with a "Jist be good enough, ma'am." They are quite astonished at the impudent air of the young fellow in a brown coat and bright buttons, who, ushering in his two companions, and walking up to the bar in as careless a manner as if he had been used to green and gold ornaments all his life, winks at one of the young ladies with singular coolness, and calls for a "kervorten and a three-out glass," just as if the place were his own. "Gin for you, sir?" says the young lady when she has drawn it: carefully looking every way but the right one, to show that the wink had no effect upon her. "For me, Mary, my dear," replies the gentleman in brown. "My name ain't Mary, as it happens," says the young girl, rather relaxing as she delivers the change. "Well, if it ain't, it ought to be," responds the irresistible one; "all the Marys as ever *I* see was handsome gals." Here the young lady, not precisely remembering how blushes are managed in such cases, abruptly ends the flirtation by addressing the female in the faded feathers who has just entered, and who, after stating explicitly, to prevent any subsequent misunderstanding, that "this gentleman pays," calls for "a glass of port wine and a bit of sugar."

Those two old men, who came in "just to have a drain," finished their third quartern a few seconds ago; they have made themselves crying drunk; and the fat comfortable-looking elderly women, who had "a glass of rum srub" each, having chimed in with their complaints on the hardness of the times, one of the women has agreed to stand a glass round, jocularly observing that "grief never mended no broken bones, and as good people's wery scarce, what I says is, make the most on 'em, and that's all about it!" a sentiment which appears to afford unlimited satisfaction to those who have nothing to pay.

It is growing late, and the throng of men, women, and children, who have been constantly going in and out, dwindles down to two or three occasional stragglers—cold, wretched-looking creatures, in the last stage of emaciation and disease. The knot of Irish labourers at the lower end of the place, who have been alternately shaking hands with, and threatening the life of, each other, for the last hour, become furious in their disputes, and finding it impossible to silence one man, who is particularly anxious to adjust the difference, they resort to the expedient of knocking him down, and jumping on him afterwards. The man in the fur cap and the potboy rush out; a scene of riot and confusion ensues; half the Irishmen get shut out, and the other half get shut in; the potboy is knocked among the tubs in no time; the landlord hits everybody, and everybody hits the landlord; the barmaids scream; the police come in; the rest is a confused mixture of arms, legs, staves, torn coats, shouting, and struggling. Some of the party are borne off to the station-house, and the remainder slink home to beat their wives for complaining, and kick the children for daring to be hungry.

We have sketched this subject very slightly, not only because our limits compel us to do so, but because, if it were pursued farther, it would be painful and repulsive. Well-disposed gentlemen and charitable ladies would alike turn with coldness and disgust from a description of the drunken besotted men, and wretched broken-down miserable women, who form no inconsiderable portion of the frequenters of these haunts; forgetting, in the pleasant consciousness of their own rectitude, the poverty of the one, and the temptation of the other. Gin-drinking is a great vice in England, but wretchedness and dirt are a greater; and until you improve the homes of the poor, or persuade a half-famished wretch not to seek relief in the temporary oblivion of his own misery, with the pittance which, divided among his family, would furnish a morsel of bread for each, gin-shops will increase in number and splendour. If Temperance Societies would suggest an antidote against hunger, filth, and foul air, or could establish dispensaries for the gratuitous distribution of bottles of Lethe-water, gin-palaces would be numbered among the things that were.

Sketches by Boz

THAT afternoon, when he had slept off his fatigue; had shaved, and washed, and dressed, and freshened himself from top to toe; when he had dined, comforted himself with a pipe, an extra Toby, a nap in the great arm-chair, and a quiet chat with Mrs Varden on everything that had happened, was happening, or about to happen, within the sphere of their domestic concern; the locksmith sat himself down at the tea-table in the little back-parlour: the rosiest, cosiest, merriest, heartiest, best-contented old buck, in Great Britain or out of it.

There he sat, with his beaming eye on Mrs V., and his shining face suffused with gladness, and his capacious waistcoat smiling in every wrinkle, and his jovial humour peeping from under the table in the very plumpness of his legs: a sight to turn the vinegar of misanthropy into purest milk of human kindness. There he sat, watching his wife as she decorated the room with flowers for the greater honour of Dolly and Joseph Willet, who had gone out walking, and for whom the tea-kettle had been singing gaily on the hob full twenty minutes, chirping as never kettle chirped before; for whom the best service of real undoubted china, patterned with divers round-faced mandarins holding up broad umbrellas, was now displayed in all its glory; to tempt whose appetites a clear, transparent, juicy ham, garnished with cool green lettuce-leaves and fragrant cucumber, reposed upon a shady table, covered with a snow-white cloth; for whose delight, preserves and jams, crisp cakes and other pastry, short to eat, with cunning twists, and cottage loaves, and rolls of bread both white and brown, were all set forth in rich profusion; in whose youth Mrs V. herself had grown quite young, and stood there in a gown of red and white: symmetrical in figure, buxom in bodice, ruddy in cheek and lip, faultless in ankle, laughing in face and mood, in all respects delicious to behold—there sat the locksmith among all and every these delights, the sun that shone upon them all: the centre of the system: the source of light, heat, life, and frank enjoyment in the bright household world.

And when had Dolly ever been the Dolly of that afternoon? To see how she came in, arm-in-arm with Joe; and how she made an effort not to blush or seem at all confused; and how she made believe she didn't care to sit on his side of the table; and how she coaxed the locksmith in a whisper not to joke; and how her colour came and went in a little restless flutter of happiness, which made her do everything wrong, and yet so charmingly wrong that it was much better than right!—why, the locksmith could have looked on at this (as he mentioned to

Mrs Varden when they retired for the night) for four-and-twenty hours at a stretch, and never wished it done.

Barnaby Rudge

CLEAR of the locksmith's house, Sim Tappertit laid aside his cautious manner, and assuming in its stead that of a ruffling, swaggering, roving blade, who would rather kill a man than otherwise, and eat him too if needful, made the best of his way along the darkened streets.

Half pausing for an instant now and then to smite his pocket and assure himself of the safety of his master key, he hurried on to Barbican, and turning into one of the narrowest of the narrow streets which diverged from that centre, slackened his pace and wiped his heated brow, as if the termination of his walk were near at hand.

It was not a very choice spot for midnight expeditions, being in truth one of more than questionable character, and of an appearance by no means inviting. From the main street he had entered, itself little better than an alley, a low-browed doorway led into a blind court, or yard, profoundly dark, unpaved, and reeking with stagnant odours. Into this ill-favoured pit, the locksmith's vagrant 'prentice groped his way; and stopping at a house from whose defaced and rotten front the rude effigy of a bottle swung to and fro like some gibbeted malefactor, struck thrice upon an iron grating with his foot. After listening in vain for some response to his signal, Mr Tappertit became impatient, and struck the grating thrice again.

A further delay ensued, but it was not of long duration. The ground seemed to open at his feet, and a ragged head appeared.

"Is that the captain?" said a voice as ragged as the head.

"Yes," replied Mr Tappertit haughtily, descending as he spoke, "who should it be?

"It's so late, we gave you up," returned the voice, as its owner stopped to shut and fasten the grating. "You're late, sir."

"Lead on," said Mr Tappertit, with a gloomy majesty, "and make remarks when I require you. Forward!"

This latter word of command was perhaps somewhat theatrical and unnecessary, inasmuch as the descent was by a very narrow, steep, and slippery flight of steps, and any rashness or departure from the beaten track must have ended in a yawning water-butt. But Mr Tappertit being, like some other great commanders, favourable to strong effects, and personal display, cried "Forward!" again, in the hoarsest voice he could assume; and led the way, with folded arms and knitted brows, to the cellar down below, where there was a small copper fixed in one corner, a chair or two, a form and table, a glimmering fire, and a truckle-bed, covered with a ragged patchwork rug.

"Welcome, noble captain!" cried a lanky figure, rising as from a nap.

The captain nodded. Then, throwing off his outer coat, he stood composed in all his dignity, and eyed his follower over.

"What news to-night?" he asked, when he had looked into his very soul.

"Nothing particular," replied the other, stretching himself—and he was so long already that it was quite alarming to see him do it—"how come you to be so late?"

"No matter," was all the captain deigned to say in answer. "Is the room prepared?"

"It is," replied his follower.

"The comrade—is he here?"

"Yes. And a sprinkling of the others—you hear 'em?"

"Playing skittles!" said the captain moodily. "Light-hearted revellers!"

There was no doubt respecting the particular amusement in which these heedless spirits were indulging, for even in the close and stifling atmosphere of the vault, the noise sounded like distant thunder. It certainly appeared, at first sight, a singular spot to choose, for that or any other purpose of relaxation, if the other cellars answered to the one in which this brief colloquy took place; for the floors were of sodden earth, the walls and roof of damp bare brick tapestried with the tracks of snails and slugs; the air was sickening, tainted, and offensive. It seemed, from one strong flavour which was uppermost among the various odours of the place, that it had, at no very distant period, been used as a storehouse for cheeses; a circumstance which, while it accounted for the greasy moisture that hung about it, was agreeably suggestive of rats. It was naturally damp besides, and little trees of fungus sprang from every mouldering corner.

The proprietor of this charming retreat, and owner of the ragged head before mentioned—for he wore an old tie-wig as bare and frowzy as a stunted hearth-broom—had by this time joined them; and stood a little apart, rubbing his hands, wagging his hoary bristled chin, and smiling in silence. His eyes were closed; but had they been wide open, it would have been easy to tell, from the attentive expression of the face he turned towards them—pale and unwholesome as might be expected in one of his underground existence—and from a certain anxious raising and quivering of the lids, that he was blind.

"Even Stagg hath been asleep," said the long comrade, nodding towards this person.

"Sound, captain, sound!" cried the blind man; "what does my noble captain drink—is it brandy, rum, usquebaugh? Is it soaked gunpowder, or blazing oil? Give it a name, heart of oak, and we'd get it for you, if it was wine from a bishop's cellar, or melted gold from King George's mint."

"See," said Mr Tappertit haughtily, "that it's something strong, and comes quick; and so long as you take care of that, you may bring it from the devil's cellar, if you like."

"Boldly said, noble captain!" rejoined the blind man. "Spoken like the 'Prentices' glory. Ha, ha! From the devil's cellar! A brave joke! The captain joketh. Ha, ha, ha!"

"I'll tell you what, my fine feller," said Mr Tappertit, eyeing the host over as he walked to a closest, and took out a bottle and glass as carelessly as if he had been in full possession of his sight, "if you make that row, you'll find that the captain's very far from joking, and so I tell you."

"He's got his eyes on me!" cried Stagg, stopping short on his way back, and affecting to screen his face with the bottle. "I feel 'em though I can't see 'em. Take 'em off, noble captain. Remove 'em, for they pierce like gimlets."

Mr Tappertit smiled grimly at his comrade; and twisting out one more look—a kind of ocular screw—under the influence of which the blind man feigned to undergo great anguish and torture, bade him, in a softened tone, approach, and hold his peace.

"I obey you, captain," cried Stagg, drawing close to him and filling out a bumper without spilling a drop, by reason that he held his little finger at the brim of the glass, and stopped at the instant the liquor touched it, "drink, noble governor. Death to all masters, life to all 'prentices, and love to all fair damsels. Drink, brave general, and warm your gallant heart!"

Mr Tappertit condescended to take the glass from his outstretched hand. Stagg then dropped on one knee, and gently smoothed the calves of his legs, with an air of humble admiration.

"That I had but eyes!" he cried, "to behold my captain's symmetrical proportions! That I had but eyes, to look upon these twin invaders of domestic peace!"

"Get out!" said Mr Tappertit, glancing downward at his favourite limbs. "Go along, will you, Stagg!"

"When I touch my own afterwards," cried the host, smiting them reproachfully, "I hate 'em. Comparatively speaking, they've no more shape than wooden legs, beside these models of my noble captain's."

"Yours!" exclaimed Mr Tappertit. "No, I should think not. Don't talk about those precious old toothpicks in the same breath with mine; that's rather too much. Here. Take the glass. Benjamin. Lead on. To business!"

With these words, he folded his arms again; and frowning with a sullen majesty, passed with his companion through a little door at the upper end of the cellar, and disappeared; leaving Stagg to his private meditations.

The vault they entered, strewn with sawdust and dimly

lighted, was between the outer one from which they had just come, and that in which the skittle-players were diverting themselves; as was manifested by the increased noise and clamour of tongues, which was suddenly stopped, however, and replaced by a dead silence, at a signal from the long comrade. Then, this young gentleman, going to a little cupboard, returned with a thigh-bone, which in former times must have been part and parcel of some individual at least as long as himself, and placed the same in the hands of Mr Tappertit; who, receiving it as a sceptre and staff of authority, cocked his three-cornered hat fiercely on the top of his head, and mounted a large table, whereupon a chair of state, cheerfully ornamented with a couple of skulls, was placed ready for his reception.

He had no sooner assumed this position, than another young gentleman appeared, bearing in his arms a huge clasped book, who made him a profound obeisance, and delivering it to the long comrade, advanced to the table, and turning his back upon it, stood there Atlas-wise. Then, the long comrade got upon the table too; and seating himself in a lower chair than Mr Tappertit's, with much state and ceremony, placed the large book on the shoulders of their mute companion as deliberately as if he had been a wooden desk, and prepared to make entries therein with a pen of corresponding size.

When the long comrade had made these preparations, he looked towards Mr Tappertit; and Mr Tappertit, flourishing the bone, knocked nine times therewith upon one of the skulls. At the ninth stroke, a third young gentleman emerged from the door leading to the skittle ground, and bowing low, awaited his commands.

"'Prentice!" said the mighty captain, "who waits without?"

The 'prentice made answer that a stranger was in attendance, who claimed admission into that secret society of 'Prentice Knights, and a free participation in their rights, privileges, and immunities. Thereupon Mr Tappertit flourished the bone and giving the other skull a prodigious rap on the nose, exclaimed "Admit him!" At these dread words the 'prentice bowed once more, and so withdrew as he had come.

There soon appeared at the same door, two other 'prentices, having between them a third, whose eyes were bandaged, and who was attired in a bag-wig, and a broad-skirted coat, trimmed with tarnished lace; and who was girded with a sword, in compliance with the laws of the Institution regulating the introduction of candidates, which required them to assume this courtly dress, and kept it constantly in lavender, for their convenience. One of the conductors of this novice held a rusty blunderbuss pointed towards his ear, and the other a very ancient sabre, with which he carved imaginary offenders as he came along in a sanguinary and anatomical manner.

As this silent group advanced, Mr Tappertit fixed his hat upon his head. The novice then laid his hand upon his breast and bent before him. When he had humbled himself sufficiently, the captain ordered the bandage to be removed, and proceeded to eye him over.

"Ha!" said the captain, thoughtfully, when he had concluded this ordeal. "Proceed."

The long comrade read aloud as follows:—"Mark Gilbert. Age, nineteen. Bound to Thomas Curzon, hosier, Golden Fleece, Aldgate. Loves Curzon's daughter. Cannot say that Curzon's daughter loves him. Should think it probable. Curzon pulled his ears last Tuesday week."

"How!" cried the captain, starting.

"For looking at his daughter, please you." said the novice.

"Write Curzon down, Denounced," said the captain. "Put a black cross against the name of Curzon."

"So please you," said the novice, "that's not the worst—he calls his 'prentice idle dog, and stops his beer unless he works to his liking. He gives Dutch cheese, too, eating Cheshire, sir, himself; and Sundays out are only once a month."

"This," said Mr Tappertit gravely, "is a flagrant case. Put two black crosses to the name of Curzon."

"If the society," said the novice, who was an ill-looking, one-sided, shambling lad, with sunken eyes set close together in his head—"if the society would burn his house down—for he's not insured—or beat him as he comes home from his club at night, or help me to carry off his daughter, and marry her at the Fleet, whether she gave consent or no—"

Mr Tappertit waved his grizzly truncheon as an admonition to him not to interrupt, and ordered three black crosses to the name of Curzon.

"Which means," he said in gracious explanation, "vengeance, complete and terrible. 'Prentice, do you love the Constitution?"

To which the novice (being to that end instructed by his attendant sponsors) replied "I do!"

"The Church, the State, and everything established—but the masters?" quoth the captain.

Again the novice said "I do."

Barnaby Rudge

Old John would have it that they must sit in the bar, and nobody objecting, into the bar they went. All bars are snug places, but the Maypole's was the very snuggest, cosiest, and completest bar, that ever the wit of man devised. Such amazing bottles in old oaken pigeon-holes; such gleaming tankards dangling from pegs at about the same inclination as thirsty men would hold them to their lips; such sturdy little Dutch kegs ranged in rows on shelves; so many lemons hanging in separate nets, and forming the fragrant grove already mentioned in this chronicle, suggestive, with goodly loaves of snowy sugar stowed away hard by, of punch, idealized beyond all mortal knowledge; such closets, such presses, such drawers full of pipes, such places for putting things away in hollow window-seats, all crammed to the throat with eatables, drinkables, or savoury condiments; lastly, and to crown all, as typical of the immense resources of the establishment, and its defiances to all visitors to cut and come again, such a stupendous cheese!

It is a poor heart that never rejoices—it must have been the poorest, weakest, and most watery heart that ever beat, which would not have warmed towards the Maypole bar. Mrs Varden's did directly. She could no more have reproached

John Willet among those household gods, the kegs and bottles, lemons, pipes, and cheese, than she could have stabbed him with his own bright carving-knife. The order for dinner too—it might have soothed a savage. "A bit of fish," said John to the cook, "and some lamb chops (breaded, with plenty of ketchup), and a good salad, and a roast spring chicken, with a dish of sausages and mashed potatoes, or something of that sort." Something of that sort! The resources of these inns! To talk carelessly about dishes, which in themselves were a first-rate holiday kind of dinner, suitable to one's wedding-day, as something of that sort: meaning, if you can't get a spring chicken, any other trifle in the way of poultry will do—such as a peacock, perhaps! The kitchen too, with its great broad cavernous chimney; the kitchen, where nothing in the way of cookery seemed impossible; where you would believe in anything to eat, they chose to tell you of. Mrs Varden returned from the contemplation of these wonders to the bar again, with a head quite dizzy and bewildered.

Barnaby Rudge

London and Elsewhere

KNOWLEDGE has a very limited power when it informs the head only; but when it informs the heart as well, it has a power over life and death, the body and the soul, and dominates the universe.

From a Speech

THERE'S a surprisin' number of men, sir, who as long as they've only got their own shoes and stockings to depend upon, will walk downhill, along the gutters quiet enough, and by themselves, and not do much harm. But set any on 'em up with a coach and horses, sir; and it's wonderful what a knowledge of drivin' he'll show, and how he'll fill his vehicle with passengers, and start off in the middle of the road, neck or nothing, to the Devil!

Martin Chuzzlewit

DREAMS are the bright creatures of poem and legend, who sport on earth in the night season, and melt away in the first beam of the sun, which lights grim care and stern reality on their daily pilgrimage through the world.

Nicholas Nickleby

AT the appointed time, my three visitors arrived together. Mr Micawber with more shirt-collar than usual, and a new ribbon to his eye-glass; Mrs Micawber with her cap in a whitey-brown paper parcel; Traddles carrying the parcel, and supporting Mrs Micawber on his arm. They were all delighted with my residence. When I conducted Mrs Micawber to my dressing-table, and she saw the scale on which it was prepared for her, she was in such raptures, that she called Mr Micawber to come in and look.

"My dear Copperfield," said Mr Micawber, "this is luxurious. This is a way of life which reminds me of the period when I was myself in a state of celibacy, and Mrs Micawber had not yet been solicited to plight her faith at the Hymeneal altar."

"He means, solicited by him, Mr Copperfield," said Mrs Micawber archly. "He cannot answer for others."

"My dear," returned Mr Micawber with sudden seriousness, "I have no desire to answer for others. I am too well aware that when, in the inscrutable decrees of Fate, you were reserved for me, it is possible you may have been reserved for one, destined, after a protracted struggle, at length to fall a victim to pecuniary involvements of a complicated nature. I understand your allusion, my love. I regret it, but I can bear it."

"Micawber!" exclaimed Mrs Micawber, in tears. "Have I

deserved this! I, who never have deserted you; who never *will* desert you, Micawber!"

"My love," said Mr Micawber, much affected, "you will forgive, and our old and tried friend Copperfield will, I am sure, forgive, the momentary laceration of a wounded spirit, made sensitive by a recent collision with the Minion of Power—in other words, with a ribald Turncock attached to the water-works—and will pity, not condemn, its excesses."

Mr Micawber then embraced Mrs Micawber, and pressed my hand; leaving me to infer from this broken allusion that his domestic supply of water had been cut off that afternoon, in consequence of default in the payment of the company's rates.

To divert his thoughts from this melancholy subject, I informed Mr Micawber that I relied upon him for a bowl of punch, and led him to the lemons. His recent despondency, not to say despair, was gone in a moment. I never saw a man so thoroughly enjoy himself amid the fragrance of lemon-peel and sugar, the odour of burning rum, and the steam of boiling water, as Mr Micawber did that afternoon. It was wonderful to see his face shining at us out of a thin cloud of these delicate fumes, as he stirred, and mixed, and tasted, and looked as if he were making, instead of punch, a fortune for his family down to the latest posterity. As to Mrs Micawber, I don't know whether it was the effect of the cap, or the lavender-water, or the pins, or the fire, or the wax candles, but she came out of my room, comparatively speaking, lovely. And the lark was never gayer than that excellent woman!

I suppose—I never ventured to inquire, but I suppose—that Mrs Crupp, after frying the soles, was taken ill. Because we broke down at that point. The leg of mutton came up very red within, and very pale without; besides having a foreign substance of a gritty nature sprinkled over it, as if it had had a fall into the ashes of that remarkable kitchen fireplace. But we were not in a condition to judge of this fact from the appearance of the gravy, forasmuch as the "young gal" had dropped it all upon the stairs—where it remained, by the by, in a long train, until it was worn out. The pigeon-pie was not bad, but it was a delusive pie: the crust being like a disappointing head, phrenologically speaking: full of lumps and bumps, with nothing particular underneath. In short, the banquet was such a failure that I should have been quite unhappy—about the failure, I mean, for I was always unhappy about Dora—if I had not been relieved by the great good-humour of my company, and by a bright suggestion from Mr Micawber.

"My dear friend Copperfield," said Mr Micawber, "accidents will occur in the best regulated families; and in families not regulated by that pervading influence which sanctifies while it enhances the—a—I would say, in short, by the influence of Woman, in the lofty character of Wife, they may be expected with confidence, and must be borne with philosophy. If you will allow me to take the liberty of remarking that there are few comestibles better, in their way, than a Devil, and that I believe, with a little division of labour, we could accomplish a good one if the young person in attendance could produce a gridiron, I would put it to you, that this little misfortune may be easily repaired."

There was a gridiron in the pantry, on which my morning rasher of bacon was cooked. We had it in, in a twinkling, and immediately applied ourselves to carrying Mr Micawber's idea into effect. The division of labour to which he had referred was this: Traddles cut the mutton into slices; Mr Micawber (who could do anything of this sort to perfection) covered them with pepper, mustard, salt, and cayenne; I put them on the gridiron, turned them with a fork, and took them off, under Mr Micawber's directions; and Mrs Micawber heated, and continually stirred, some mushroom ketchup in a little saucepan. When we had slices enough done, to begin upon, we fell to, with our sleeves still tucked up at the wrists, more slices sputtering and blazing on the fire, and our attention divided between the mutton on our plates, and the mutton then preparing.

What with the novelty of this cookery, the excellence of it, the bustle of it, the frequent starting up to look after it, the frequent sitting down to dispose of it as the crisp slices came off the gridiron hot and hot, the being so busy, so flushed with the fire, so amused, and in the midst of such a tempting noise and savour, we reduced the leg of mutton to the bone. My own appetite came back miraculously. I am ashamed to record it, but I really believe I forgot Dora for a little while. I am satisfied that Mr and Mrs Micawber could not have enjoyed the feast more if they had sold a bed to provide it. Traddles laughed as heartily, almost the whole time, as he ate and worked. Indeed we all did, all at once; and I daresay there never was a greater success.

David Copperfield

MEN who look on nature, and their fellow-men, and cry that all is dark and gloomy, are in the right; but the sombre colours are reflections from their own jaundiced eyes and hearts. The real hues are delicate, and need a clearer vision.

Oliver Twist

WE had made a very pretty course, and taken great pains. Encouraged by the cricket matches experience, I allowed the landlord of the Falstaff to have a drinking-booth on the ground. Not to seem to dictate or distrust, I gave all the prizes (about ten pounds in the aggregate) in money. The great mass of the crowd were labouring men of all kinds, soldiers, sailors, and navvies. They did not, between half-past ten, when we began, and sunset, displace a rope or a stake; and they left every barrier and flag as neat as they found it. There was not a dispute, and there was no drunkenness whatever. I made them a little speech from the lawn, at the end of the games, saying that please God we would do it again next year. They cheered most lustily and dispersed. The road between this and Chatham was like a Fair all day; and surely it is a fine thing to get such perfect behaviour out of a reckless seaport town. Among other oddities we had A Hurdle Race for Strangers. One man (he came in second) ran 120 yards and leaped over ten hurdles, in twenty seconds, *with a pipe in his mouth, and smoking it all the time.* "If it hadn't been for your pipe," I said to him at the winning-post, "you would have been first." "I beg your pardon, sir," he answered, "but if it hadn't been for my pipe, I should have been nowhere."

Letter to Gadshill, 1857

"AH!" said the old lady, "painters always make ladies out prettier than they are, or they wouldn't get any custom, child. The man that invented the machine for taking likenesses might have known *that* would never succeed; it's a deal too honest."

Oliver Twist

YOU will be greatly shocked and grieved to hear that the Raven is no more. He expired today at a few minutes after twelve o'clock at noon. He had been ailing for a few days, but we anticipated no serious result, conjecturing that a portion of the white paint he swallowed last summer might be lingering about his vitals without having any serious effect upon his constitution. Yesterday afternoon he was taken so much worse that I sent an express for the medical gentleman (Mr Herring), who promptly attended, and administered a powerful dose of castor oil. Under the influence of this medicine, he recovered so far as to be able at eight o'clock p.m. to bite Topping. His night was peaceful. This morning at daybreak he appeared better; received (agreeably to the doctor's directions) another dose of castor oil; and partook plentifully of some warm gruel, the flavour of which he appeared to relish. Towards eleven o'clock he was so much worse that it was found necessary to muffle the stable-knocker. At half-past, or thereabouts, he was heard talking to himself about the horse and Topping's family, and to add some incoherent expressions which are supposed to have been either a foreboding of his approaching dissolution, or some wishes relative to the disposal of his little property: consisting chiefly of half-pence which he had buried in different parts of the garden. On the clock striking twelve he appeared slightly agitated, but he soon recovered, walked twice or thrice along the coach-house, stopped to bark, staggered, exclaimed *Halloa old girl!* (his favourite expression), and died.

He behaved throughout with a decent fortitude, equanimity, and self-possession, which cannot be too much admired. I deeply regret that being in ignorance of his danger I did not attend to receive his last instructions. Something remarkable about his eyes occasioned Topping to run for the doctor at twelve. When they returned together our friend was gone. It was the medical gentleman who informed me of his decease. He did it with great caution and delicacy, preparing me by the remark that "a jolly queer start had taken place"; but the shock was very great notwithstanding. I am not wholly free from suspicions of poison. A malicious butcher has been heard to say that he would "do" for him: his plea was that he would not be molested in taking orders down the mews, by any bird that wore a tail.

Letter to John Forster, 1841

HE drank a quantity of wine after dinner, in vain. No such artificial means would bring sleep to his eyes. His thoughts, more incoherent, dragged him more unmercifully after them—as if a wretch, condemned to such expiation, were drawn at the heels of wild horses. No oblivion, and no rest.

How long he sat, drinking and brooding, and being dragged in imagination hither and thither, no one could have told less correctly than he. But he knew that he had been sitting a long time by candle-light, when he started up and listened, in a sudden terror.

For now, indeed, it was no fancy. The ground shook, the house rattled, the fierce impetuous rush was in the air! He felt it come up, and go darting by; and even when he hurried to the window, and saw what it was, he stood, shrinking from it, as if it were not safe to look.

A curse upon the fiery devil, thundering along so smoothly, tracked through the distant valley by a glare of light and lurid smoke, and gone! He felt as if he had been plucked out of its path, and saved from being torn asunder. It made him shrink and shudder even now, when its faintest hum was hushed, and when the lines of iron road he could trace in the moonlight, running to a point, were as empty and as silent as a desert.

Unable to rest, and irresistibly attracted—or he thought so—to this road, he went out and lounged on the brink of it, marking the way the train had gone, by the yet smoking cinders that were lying in its track. After a lounge of some half-hour in the direction by which it had disappeared, he turned and walked the other way—still keeping to the brink of the road—past the inn garden, and a long way down; looking curiously at the bridges, signals, lamps, and wondering when another devil would come by.

A trembling of the ground, and quick vibration in his ears; a distant shriek; a dull light advancing, quickly changed to two red eyes, and a fierce fire, dropping glowing coals; an irresistible bearing on of a great roaring and dilating mass; a high wind, and a rattle—another come and gone, and he holding to a gate, as if to save himself!

He waited for another, and for another. He walked back to his former point, and back again to that, and still through the wearisome vision of his journey, looked for these approaching monsters. He loitered about the station, waiting until one should stay to call there; and when one did, and was detached for water, he stood parallel with it, watching its heavy wheels and brazen front, and thinking what a cruel power and might it had. Ugh! To see the great wheels slowly turning, and to think of being run down and crushed!

Disordered with wine and want of rest—that want which

nothing, although he was so weary, would appease—these ideas and objects assumed a diseased importance in his thoughts. When he went back to his room, which was not until near midnight, they still haunted him, and he sat listening for the coming of another.

So in his bed, whither he repaired with no hope of sleep. He still lay listening; and when he felt the trembling and vibration, got up and went to the window, to watch (as he could from its position) the dull light changing to the two red eyes, and the fierce fire dropping glowing coals, and the rush of the giant as it fled past, and the track of glare and smoke along the valley. Then he would glance in the direction by which he intended to depart at sunrise, as there was no rest for him there; and would lie down again to be troubled by the vision of his journey, and the old monotony of bells and wheels and horses' feet, until another came. This lasted all night. So far from resuming the mastery of himself, he seemed, if possible, to lose it more and more, as the night crept on. When the dawn appeared, he was still tormented with thinking, still postponing thought until he should be in a better state; the past, present, and future, all floated confusedly before him, and he had lost all power of looking steadily at any one of them.

"At what time," he asked the man who had waited on him over-night, now entering with a candle, "do I leave here, did you say?"

"About a quarter after four, sir. Express comes through at four, sir.—Don't stop."

He passed his hand across his throbbing head, and looked at his watch. Nearly half-past three.

"Nobody going with you, sir, probably," observed the man. "Two gentlemen here, sir, but they're waiting for the train to London."

"I thought you said there was nobody here," said Carker, turning upon him with the ghost of his old smile, when he was angry or suspicious.

"Not then, sir. Two gentlemen came in the night by the short train that stops here, sir. Warm water, sir?"

"No; and take away the candle. There's day enough for me."

Having thrown himself upon the bed, half-dressed, he was at the window as the man left the room. The cold light of morning had succeeded to night, and there was already, in the sky, the red suffusion of the coming sun. He bathed his head and face with water—there was no cooling influence in it for him—hurriedly put on his clothes, paid what he owed, and went out.

The air struck chill and comfortless as it breathed upon him. There was a heavy dew; and, hot as he was, it made him shiver. After a glance at the place where he had walked last night, and at the signal-lights burning feebly in the morning, and bereft of their significance, he turned to where the sun was rising, and beheld it, in its glory, as it broke upon the scene.

So awful, so transcendent in its beauty, so divinely solemn. As he cast his faded eyes upon it, where it rose, tranquil and serene, unmoved by all the wrong and wickedness on which its beams had shone since the beginning of the world, who shall say that some weak sense of virtue upon Earth, and its reward in Heaven, did not manifest itself, even to him? If ever he remembered sister or brother with a touch of tenderness and remorse, who shall say it was not then?

He needed some such touch then. Death was on him. He was marked off from the living world, and going down into his grave.

He paid the money for his journey to the country-place he had thought of; and was walking to and fro, alone, looking along the lines of iron, across the valley in one direction, and towards a dark bridge near at hand in the other; when, turning in his walk, where it was bounded by one end of the wooden stage on which he paced up and down, he saw the man from whom he had fled, emerging from the door by which he himself had entered there. And their eyes met.

In the quick unsteadiness of the surprise, he staggered, and slipped on to the road below him. But recovering his feet immediately, he stepped back a pace or two upon that road, to interpose some wider space between them, and looked at his pursuer, breathing short and quick.

He heard a shout—another—saw the face change from its vindictive passion to a faint sickness and terror—felt the earth tremble—knew in a moment that the rush was come—uttered a shriek—looked round—saw the red eyes, bleared and dim, in the daylight, close upon him—was beaten down, caught up, and whirled away upon a jagged mill, that spun him round and round, and struck him limb from limb, and licked his stream of life with its fiery heat, and cast his mutilated fragments in the air.

When the traveller, who had been recognised, recovered from a swoon, he saw them bringing from a distance something covered, that lay heavy and still, upon a board, between four men, and saw that others drove some dogs away that sniffed upon the road, and soaked his blood up, with a train of ashes.

Dombey and Son

MR AND MRS VENEERING were bran-new people in a bran-new house in a bran-new quarter of London. Everything about the Veneerings was spick and span new. All their furniture was new, all their friends were new, all their servants were new, their plate was new, their carriage was new, their harness was new, their horses were new, their pictures were new, they themselves were new, they were as newly married as was lawfully compatible with their having a bran-new baby, and if they had set up a great-grandfather, he would have come home in matting from the Pantechnicon, without a scratch upon him, French polished to the crown of his head.

For, in the Veneering establishment, from the hall-chairs with the new coat of arms, to the grand pianoforte with the new action, and upstairs again to the new fire-escape, all things were in a state of high varnish and polish. And what was observable in the furniture, was observable in the Veneerings—the surface smelt a little too much of the workshop and was a trifle sticky.

There was an innocent piece of dinner-furniture that went

upon easy castors and was kept over a livery stable-yard in Duke Street, St James's, when not in use, to whom the Veneerings were a source of blind confusion. The name of this article was Twemlow. Being first cousin to Lord Snigsworth, he was in frequent requisition, and at many houses might be said to represent the dining-table in its normal state. Mr and Mrs Veneering, for example, arranging a dinner, habitually started with Twemlow, and then put leaves in him, or added guests to him. Sometimes, the table consisted of Twemlow and half-a-dozen leaves; sometimes, of Twemlow and a dozen leaves; sometimes, Twemlow was pulled out to his utmost extent of twenty leaves. Mr and Mrs Veneering on occasions of ceremony faced each other in the centre of the board, and thus the parallel still held; for, it always happened that the more Twemlow was pulled out, the further he found himself from the centre, and the nearer to the sideboard at one end of the room, or the window-curtains at the other.

But, it was not this which steeped the feeble soul of Twemlow in confusion. This he was used to, and could take soundings of. The abyss to which he could find no bottom, and from which started forth the engrossing and ever-swelling difficulty of his life, was the insoluble question whether he was Veneering's oldest friend, or newest friend. To the excogitation of this problem, the harmless gentleman had devoted many anxious hours, both in his lodgings over the livery stable-yard, and in the cold gloom, favourable to meditation, of St James's Square. Thus. Twemlow had first known Veneering at his club, where Veneering then knew nobody but the man who made them known to one another, who seemed to be the most intimate friend he had in the world, and whom he had known two days—the bond of union between their souls, the nefarious conduct of the committee respecting the cookery of a fillet of veal, having been accidentally cemented at that date. Immediately upon this, Twemlow received an invitation to dine with Veneering, and dined: the man being of the party. Immediately upon that, Twemlow received an invitation to dine with the man, and dined: Veneering being of the party. At the man's were a

Member, an Engineer, a Payer-off of the National Debt, a Poem on Shakespeare, a Grievance, and a Public Office, who all seemed to be utter strangers to Veneering. And yet immediately after that, Twemlow received an invitation to dine at Veneering's, expressly to meet the Member, the Engineer, the Payer-off of the National Debt, the Poem on Shakespeare, the Grievance, and the Public Office, and, dining, discovered that all of them were the most intimate friends Veneering had in the world, and that the wives of all of them (who were all there) were the objects of Mrs Veneering's most devoted affection and tender confidence.

Thus it had come about, that Mr Twemlow had said to himself in his lodgings, with his hand to his forehead: "I must not think of this. This is enough to soften any man's brain,"—and yet was always thinking of it, and could never form a conclusion.

This evening the Veneerings give a banquet. Eleven leaves in the Twemlow; fourteen in company all told. Four pigeon-breasted retainers in plain clothes stand in line in the hall. A fifth retainer, proceeding up the staircase with a mournful air—as who should say, "Here is another wretched creature come to dinner; such is life!"—announces, "Mis-ter Twemlow!"

Mrs Veneering welcomes her sweet Mr Twemlow. Mr Veneering welcomes his dear Twemlow. Mrs Veneering does not expect that Mr Twemlow can in nature care much for such insipid things as babies, but so old a friend must please look at baby. "Ah! You will know the friend of your family better, Tootleums," says Mr Veneering, nodding emotionally at that new article, "when you begin to take notice." He then begs to make his dear Twemlow known to his two friends, Mr Boots and Mr Brewer—and clearly has no distinct idea which is which.

But now a fearful circumstance occurs.

"Mis-ter and Mis-sis Podsnap!"

"My dear," says Mr Veneering to Mrs Veneering, with an air of much friendly interest, while the door stands open, "the Podsnaps."

A too, too smiling large man, with a fatal freshness on him, appearing with his wife, instantly deserts his wife and darts at Twemlow with:

"How do you do? So glad to know you. Charming house you have here. I hope we are not late. So glad of this opportunity, I am sure!"

When the first shock fell upon him, Twemlow twice skipped back in his neat little shoes and his neat little silk stockings of a bygone fashion, as if impelled to leap over a sofa behind him; but the large man closed with him and proved too strong.

"Let me," says the large man, trying to attract the attention of his wife in the distance, "have the pleasure of presenting Mrs Podsnap to her host. She will be," in his fatal freshness he seems to find perpetual verdure and eternal youth in the phrase, "she will be so glad of the opportunity, I am sure!"

In the meantime, Mrs Podsnap, unable to originate a mistake on her own account, because Mrs Veneering is the only other lady there, does her best in the way of handsomely supporting her husband's, by looking towards Mr Twemlow with a plaintive countenance and remarking to Mrs Veneering in a feeling manner, firstly, that she fears he has been rather bilious of late, and, secondly, that the baby is already very like him.

It is questionable whether any man quite relishes being mistaken for any other man; but Mr Veneering having this very evening set up the shirt-front of the young Antinous (in new worked cambric just come home) is not at all complimented by being supposed to be Twemlow, who is dry and weazen and some thirty years older. Mrs Veneering equally resents the imputation of being the wife of Twemlow. As to Twemlow, he is so sensible of being a much better bred man than Veneering, that he considers the large man an offensive ass.

In this complicated dilemma, Mr Veneering approaches the large man with extended hand, and smilingly assures that incorrigible personage that he is delighted to see him: who in his fatal freshness instantly replies:

"Thank you. I am ashamed to say that I cannot at this

moment recall where we met, but I am so glad of this opportunity, I am sure!"

Then pouncing upon Twemlow, who holds back with all his feeble might, he is haling him off to present him, as Veneering, to Mrs Podsnap, when the arrival of more guests unravels the mistake. Whereupon, having re-shaken hands with Veneering as Veneering, he re-shakes hands with Twemlow as Twemlow, and winds it all up to his own perfect satisfaction by saying to the last-named, "Ridiculous opportunity—but so glad of it, I am sure!"

Now, Twemlow having undergone this terrific experience, having likewise noted the fusion of Boots in Brewer and Brewer in Boots, and having further observed that of the remaining seven guests four discreet characters enter with wandering eyes and wholly decline to commit themselves as to which is Veneering, until Veneering has them in his grasp;—Twemlow having profited by these studies, finds his brain wholesomely hardening as he approaches the conclusion that he really is Veneering's oldest friend, when his brain softens again and all is lost, through his eyes encountering Veneering and the large man linked together as twin brothers in the back drawing-room near the conservatory door, and through his ears informing him in the tones of Mrs Veneering that the same large man is to be baby's godfather.

"Dinner is on the table!"

Thus the melancholy retainer, as who should say, "Come down and be poisoned, ye unhappy children of men!"

Twemlow, having no lady assigned to him, goes down in the rear, with his hand to his forehead. Boots and Brewer, thinking him indisposed, whisper, "Man faint. Had no lunch." But he is only stunned by the unvanquishable difficulty of his existence.

Revived by soup, Twemlow discourses mildly of the Court Circular with Boots and Brewer. Is appealed to, at the fish stage of the banquet, by Veneering, on the disputed question whether his cousin Lord Snigsworth is in or out of town? Gives it that his cousin is out of town. "At Snigsworthy Park?" Veneering inquires. "At Snigsworthy," Twemlow rejoins.

Boots and Brewer regard this as a man to be cultivated; and Veneering is clear that he is a remunerative article. Meantime the retainer goes round, like a gloomy Analytical Chemist; always seeming to say, after "Chablis, sir?"—"You wouldn't if you knew what its' made of."

The great looking-glass above the sideboard reflects the table and the company. Reflects the new Veneering crest, in gold and eke in silver frosted and also thawed, a camel of all work. The Herald's College found out a Crusading ancestor for Veneering who bore a camel on his shield (or might have done it if he had thought of it), and a caravan of camels take charge of the fruits and flowers and candles, and kneel down to be loaded with the salt. Reflects Veneering; forty, wavy-haired, dark, tending to corpulence, sly, mysterious, filmy—a kind of sufficiently well-looking veiled-prophet, not prophesying. Reflects Mrs Veneering; fair, aquiline-nosed and fingered, not so much light hair as she might have, gorgeous in raiment and jewels, enthusiastic, propitiatory, conscious that a corner of her husband's veil is over herself. Reflects Podsnap; prosperously feeding, two little light-coloured wiry wings, one on either side of his else bald head, looking as like his hair-brushes as his hair, dissolving view of red beads on his forehead, large allowance of crumpled shirt-collar up behind. Reflects Mrs Podsnap; fine woman for Professor Owen, quantity of bone, neck and nostrils like a rocking-horse, hard features, majestic head-dress in which Podsnap has hung golden offerings. Reflects Twemlow; grey, dry, polite, susceptible to east wind, First-Gentleman-in-Europe collar and cravat, cheeks drawn in as if he had made a great effort to retire into himself some years ago, and had got so far and had never got any farther. Reflects mature young lady; raven locks, and complexion that lights up well when well-powdered—as it is—carrying on considerably in the captivation of mature young gentleman; with too much nose in his face, too much ginger in his whiskers, too much torso in his waistcoat, too much sparkle in his studs, his eyes, his buttons, his talk, and his teeth. Reflects charming old Lady Tippins on Veneering's right; with an immense obtuse drab oblong face, like a face in a tablespoon, and a dyed Long Walk up the top of her head, as a convenient public approach to the bunch of false hair behind, pleased to patronise Mrs Veneering opposite, who is pleased to be patronised. Reflects a certain "Mortimer," another of Veneering's oldest friends; who never was in the house before, and appears not to want to come again, who sits disconsolate on Mrs Veneering's left, and who was inveigled by Lady Tippins (a friend of his boyhood) to come to these people's and talk, and who won't talk. Reflects Eugene, friend of Mortimer; buried alive in the back of his chair, behind a shoulder—with a powder-epaulette on it—of the mature young lady, and gloomily resorting to the champagne chalice whenever proffered by the Analytical Chemist. Lastly, the looking-glass reflects Boots and Brewer, and two other stuffed Buffers interposed between the rest of the company and possible accidents.

The Veneering dinners are excellent dinners—or new people wouldn't come—and all goes well.

Our Mutual Friend

THE lodgers to whom Crowl had made allusion under the designation of "the Kenwigses," were the wife and olive branches of one Mr Kenwigs, a turner in ivory, who was looked upon as a person of some consideration on the premises, inasmuch as he occupied the whole of the first floor, comprising a suite of two rooms. Mrs Kenwigs, too, was quite a lady in her manners, and of a very genteel family, having an uncle who collected a water-rate; besides which distinction, the two eldest of her little girls went twice a week to a dancing school in the neighbourhood, and had flaxen hair, tied with blue ribands, hanging in luxuriant pigtails down their backs; and wore little white trousers with frills round the ankles—for all of which reasons, and many more equally valid but too numerous to mention, Mrs Kenwigs was considered a very desirable person to know, and was the constant theme of all the gossips in the street, and even three or four doors round the corner at both ends.

It was the anniversary of that happy day on which the Church of England as by law established, had bestowed Mrs Kenwigs upon Mr Kenwigs; and in grateful commemoration of the same, Mrs Kenwigs had invited a few select friends to cards and a supper in the first floor, and had put on a new gown to receive them in; which gown, being of a flaming colour and made upon a juvenile principle, was so successful that Mr Kenwigs said the eight years of matrimony and the five children seemed all a dream, and Mrs Kenwigs younger and more blooming than on the very first Sunday he had kept company with her.

Beautiful as Mrs Kenwigs looked when she was dressed though, and so stately that you would have supposed she had a cook and housemaid at least, and nothing to do but order them about, she had a world of trouble with the preparations; more, indeed, than she, being of a delicate and genteel constitution, could have sustained, had not the pride of housewifery upheld her. At last, however, all the things that had to be got together were got together, and all the things that had to be got out of the way were got out of the way, and everything was ready, and the collector himself having promised to come, fortune smiled upon the occasion.

The party was admirably selected. There were, first of all, Mr Kenwigs and Mrs Kenwigs, and four olive Kenwigses who sat up to supper; firstly, because it was but right that they should have a treat on such a day; and secondly, because their going to bed, in presence of the company, would have been inconvenient, not to say improper. Then, there was a young lady who had made Mrs Kenwigs's dress, and who—it was the most convenient thing in the world—living in the two-pair back, gave up her bed to the baby, and got a little girl to watch it. Then, to match this young lady, was a young man, who had known Mr Kenwigs when he was a bachelor, and was much esteemed by the ladies, as bearing the reputation of a rake. To these, were added a newly-married couple, who had visited Mr and Mrs Kenwigs in their courtship; and a sister of Mrs Kenwigs's, who was quite a beauty; besides whom, there was another young man, supposed to entertain honourable designs upon the lady last mentioned; and Mr Noggs, who was a genteel person to ask, because he had been a gentleman once. There were also an elderly lady from the back parlour, and one more young lady, who, next to the collector, perhaps was the great lion of the party, being the daughter of a theatrical fireman, who "went on" in the pantomime, and had the greatest turn for the stage that was ever known, being able to sing and recite in a manner that brought the tears into Mrs Kenwigs's eyes. There was only one drawback upon the pleasure of seeing such friends, and that was, that the lady in the back-parlour, who was very fat, and turned of sixty, came in a low book-muslin dress and short kid gloves, which so exasperated Mrs Kenwigs, that that lady assured her visitors, in private, that if it hadn't happened that the supper was cooking at the back-parlour grate at that moment, she certainly would have requested its representative to withdraw.

"My dear," said Mr Kenwigs, "wouldn't it be better to begin a round game?"

"Kenwigs, my dear," returned his wife, "I am surprised at you. Would you begin without my uncle?"

"I forgot the collector," said Kenwigs; "oh no, that would never do."

"He's so particular," said Mrs Kenwigs, turning to the other married lady, "that if we began without him, I should be out of his will for ever."

"Dear!" cried the married lady.

"You've no idea what he is," replied Mrs Kenwigs; "and yet as good a creature as ever breathed."

"The kindest-hearted man as ever was," said Kenwigs.

"It goes to his heart, I believe, to be forced to cut the water off, when the people don't pay," observed the bachelor friend, intending a joke.

"George," said Mr Kenwigs, solemnly, "none of that, if you please."

"It was only my joke," said the friend, abashed.

"George," rejoined Mr Kenwigs, "a joke is a wery good thing—a wery good thing—but when that joke is made at the expense of Mrs Kenwigs's feeling, I set my face against it. A man in public life expects to be sneered at—it is the fault of his elewated sitiwation, and not of himself. Mrs Kenwigs's relation is a public man, and that he knows, George, and that he can bear; but putting Mrs Kenwigs out of the question (if I *could* put Mrs Kenwigs out of the question on such an occasion as this), I have the honour to be connected with the collector by marriage; and I cannot allow these remarks in my—" Mr Kenwigs was going to say "house," but he rounded the sentence with "apartments."

At the conclusion of these observations, which drew forth evidences of acute feeling from Mrs Kenwigs, and had the intended effect of impressing the company with a deep sense of the collector's dignity, a ring was heard at the bell.

"That's him," whispered Mr Kenwigs, greatly excited. "Morleena, my dear, run down and let your uncle in, and kiss him directly you get the door open. Hem! Let's be talking."

Adopting Mr Kenwigs's suggestion, the company spoke very loudly, to look easy and unembarrassed; and almost as soon as they had begun to do so, a short old gentleman in drabs and gaiters, with a face that might have been carved out of *lignum vitae*, for anything that appeared to the contrary, was led playfully in by Miss Morleena Kenwigs, regarding whose uncommon Christian name it may be here remarked that it had been invented and composed by Mrs Kenwigs previous to her first lying-in, for the special distinction of her eldest child, in case it should prove a daughter.

"Oh uncle, I am *so* glad to see you," said Mrs Kenwigs, kissing the collector affectionately on both cheeks. "So glad!"

"Many happy returns of the day, my dear," replied the collector, returning the compliment.

Now this was an interesting thing. Here was a collector of water-rates, without his book, without his pen and ink, without his double knock, without his intimidation, kissing—actually kissing—an agreeable female, and leaving taxes, summonses, notices that he had called, or announcements that he would never call again, for two quarters' due, wholly out of the question. It was pleasant to see how the company looked on, quite absorbed in the sight, and to behold the nods and winks with which they expressed their gratification at finding so much humanity in a tax-gatherer.

"Where will you sit, uncle?" said Mrs Kenwigs, in the full glow of family pride, which the appearance of her distinguished relation occasioned.

"Anywheres, my dear," said the collector, "I am not particular."

Not particular! What a meek collector. If he had been an author, who knew his place, he couldn't have been more humble.

"Mr Lillyvick," said Kenwigs, addressing the collector, "some friends here, sir, are very anxious for the honour of—thank you—Mr and Mrs Cutler, Mr Lillyvick."

"Proud to know you, sir," said Mr Cutler, "I've heard of you very often." These were not mere words of ceremony; for, Mr Cutler, having kept house in Mr Lillyvick's parish, had heard of him very often indeed. His attention in calling had been quite extraordinary.

"George, you know, I think, Mr Lillyvick," said Kenwigs; "lady from down-stairs—Mr Lillyvick. Mr Snewkes—Mr Lillyvick. Miss Green—Mr Lillyvick. Mr Lillyvick—Miss Petowker of the Theatre Royal, Drury Lane. Very glad to make two public characters acquainted! Mrs Kenwigs, my dear, will you sort the counters?"

Mrs Kenwigs, with the assistance of Newman Noggs (who, as he performed sundry little acts of kindness for the children, at all times and seasons, was humoured in his request to be taken no notice of, and was merely spoken about, in a whisper, as the decayed gentleman), did as she was desired; and the greater part of the guests sat down to speculation, while Newman himself, Mrs Kenwigs, and Miss Petowker of the Theatre Royal, Drury Lane, looked after the supper-table.

While the ladies were thus busying themselves, Mr Lillyvick was intent upon the game in progress, and as all should be fish that comes to a water-collector's net, the dear old gentleman was by no means scrupulous in appropriating to himself the property of his neighbours, which, on the contrary, he abstracted whenever an opportunity presented itself, smiling good-humouredly all the while, and making so many condescending speeches to the owners, that they were delighted with his amiability, and thought in their hearts that he deserved to be Chancellor of the Exchequer at least.

After a great deal of trouble, and the administration of many slaps on the head to the infant Kenwigses, whereof two of the most rebellious were summarily banished, the cloth was laid with much elegance, and a pair of boiled fowls, a large piece of pork, apple-pie, potatoes and greens, were served; at sight of which, the worthy Mr Lillyvick vented a great many witticisms, and plucked up amazingly: to the immense delight and satisfaction of the whole body of admirers.

Very well and very fast the supper went off; no more serious difficulties occurring, than those which arose from the incessant demand for clean knives and forks: which made poor Mrs Kenwigs wish, more than once, that private society adopted the principle of schools, and required that every guest should bring his own knife, fork, and spoon; which doubtless would be a great accommodation in many cases, and to no one more so than to the lady and gentleman of the house, especially if the school principle were carried out to the full extent, and the articles were expected, as a matter of delicacy, not to be taken away again.

Everybody having eaten everything, the table was cleared in a most alarming hurry, and with great noise; and the spirits, whereat the eyes of Newman Noggs glistened, being arranged in order, with water both hot and cold, the party composed themselves for conviviality; Mr Lillyvick being stationed in a large arm-chair by the fireside, and the four little Kenwigses disposed on a small form in front of the company with their flaxen tails towards them, and their faces to the fire; an arrangement which was no sooner perfected, than Mrs Kenwigs was overpowered by the feelings of a mother, and fell upon the left shoulder of Mr Kenwigs dissolved in tears.

"They are so beautiful!" said Mrs Kenwigs, sobbing.

"Oh, dear," said all the ladies, "so they are! it's very natural you should feel proud of that; but don't give way, don't."

"I can—not help it, and it don't signify," sobbed Mrs Kenwigs; "oh! they're too beautiful to live, much too beautiful!"

On hearing this alarming presentiment of their being doomed to an early death in the flower of their infancy, all four little girls raised a hideous cry, and burying their heads in their mother's lap simultaneously, screamed until the eight flaxen tails vibrated again; Mrs Kenwigs meanwhile clasping them alternately to her bosom, with attitudes expressive of distraction, which Miss Petowker herself might have copied.

At length, the anxious mother permitted herself to be smoothed into a more tranquil state, and the little Kenwigses, being also composed, were distributed among the company, to prevent the possibility of Mrs Kenwigs being again overcome by the blaze of their combined beauty. This done, the ladies and gentlemen united in prophesying that they would live for many, many years and that there was no occasion at all for Mrs Kenwigs to distress herself: which, in good truth, there did not appear to be: the loveliness of the children by no means justifying her apprehensions.

"This day eight year," said Mr Kenwigs after a pause. "Dear me—ah!"

This reflection was echoed by all present, who said "Ah!" first, and "dear me," afterwards.

"I was younger then," tittered Mrs Kenwigs.

"No," said the collector.

"Certainly not," added everybody.

"I remember my niece," said Mr Lillyvick, surveying his audience with a grave air; "I remember her, on that very afternoon, when she first acknowledged to her mother a partiality for Kenwigs. 'Mother,' she says, 'I love him.' "

" 'Adore him,' I said, uncle," interposed Mrs Kenwigs.

" 'Love him,' I think, my dear," said the collector, firmly.

"Perhaps you are right, uncle," replied Mrs Kenwigs, submissively. "I thought it was 'adore.' "

" 'Love,' my dear," retorted Mr Lillyvick. " 'Mother,' she says, 'I love him!' 'What do I hear?' cries her mother; and instantly falls into strong conwulsions."

A general exclamation of astonishment burst from the company.

"Into strong conwulsions," repeated Mr Lillyvick, regarding them with a rigid look. "Kenwigs will excuse my saying, in the presence of friends, that there was a very great objection to him, on the ground that he was beneath the family, and would disgrace it. You remember, Kenwigs?"

"Certainly," replied that gentleman, in no way displeased at the reminiscence, inasmuch as it proved, beyond all doubt, what a high family Mrs Kenwigs came of.

"I shared in that feeling," said Mr Lillyvick: "perhaps it was natural; perhaps it wasn't."

A gentle murmur seemed to say, that, in one of Mr Lillyvick's station, the objection was not only natural, but highly praiseworthy.

"I came round to him in time," said Mr Lillyvick. "After they were married, and there was no help for it, I was one of the first to say that Kenwigs must be taken notice of. The family *did* take notice of him, in consequence, and on my representation; and I am bound to say—and proud to say—that I have always found him a very honest, well-behaved, upright, respectable sort of man. Kenwigs, shake hands."

"I am proud to do it, sir," said Mr Kenwigs.

"So am I, Kenwigs," rejoined Mr Lillyvick.

"A very happy life I have led with your niece, sir," said Kenwigs.

"It would have been your own fault if you had not, sir," remarked Mr Lillyvick.

"Morleena Kenwigs," cried her mother, at this crisis, much affected, "kiss your dear uncle!"

The young lady did as she was requested, and the three other little girls were successively hoisted up to the collector's countenance, and subjected to the same process, which was afterwards repeated on them by the majority of those present.

"Oh dear, Mrs Kenwigs," said Miss Petowker, "while Mr Noggs is making that punch to drink happy returns in, do let Morleena go through that figure dance before Mr Lillyvick."

"No, no, my dear," replied Mrs Kenwigs, "it will only worry my uncle."

"It can't worry him, I am sure," said Miss Petowker. "You will be very much pleased, won't you, sir?"

"That I am sure I shall," replied the collector, glancing at the punch-mixer.

"Well then, I'll tell you what," said Mrs Kenwigs, "Morleena shall do the steps, if uncle can persuade Miss Petowker to recite us the Blood-Drinker's Burial, afterwards."

There was a great clapping of hands and stamping of feet, at this proposition; the subject whereof, gently inclined her head several times, in acknowledgment of the reception.

"You know," said Miss Petowker, reproachfully, "that I dislike doing anything professional in private parties."

"Oh, but not here!" said Mrs Kenwigs. "We are all so very friendly and pleasant, that you might as well be going through it in your own room; besides, the occasion—"

"I can't resist that," interrupted Miss Petowker; "anything in my humble power I shall be delighted to do."

Mrs Kenwigs and Miss Petowker had arranged a small *programme* of the entertainments between them, of which this was the prescribed order, but they had settled to have a little pressing on both sides, because it looked more natural. The company being all ready, Miss Petowker hummed a tune, and Morleena danced a dance, having previously had the soles of her shoes chalked, with as much care as if she were going on the tight-rope. It was a very beautiful figure, comprising a great deal of work for the arms, and was received with unbounded applause.

"If I was blessed with a—a child—" said Miss Petowker, blushing, "of such genius as that, I would have her out at the Opera instantly."

Mrs Kenwigs sighed, and looked at Mr Kenwigs, who shook his head, and observed that he was doubtful about it.

"Kenwigs is afraid," said Mrs K.

"What of?" inquired Miss Petowker, "not of her failing?"

"Oh no," replied Mrs Kenwigs, "but if she grew up what she is now,—only think of the young dukes and marquises."

"Very right," said the collector.

"Still," submitted Miss Petowker, "if she took a proper pride in herself, you know—"

"There's a good deal in that," observed Mrs Kenwigs, looking at her husband.

"I only know—" faltered Miss Petowker,—"it may be no rule to be sure—but *I* have never found any inconvenience or unpleasantness of that sort."

Mr Kenwigs, with becoming gallantry, said that settled the question at once, and that he would take the subject into his serious consideration. This being resolved upon, Miss Petowker was entreated to begin the Blood-Drinker's Burial; to which end, that young lady let down her back-hair, and taking up her position at the other end of the room, with the bachelor friend posted in a corner, to rush out at the cue "in death expire," and catch her in his arms when she died raving mad, went through the performance with extraordinary spirit, and to the great terror of the little Kenwigses, who were all but frightened into fits.

Nicholas Nickleby

CANT as we may, and as we shall to the end of all things, it is very much harder for the poor to be virtuous than it is for the rich; and the good that is in them, shines the brighter for it.

Letter to John Forster, 1842

IT was a foggy day in London, and the fog was heavy and dark. Animate London, with smarting eyes and irritated lungs, was blinking, wheezing, and choking; inanimate London was a sooty spectre, divided in purpose between being visible and invisible, and so being wholly neither. Gaslights flared in the shops with a haggard and unblest air, as knowing themselves to be night-creatures that had no business abroad under the sun; while the sun itself, when it was for a few moments dimly indicated through circling eddies of fog, showed as if it had gone out, and were collapsing flat and cold. Even in the surrounding country it was a foggy day, but there the fog was grey, whereas in London it was, at about the boundary line, dark yellow, and a little within it brown, and then browner, and then browner, until at the heart of the City—which call St Mary Axe—it was rusty-black. From any point of the high ridge of land northward, it might have been discerned that the loftiest buildings made an occasional struggle to get their heads above the foggy sea, and especially that the great dome of St Paul's seemed to die hard; but this was not perceivable in the streets at their feet, where the whole metropolis was a heap of vapour charged with muffled sound of wheels, and enfolding a gigantic catarrh.

Our Mutual Friend

BY the time they had turned into the Bethnal Green Road, the day had fairly begun to break. Many of the lamps were already extinguished; a few country waggons were slowly toiling on towards London; now and then a stage-coach, covered with mud, rattled briskly by: the driver bestowing, as he passed, an admonitory lash upon the heavy waggoner who, by keeping on the wrong side of the road, had endangered his arriving at the office a quarter of a minute after his time. The public-houses, with gas-lights burning inside, were already open. By degrees, other shops began to be unclosed, and a few scattered people were met with. Then came straggling groups of labourers going to their work: then men and women with fish-baskets on their heads; donkey-carts laden with vegetables; chaise-carts filled with live-stock or whole carcases of meat; milk-women with pails; an unbroken concourse of people, trudging out with various supplies to the eastern suburbs of the town. As they approached the City, the noise and traffic gradually increased; when they threaded the streets between Shoreditch and Smithfield it had swelled into a roar of sound and bustle. It was as light as it was likely to be, till night came on again, and the busy morning of half the London population had begun.

Turning down Sun Street and Crown Street, and crossing Finsbury Square, Mr Sikes struck, by way of Chiswell Street, into Barbican; thence into Long Lane, and so into Smithfield; from which latter place arose a tumult of discordant sounds that filled Oliver Twist with amazement.

It was market-morning. The ground was covered, nearly ankle-deep, with filth and mire; a thick steam, perpetually rising from the reeking bodies of the cattle, and mingling with the fog, which seemed to rest upon the chimney-tops, hung heavily above. All the pens in the centre of the large area, and as many temporary pens as could be crowded into the vacant space, were filled with sheep; tied up to posts by the gutter side were long lines of beasts and oxen, three or four deep. Countrymen, butchers, drovers, hawkers, boys, thieves, idlers, and vagabonds of every low grade, were mingled together in a mass; the whistling of drovers, the barking of dogs, the bellowing and plunging of oxen, the bleating of sheep, the grunting and squeaking of pigs, the cries of hawkers, the shouts, oaths, and quarrelling on all side; the ringing of bells and roar of voices that issued from every public-house; the crowding, pushing, driving, beating, whooping, and yelling; the hideous and discordant din that resounded from every corner of the market; and the unwashed, unshaven, squalid, and dirty figures constantly running to and fro, and bursting in and out of the throng, rendered it a stunning and bewildering scene, which quite confounded the senses.

Mr Sikes, dragging Oliver after him, elbowed his way through the thickest of the crowd, and bestowed very little attention on the numerous sights and sounds which so astonished the boy. He nodded, twice or thrice to a passing friend; and, resisting as many invitations to take a morning dram, pressed steadily onward, until they were clear of the turmoil, and had made their way through Hosier Lane into Holborn.

"Now, young un!" said Sikes, looking up at the clock of St Andrew's Church, "hard upon seven! you must step out. Come, don't lag behind already, Lazy-legs!"

Mr Sikes accompanied this speech with a jerk at his little companion's wrist; Oliver, quickening his pace into a kind of trot, between a fast walk and a run, kept up with the rapid strides of the housebreaker as well as he could.

They held their course at this rate until they had passed Hyde Park Corner, and were on their way to Kensington, when Sikes relaxed his pace, until an empty cart which was at some little distance behind came up. Seeing "Hounslow" written on it, he asked the driver with as much civility as he could assume, if he would give them a lift as far as Isleworth.

"Jump up," said the man. "Is that your boy?"

"Yes; he's my boy," replied Sikes, looking hard at Oliver, and putting his hand abstractedly into the pocket where the pistol was.

"Your father walks rather too quick for you, don't he, my man?" inquired the driver, seeing that Oliver was out of breath.

"Not a bit of it," replied Sikes, interposing. "He's used to it. Here, take hold of my hand, Ned. In with you!"

Thus addressing Oliver, he helped him into the cart; and the driver, pointing to a heap of sacks, told him to lie down there, and rest himself.

As they passed the different milestones, Oliver wondered more and more where his companion meant to take him. Kensington, Hammersmith, Chiswick, Kew Bridge, Brentford, were all passed; and yet they went on as steadily as if they had only just begun their journey. At length they came to a public-house called the Coach and Horses, a little way beyond which another road appeared to turn off. And here the cart stopped.

Sikes dismounted with great precipitation, holding Oliver by the hand all the while; and lifting him down directly, bestowed a furious look upon him, and rapped the side-pocket with his fist in a significant manner.

"Good-bye, boy," said the man.

"He's sulky," replied Sikes, giving him a shake; "he's sulky. A young dog! Don't mind him."

"Not I!" rejoined the other, getting into his cart. "It's a fine day after all." And he drove away.

Sikes waited until he had fairly gone; and then, telling Oliver he might look about him if he wanted, once again led him onward on his journey.

They turned round to the left, a short way past the public-house; and then, taking a right-hand road, walked on for a long time, passing many large gardens and gentlemen's houses on both sides of the way, and stopping for nothing but a little beer, until they reached a town. Here against the wall of a house Oliver saw written up in pretty large letters, "Hampton." They lingered about, in the fields, for some hours. At length they came back into the town; and, turning into an old public-house with a defaced signboard, ordered some dinner by the kitchen fire.

The kitchen was an old, low-roofed room; with a great beam across the middle of the ceiling, and benches, with high backs to them, by the fire; on which were seated several rough men in smock-frocks, drinking and smoking. They took no notice of Oliver, and very little of Sikes; and, as Sikes took very little notice of them, he and his young comrade sat in a corner by themselves, without being much troubled by their company.

They had some cold meat for dinner, and sat so long after it, while Mr Sikes indulged himself with three or four pipes, that Oliver began to feel quite certain they were not going any further. Being much tired with the walk, and getting up so early, he dozed a little at first; then, quite overpowered by fatigue and the fumes of the tobacco, fell asleep.

It was quite dark when he was awakened by a push from Sikes. Rousing himself sufficiently to sit up and look about him, he found that worthy in close fellowship and communication with a labouring man, over a pint of ale.

"So, you're going on to Lower Halliford, are you?" inquired Sikes.

"Yes, I am," replied the man, who seemed a little the worse—or better, as the case might be—for drinking; "and not slow about it neither. My horse hasn't got a load behind him going back, as he had coming up in the mornin'; and he won't be long a-doing of it. Here's luck to him! Ecod! he's a good un!"

"Could you give me boy and me a lift as far as there?" demanded Sikes, pushing the ale towards his new friend.

"If you're going directly, I can," replied the man, looking out of the pot. "Are you going to Halliford?"

"Going on to Shepperton," replied Sikes.

"I'm your man, as far as I go," replied the other. "Is all paid, Becky?"

"Yes, the other gentleman's paid," replied the girl.

"I say!" said the man, with tipsy gravity; "that won't do, you know."

"Why not?" rejoined Sikes. "You're a-going to accommodate us, and wot's to prevent my standing treat for a pint or so in return?"

The stranger reflected upon this argument with a very profound face; having done so, he seized Sikes by the hand, and declared he was a real good fellow. To which Mr Sikes replied, he was joking; as, if he had been sober, there would have been strong reason to suppose he was.

After the exchange of a few more compliments, they bade the company good night, and went out; the girl gathering up the pots and glasses as they did so, and lounging out to the door, with her hands full, to see the party start.

The horse, whose health had been drunk in his absence, was standing outside, ready harnessed to the cart. Oliver and Sikes got in without any further ceremony; and the man to whom he belonged, having lingered for a minute or two "to bear him up," and to defy the hostler and the world to produce his equal, mounted also. Then the hostler was told to give the horse his head; and his head being given him, he made a very unpleasant use of it, tossing it into the air with great disdain, and running into the parlour windows over the way; after performing those feats, and supporting himself for a short time on his hind-legs, he started off at great speed, and rattled out of the town right gallantly.

The night was very dark. A damp mist rose from the river, and the marshy ground about, and spread itself over the dreary fields. It was piercing cold, too; all was gloomy and black. Not a word was spoken; for the driver had grown sleepy, and Sikes was in no mood to lead him into conversation. Oliver sat huddled together in a corner of the cart; bewildered with alarm and apprehension; and figuring strange objects in the gaunt trees, whose branches waved grimly to and fro, as if in some fantastic joy at the desolation of the scene.

As they passed Sunbury Church the clock struck seven. There was a light in the ferry-house window opposite, which streamed across the road, and threw into more sombre shadow a dark yew tree with graves beneath it. There was a dull sound of falling water not far off; and the leaves of the old trees stirred gently in the night wind. It seemed like quiet music for the repose of the dead.

Sunbury was passed through, and they came again into the lonely road. Two or three miles more, and the cart stopped. Sikes alighted, took Oliver by the hand, and they once again walked on.

They turned into no house at Shepperton, as the weary boy had expected; but still kept walking on, in mud and darkness, through gloomy lanes and over cold open wastes, until they came within sight of the lights of a town at no great distance. On looking intently forward, Oliver saw that the water was just below them, and that they were coming to the foot of a bridge.

Sikes kept straight on, until they were close upon the bridge; then turned suddenly down a bank upon the left.

"The water!" thought Oliver, turning sick with fear. "He has brought me to this lonely place to murder me!"

He was about to throw himself on the ground, and make one struggle for his young life, when he saw that they stood before a solitary house, all ruinous and decayed. There was a window on each side of the dilapidated entrance; and one storey above;

but no light was visible. The house was dark, dismantled, and, to all appearance, uninhabited.

Sikes, with Oliver's hand still in his, softly approached the low porch, and raised the latch. The door yielded to the pressure, and they passed in together.

Oliver Twist

SOME years ago, being in Scotland, I went with one of the most humane members of the most humane of professions, on a morning tour among some of the worst lodged inhabitants of the old town of Edinburgh. In the closes and wynds of that picturesque place (I am sorry to remind you what fast friends picturesqueness and typhus often are), we saw more poverty and sickness in an hour than many people would believe in, in a life. Our way lay from one to another of the most wretched dwellings, reeking with horrible odours; shut out from the sky and from the air, mere pits and dens. In a room in one of these places, where there was an empty porridge-pot on the cold hearth, a ragged woman and some ragged children crouching on the bare ground near it,—and, I remember as I speak, where the very light, refracted from a high damp-stained wall outside, came in trembling, as if the fever which had shaken everything else had shaken even it,—there lay, in an old egg-box which the mother had begged from a shop, a little, feeble, wan, sick child. With his little wasted face, and his little hot worn hands folded over his breast, and his little bright attentive eyes, I can see him now, as I have seen him for several years, looking steadily at us. There he lay in his small frail box, which was not at all a bad emblem of the small body from which he was slowly parting—there he lay, quite quiet, quite patient, saying never a word. He seldom cried, the mother said; he seldom complained; "he lay there, seemin' to woonder what it was a' aboot." God knows, I thought, as I stood looking at him, he had his reasons for wondering. . . . Many a poor child, sick and neglected, I have seen since that time in London; many have I also seen most affectionately tended, in unwholesome houses and hard circumstances where recovery was impossible: but at all such times I have seen my little drooping friend in his egg-box, and he has always addressed his dumb wonder to me what it meant, and why, in the name of a gracious God, such things should be! . . . But, ladies and gentlemen, such things need NOT be, and will not be, if this company, which is a drop of the life-blood of the great compassionate public heart, will only accept the means of rescue and prevention which it is mine to offer. Within a quarter of a mile of this place where I speak, stands a once courtly old house, where blooming children were born, and grew up to be men and women, and married, and brought their own blooming children back to patter up the old oak staircase which stood but the other day, and to wonder at the old oak carvings on the chimney-pieces. In the airy wards into which the old state drawing-rooms and family bedchambers of that house are now converted, are lodged such small patients that the attendant nurses look like reclaimed giantesses, and the kind medical practitioner like an amiable Christian ogre. Grouped about the little low tables in the centre of the rooms, are such tiny convalescents that they seem to be playing at having been ill. On the doll's beds are such diminutive creatures that each poor sufferer is supplied with its tray of toys: and, looking round, you may see how the little tired flushed cheek has toppled over half the brute creation on its way into the ark; or how one little dimpled arm has mowed down (as I saw myself) the whole tin soldiery of Europe. On the walls of these rooms are graceful, pleasant, bright, childish pictures. At the beds' heads, hang representations of the figure which is the universal embodiment of all mercy and compassion, the figure of Him who was once a child Himself, and a poor one. But alas! reckoning up the number of beds that are there, the visitor to this Child's Hospital will find himself perforce obliged to stop at very little over thirty; and will learn, with sorrow and surprise, that even that small number, so forlornly, so miserably diminutive compared with this vast London, cannot possibly be maintained unless the Hospital be made better known. I limit myself to saying better known, because I will not believe that in a Christian community of fathers and mothers, and brothers and sisters, it can fail, being better known, to be well and richly endowed.

Speech at a Public Dinner to raise funds for the Hospital for Sick Children, Great Ormond Street, 1856

THE first of May! There is a merry freshness in the sound, calling to our minds a thousand thoughts of all that is pleasant and beautiful in nature in her most delightful form. What man is there over whose mind a bright spring morning does not exercise a magic influence—carrying him back to the days of his childish sports, and conjuring up before him the old green field with its gently-waving trees, where the birds sang as he has never heard them since—where the butterfly fluttered far more gaily than he ever sees him now, in all his ramblings—where the sky seemed bluer, and the sun shone more brightly—where the air blew more freshly over greener grass and sweeter-smelling flowers—where everything wore a richer and more brilliant hue than it is ever dressed in now! Such are the deep feelings of childhood, and such are the impressions which every lovely object stamps upon its heart! The hardy traveller wanders through the maze of thick and pathless woods, where the sun's rays never shone, and Heaven's pure air never played; he stands on the brink of the roaring water-fall, and, giddy and bewildered, watches the foaming mass as it leaps from stone to stone, and from crag to crag; he lingers in the fertile plains of a land of perpetual sunshine, and revels in the luxury of their balmy breath. But what are the deep forests, or the thundering waters, or the richest landscapes that bounteous nature ever spread, to charm the eyes and captivate the senses of man, compared with the recollection of the old scenes of his early youth? Magic scenes indeed, for the fancies of childhood dressed them in colours brighter than the rainbow, and almost as fleeting!

The First of May

DON'T be afraid! We won't make an author of you, while there's an honest trade to be learnt, or brick-making to turn to.

Oliver Twist

TO see the butcher slap the steak, before he laid it on the block, and give his knife a sharpening, was to forget breakfast instantly. It was agreeable, too—it really was—to see him cut it off, so smooth and juicy. There was nothing savage in the act, although the knife was large and keen; it was a piece of art, high art; there was delicacy of touch, clearness of tone, skilful handling of the subject, fine shading. It was the triumph of mind over matter; quite.

Perhaps the greenest cabbage-leaf ever grown in a garden was wrapped about this steak, before it was delivered over to Tom. But the butcher had a sentiment for his business, and knew how to refine upon it. When he saw Tom putting the cabbage-leaf into his pocket awkwardly, he begged to be allowed to do it for him; "for meat," he said with some emotion, "must be humoured, not drove."

Martin Chuzzlewit

THERE'S romance enough at home without going half a mile for it; only people never think of it.

Pickwick Papers

IT was a hard frost that day. The air was bracing, crisp, and clear. The wintry sun, though powerless for warmth, looked brightly down upon the ice it was too weak to melt, and set a radiant glory there.

The Year was Old that day. The patient Year had lived through the reproaches and misuses of its slanderers, and faithfully performed its work.

The streets were full of motion, and the shops were decked out gaily. The New Year, like an Infant Heir to the whole world, was waited for with welcomes, presents, and rejoicings. There were books and toys for the New Year, glittering trinkets for the New Year, dresses for the New Year, schemes of fortune for the New Year; new inventions to beguile it. Its life was parcelled out in almanacs and pocket-books; the coming of its moons, and stars, and tides was known beforehand to the moment: all the workings of its seasons, in their days and nights, were calculated with as much precision as Mr Filer could work sums in men and women.

The New Year, the New Year! Everywhere the New Year! The Old Year was already looked upon as dead; and its effects were selling cheap, like some drowned mariner's aboard ship. Its patterns were Last Year's, and going at a sacrifice, before its breath was gone. Its treasures were mere dirt beside the riches of its unborn successor!

The Chimes

AS if the aspiring city had become puffed up in the very ground on which it stood, the ground had so risen about Bleeding Heart Yard that you got into it down a flight of steps which formed no part of the original approach, and got out of it by a low gateway into a maze of shabby streets, which went about and about, tortuously ascending to the level again. At this end of the Yard and over the gateway, was the factory of Daniel Doyce, often heavily beating like a bleeding heart of iron, with the clink of metal upon metal.

The opinion of the Yard was divided respecting the derivation of its name. The more practical of its inmates abided by the tradition of a murder; the gentler and more imaginative inhabitants, including the whole of the tender sex, were loyal to the legend of a young lady of former times closely imprisoned in her chamber by a cruel father for remaining true to her own true love, and refusing to marry the suitor he chose for her. The legend related how that the young lady used to be seen up at her window behind the bars, murmuring a love-lorn song of which the burden was, "Bleeding Heart, Bleeding Heart, bleeding away," until she died. It was objected by the murderous party that this Refrain was notoriously the invention of a tambour-worker, a spinster and romantic, still lodging in the Yard. But, forasmuch as all favourite legends must be associated with the affections, and as many more people fall in love than commit murder—which it may be hoped, howsoever bad we are, will continue until the end of the world to be the dispensation under which we shall live—the Bleeding Heart, Bleeding Heart, bleeding away story, carried the day by a great majority. Neither party would listen to the antiquaries who delivered learned lectures in the neighbourhood, showing the Bleeding Heart to have been the heraldic cognizance of the old family to whom the property had once belonged. And, considering that the hour-glass they turned from year to year was filled with the earthiest and coarsest sand, the Bleeding Heart Yarders had reason enough for objecting to be despoiled of the one little golden grain of poetry that sparkled in it.

Little Dorrit

IT was the best of times, it was the worst of times, it was the age of wisdom, it was the age of foolishness, it was the epoch of belief, it was the epoch of incredulity, it was the season of Light, it was the season of Darkness, it was the spring of hope, it was the winter of despair, we had everything before us, we had nothing before us, we were all going direct to Heaven, we were all going direct the other way—in short, the period was so far like the present period, that some of its noisiest authorities insisted on its being received, for good or for evil, in the superlative degree of comparison only.

A Tale of Two Cities

A LARGE cask of wine had been dropped and broken, in the street. The accident had happened in getting it out of a cart; the cask had tumbled out with a run, the hoops had burst, and it lay on the stones just outside the door of the wine-shop, shattered like a walnut-shell.

All the people within reach had suspended their business, or their idleness, to run to the spot and drink the wine. The rough, irregular stones of the street, pointing every way, and designed, one might have thought, expressly to lame all living creatures that approached them, had dammed it into little pools; these were surrounded, each by its own jostling group or crowd, according to its size. Some men kneeled down, made scoops of their two hands joined, and sipped, or tried to help women, who bent over their shoulders, to sip, before the wine had all run out between their fingers. Others, men and women, dipped in the puddles with little mugs of mutilated earthenware, or even with handkerchiefs from women's heads, which were squeezed dry into infants' mouths; others made small mud-embankments, to stem the wine as it ran; others, directed by lookers-on up at high windows, darted here and there, to cut off little streams of wine that started away in new directions; others devoted themselves to the sodden and lee-dyed pieces of the cask, licking, and even champing the moister wine-rotted fragments with eager relish. There was no drainage to carry off the wine, and not only did it all get taken up, but so much mud got taken up along with it that there might have been a scavenger in the street, if anybody acquainted with it could have believed in such a miraculous presence.

A shrill sound of laughter and of amused voices—voices of men, women, and children—resounded in the street while this wine game lasted. There was little roughness in the sport, and much playfulness. There was a special companionship in it, an observable inclination on the part of every one to join some other one, which led, especially among the luckier or lighter-hearted, to frolicsome embraces, drinking of healths, shaking of hands, and even joining of hands and dancing, a dozen together. When the wine was gone, and the places where it had been most abundant were raked into a gridiron-pattern by fingers, these demonstrations ceased, as suddenly as they had broken out. The man who had left his saw sticking in the firewood he was cutting, set it in motion again; the woman who had left on a doorstep the little pot of hot ashes, at which she had been trying to soften the pain in her own starved fingers and toes, or in those of her child, returned to it; men with bare arms, matted locks, and cadaverous faces, who had emerged into the winter light from cellars, moved away, to descend again; and a gloom gathered on the scene that appeared more natural to it than sunshine.

The wine was red wine, and had stained the ground of the narrow street in the suburb of St Antoine, in Paris, where it was spilled. It had stained many hands, too, and many faces, and many naked feet, and many wooden shoes. The hands of the man who sawed the wood, left red marks on the billets; and the forehead of the woman who nursed her baby, was stained with the strain of the old rag she wound about her head again. Those who had been greedy with the staves of the cask, had acquired a tigerish smear about the mouth; and one tall joker so besmirched, his head more out of a long squalid bag of a night-cap than in it, scrawled upon a wall with his finger dipped in muddy wine-lees—BLOOD.

The time was to come, when that wine too would be spilled on the street-stones, and when the stain of it would be red upon many there.

And now that the cloud settled on St Antoine, which a momentary gleam had driven from his sacred countenance, the darkness of it was heavy—cold, dirt, sickness, ignorance, and want, were the lords in waiting on the saintly presence—nobles of great power all of them; but, most especially the last. Samples of a people that had undergone a terrible grinding and re-grinding in the mill, and certainly not in the fabulous mill which ground old people young, shivered at every corner, passed in and out at every doorway, looked from every window, fluttered in every vestige of a garment that the wind shook. The mill which had worked them down, was the mill that grinds young people old; the children had ancient faces and grave voices; and upon them, and upon the grown faces, and ploughed into every furrow of age and coming up afresh, was the sign, Hunger. It was prevalent everywhere. Hunger was pushed out of the tall houses, in the wretched clothing that hung upon poles and lines; Hunger was patched into them with straw and rag and wood and paper; Hunger was repeated in every fragment of the small modicum of firewood that the man sawed off; Hunger stared down from the smokeless chimneys, and started up from the filthy street that had no offal, among its refuse, of anything to eat. Hunger was the inscription on the baker's shelves, written in every small loaf of his scanty stock of bad bread; at the sausage-shop, in every dead-dog preparation that was offered for sale. Hunger rattled its dry bones among the roasting chestnuts in the turned cylinder; Hunger was shred into atomies in every farthing porringer of husky chips of potato, fried with some reluctant drops of oil.

A Tale of Two Cities

IN the venerable suburb—it was a suburb once—of Clerkenwell, towards that part of its confines which is nearest to the Charter House, and in one of those cool, shady streets, of which a few, widely scattered and dispersed, yet remain in such old parts of the metropolis,—each tenement quietly vegetating like an ancient citizen who long ago retired from business, and dozing on in its infirmity until in course of time it tumbles down, and is replaced by some extravagant young heir, flaunting in stucco and ornamental work, and all the vanities of modern days,—in this quarter, and in a street of this description, the business of the present chapter lies.

At the time of which it treats, though only six-and-sixty years ago, a very large part of what is London now had no existence. Even in the brains of the wildest speculators, there had sprung up no long rows of streets connecting Highgate with Whitechapel, no assemblages of palaces in the swampy levels, nor little cities in the open fields. Although this part of town was then, as now, parcelled out in streets and plentifully peopled, it wore a different aspect. There were gardens to many of the houses, and trees by the pavement side; with an air of freshness breathing up and down, which in these days would be sought in vain. Fields were nigh at hand, through which the New River took its winding course, and where there was merry hay-making in the summer time. Nature was not so far removed or hard to get at, as in these days; and although there were busy trades in Clerkenwell, and working jewellers by scores, it was a purer place, with farm-houses nearer to it than many modern Londoners would readily believe, and lovers' walks at no great distance, which turned into squalid courts, long before the lovers of this age were born, or, as the phrase goes, thought of.

In one of these streets, the cleanest of them all, and on the shady side of the way—for good housewives know that sunlight damages their cherished furniture, and so choose the shade rather than its intrusive glare—there stood the house with which we have to deal. It was a modest building, not over newly-fashioned, not very straight, not large, not tall; not bold-faced, with great staring windows, but a shy, blinking house, with a conical roof going up into a peak over its garret window of four small panes of glass, like a cocked hat on the head of an elderly gentleman with one eye. It was not built of brick or lofty stone, but of wood and plaster; it was not planned with a dull and wearisome regard to regularly, for no one window matched the other, or seemed to have the slightest reference to anything besides itself.

The shop—for it had a shop—was, with reference to the first

floor, where shops usually are; and there all resemblance between it and any other shop stopped short and ceased. People who went in and out didn't go up a flight of steps to it, or walk easily in upon a level with the street, but dived down three steep stairs, as into a cellar. Its floor was paved with stone and brick, as that of any other cellar might be; and in lieu of window framed and glazed it had a great black wooden flap or shutter, nearly breast high from the ground, which turned back in the daytime, admitting as much cold air as light, and very often more. Behind this shop was a wainscoted parlour, looking first into a paved yard, and beyond that again into a little terrace garden, raised some few feet above it. Any stranger would have supposed that this wainscoted parlour, saving for the door of communication by which he had entered, was cut off and detached from all the world; and indeed most strangers on their first entrance were observed to grow extremely thoughtful, as weighing and pondering in their minds whether the upper rooms were only approachable by ladders from without; never suspecting that two of the most unassuming and unlikely doors in existence, which the most ingenious mechanician on earth must of necessity have supposed to be the doors of closets, opened out of this room—each without the smallest preparation, or so much as a quarter of an inch of passage—upon two dark winding flights of stairs, the one upward, the other downward, which were the sole means of communication between that chamber and the other portions of the house.

Barnaby Rudge

BUT such awful workers, and such awful work! The grindstone had a double handle, and, turning at it madly were two men, whose faces, as their long hair flapped back when the whirlings of the grindstone brought their faces up, were more horrible and cruel than the visages of the wildest savages in their most barbarous disguise. False eyebrows and false moustaches were stuck upon them, and their hideous countenances were all bloody and sweaty, and all awry with howling, and all staring and glaring with beastly excitement and want of sleep. As these ruffians turned and turned, their matted locks now flung forward over their eyes, now flung backward over their necks, some women held wine to their mouths that they might drink; and what with dropping blood, and what with dropping wine, and what with the stream of sparks struck out of the stone, all their wicked atmosphere seemed gore and fire. The eye could not detect one creature in the group free from the smear of blood. Shouldering one another to get next at the sharpening-stone, were men stripped to the waist, with the stain all over their limbs and bodies; men in all sorts of rags, with the stain upon those rags; men devilishly set off with spoils of women's lace and silk and ribbon, with the stain dyeing those trifles through and through. Hatches, knives, bayonets, swords, all brought to be sharpened, were all red with it. Some of the hacked swords were tied to the wrists of those who carried them, with strips of linen and fragments of dress: ligatures various in kind, but all deep of the one colour. And as the frantic wielders of these weapons snatched them from the stream of sparks and tore away into the streets, the same red hue was red in their frenzied eyes;—eyes which any unbrutalized beholder would have given twenty years of life, to petrify with a well directed gun.

A Tale of Two Cities

ST Antoine had been, that morning, a vast dusky mass of scarecrows heaving to and fro, with frequent gleams of light above the billowy heads, where steel blades and bayonets shone in the sun. A tremendous roar arose from the throat of St Antoine, and a forest of naked arms struggled in the air like shrivelled branches of trees in a winter wind: all the fingers convulsively clutching at every weapon or semblance of a weapon that was thrown up from the depths below, no matter how far off.

Who gave them out, whence they last came, where they began, through what agency they crookedly quivered and jerked, scores at a time, over the heads of the crowd, like a kind of lightning, no eye in the throng could have told; but, muskets were being distributed—so were cartridges, powder and ball, bars of iron and wood, knives, axes, pikes, every weapon that distracted ingenuity could discover or devise. People who could lay hold of nothing else, set themselves with bleeding hands to force stones and bricks out of their places in walls. Every pulse and heart in St Antoine was on high-fever strain and at high-fever heat. Every living creature there held life as of no account, and was demented with a passionate readiness to sacrifice it.

As a whirlpool of boiling waters has a centre point, so, all this raging circled round Defarge's wine-shop, and every human drop in the caldron had a tendency to be sucked towards the vortex where Defarge himself, already begrimed with gunpowder and sweat, issued orders, issued arms, thrust this man back, dragged this man forward, disarmed one to arm another, laboured and strove in the thickest of the uproar.

"Keep near to me, Jacques Three," cried Defarge; "and do you, Jacques One and Two, separate and put yourselves at the head of as many of these patriots as you can. Where is my wife?"

"Eh, well! Here you see me!" said madame, composed as ever, but not knitting to-day. Madame's resolute right hand was occupied with an axe, in place of the usual softer implements, and in her girdle were a pistol and a cruel knife.

"Where do you go, my wife?"

"I go," said madame, "with you at present. You shall see me at the head of women, by-and-by."

"Come then!" cried Defarge, in a resounding voice. "Patriots and friends, we are ready! The Bastille!"

With a roar that sounded as if all the breath in France had been shaped into the detested word, the living sea rose, wave on wave, depth on depth, and overflowed the city to that point. Alarm-bells ringing, drums beating, the sea raging and thundering on its new beach, the attack begun.

Deep ditches, double drawbridge, massive stone walls, eight great towers, cannon, muskets, fire and smoke. Through the fire and through the smoke—in the fire and in the smoke, for the sea cast him up against a cannon, and on the instant he became a cannonier—Defarge of the wine-shop worked like a manful soldier, Two fierce hours.

Deep ditch, single drawbridge, massive stone walls, eight great towers, cannon, muskets, fire and smoke. One drawbridge down! "Work, comrades all, work! Work, Jacques One, Jacques Two, Jacques One Thousand, Jacques Two Thousand, Jacques Five-and-Twenty Thousand; in the name of all the Angels or the Devils—which you prefer—work!" Thus Defarge of the wine-shop, still at his gun, which had long grown hot.

"To me, women!" cried madame his wife. "What! We can kill as well as the men when the place is taken!" And to her, with a shrill thirsty cry, trooping women variously armed, but all armed alike in hunger and revenge.

Cannon, muskets, fire and smoke; but, still the deep ditch, the single drawbridge, the massive stone walls, and the eight great towers. Slight displacements of the raging sea, made by the falling wounded. Flashing weapons, blazing torches, smoking waggon-loads of wet straw, hard work at neighbouring barricades in all directions, shrieks, volleys, execrations, bravery without stint, boom smash and rattle, and the furious sounding of the living sea; but, still the deep ditch, and the single drawbridge, and the massive stone walls, and the eight great towers, and still Defarge of the wine-shop at his gun, grown doubly hot by the service of Four fierce hours.

A white flag from within the fortress, and a parley—this dimly perceptible through the raging storm, nothing audible in it—suddenly the sea rose immeasurably wider and higher, and swept Defarge of the wine-shop over the lowered drawbridge, past the massive stone outer walls, in among the eight great towers surrendered!

A Tale of Two Cities

THE vintner's house, with half a dozen others near at hand, was one great, glowing blaze. All night, no one had essayed to quench the flames or stop their progress; but now a body of soldiers were actively engaged in pulling down two old wooden houses, which were every moment in danger of taking fire, and which could scarcely fail, if they were left to burn, to extend the conflagration immensely. The tumbling down of nodding walls and heavy blocks of wood, the hooting and the execrations of the crowd, the distant firing of other military detachments, the distracted looks and cries of those whose habitations were in danger, the hurrying to and fro of frightened people with their goods; the reflections in every quarter of the sky, of deep red, soaring flames, as though the last day had come and the whole universe were burning; the dust, and smoke, and drift of fiery particles, scorching and kindling all it fell upon; the hot unwholesome vapour, the blight on everything; the stars, and moon, and very sky, obliterated;—made up such a sum of dreariness and ruin, that it seemed as if the face of Heaven were blotted out, and night, in its rest and quiet, and softened light, never could look upon the earth again.

But there was a worse spectacle than this—worse by far than fire and smoke, or even the rabble's unappeasable and maniac rage. The gutters of the street and every crack and fissure in the stone, ran with scorching spirit, which being dammed up by busy hands, overflowed the road and pavement, and formed a great pool, in which the people dropped down dead by dozens. They lay in heaps all round this fearful pond, husbands and wives, fathers and sons, mothers and daughters, women with children in their arms and babies at their breasts, and drank until they died. While some stooped with their lips to the brink and never raised their heads again, others sprang up from their fiery draught, and danced, half in a mad triumph, and half in the agony of suffocation, until they fell and steeped their corpses in the liquor that had killed them. Nor was even this the worst or most appalling kind of death that happened on this fatal night. From the burning cellars, where they drank out of hats, pails, buckets, tubs, and shoes, some men were drawn, alive, but all alight from head to foot; who, in their unendurable anguish and suffering, making for anything that had the look of water, rolled, hissing, in this hideous lake, and splashed up liquid fire which lapped in all it met with as it ran along the surface, and neither spared the living nor the dead. On this last night of the great riots—for the last night it was—the wretched victims of a senseless outcry became themselves the dust and ashes of the flames they had kindled, and strewed the public streets of London.

Barnaby Rudge

TO surround anything, however monstrous or ridiculous, with an air of mystery, is to invest it with a secret charm, and power of attraction which to the crowd is irresistible. False priests, false prophets, false doctors, false patriots, false prodigies of every kind, veiling their proceedings in mystery, have always addressed themselves at an immense advantage to the popular credulity, and have been, perhaps, more indebted to that resource in gaining and keeping for a time the upper hand of Truth and Common Sense, than to any half-dozen items in the whole catalogue of imposture. Curiosity is, and has been from the creation of the world, a master-passion. To awaken it, to gratify it by slight degrees, and yet leave something always in suspense, is to establish the surest hold that can be had, in wrong, on the unthinking portion of mankind.

Barnaby Rudge

THE first shock of a great earthquake had, just at that period, rent the whole neighbourhood to its centre. Traces of its course were visible on every side. Houses were knocked down; streets broken through and stopped; deep pits and trenches dug in the ground; enormous heaps of earth and clay thrown up;

buildings that were undermined and shaking, propped by great beams of wood. Here, a chaos of carts, overthrown and jumbled together, lay topsy-turvy at the bottom of a steep unnatural hill; there, confused treasures of iron soaked and rusted in something that had accidentally become a pond. Everywhere were bridges that led nowhere; thoroughfares that were wholly impassable; Babel towers of chimneys, wanting half their height; temporary wooden houses and enclosures, in the most unlikely situations; carcases of ragged tenements, and fragments of unfinished walls and arches, and piles of scaffolding, and wildernesses of bricks, and giant forms of cranes, and tripods straddling above nothing. There were a hundred thousand shapes and substances of incompleteness, wildly mingled out of their places, upside down, burrowing in the earth, aspiring in the air, mouldering in the water, and unintelligible as any dream. Hot springs and fiery eruptions, the usual attendants upon earthquakes, lent their contributions of confusion to the scene. Boiling water hissed and heaved within dilapidated walls; whence also, the glare and roar of flames came issuing forth; and mounds of ashes blocked up rights of way, and wholly changed the law and custom of the neighbourhood.

In short, the yet unfinished and unopened railroad was in progress; and from the very core of all this dire disorder, trailed smoothly away, upon its mighty course of civilization and improvement.

But as yet, the neighbourhood was shy to own the railroad. One or two bold speculators had projected streets; and one had built a little, but had stopped among the mud and ashes to consider farther of it. A bran-new tavern, redolent of fresh mortar and size, and fronting nothing at all, had taken for its sign The Railway Arms; but that might be rash enterprise—and then it hoped to sell drink to the workmen. So, the Excavators' House of Call had sprung up from a beer shop; and the old-established ham and beef shop had become The Railway Eating House, with a roast leg of pork daily, through interested motives of a similar immediate and popular description.

Lodging-house keepers were favourable in like manner; and for the like reasons were not to be trusted. The general belief was very slow. There were frowzy fields, and cowhouses, and dunghills, and dustheaps, and ditches, and gardens, and summer-houses, and carpet-beating grounds, at the very door of the railway. Little tumuli of oyster shells in the oyster season, and of lobster shells in the lobster season, and of broken crockery and faded cabbage leaves in all seasons, encroached upon its high places. Posts, and rails, and old cautions to trespassers, and backs of mean houses, and patches of wretched vegetation, stared it out of countenance. Nothing was the better for it, or thought of being so. If the miserable waste ground lying near it could have laughed, it would have laughed it to scorn, like many of the miserable neighbours.

Staggs's Gardens was uncommonly incredulous. It was a little row of houses, with little squalid patches of ground before them, fenced off with old doors, barrel staves, scraps of tarpaulin, and dead bushes; with bottomless tin kettles and exhausted iron fenders, thrust into the gaps. Here, the Staggs's Gardeners trained scarlet beans, kept fowls and rabbits, erected rotten summer-houses (one was an old boat), dried clothes, and smoked pipes. Some were of opinion that Staggs's Gardens derived its name from a deceased capitalist, one Mr Staggs, who had built it for his delectation. Others, who had a natural taste for the country, held that it dated from those rural times when the antlered herd, under the familiar denomination of Staggses, had resorted to its shady precincts. Be this as it may, Staggs's Gardens was regarded by its population as a sacred grove not to be withered by railroads; and so confident were they generally of its long outliving any such ridiculous inventions, that the master chimney-sweeper at the corner, who was understood to take the lead in the local politics of the Gardens, had publicly declared that on the occasion of the railroad opening, if ever it did open, two of his boys should ascend the flues of his dwelling, with instructions to hail the failure with derisive jeers from the chimney-pots.

Dombey and Son

ALONG the Paris streets, the death-carts rumble, hollow and harsh. Six tumbrils carry the day's wine to La Guillotine. All the devouring and insatiate Monsters imagined since imagination could record itself, are fused in the one realization, Guillotine. And yet there is not in France, with its rich variety of soil and climate, a blade, a leaf, a root, a sprig, a peppercorn, which will grow to maturity under conditions more certain than those that have produced this horror. Crush humanity out of shape once more, under similar hammers, and it will twist itself into the same tortured forms. Sow the same seed of rapacious license and oppression over again, and it will surely yield the same fruit according to its kind.

Six tumbrils roll along the streets. Change these back again to what they were, thou powerful enchanter, Time, and they shall be seen to be the carriages of absolute monarchs, the equipages of feudal nobles, the toilettes of flaring Jezabels, the churches that are not my Father's house but dens of thieves, the huts of millions of starving peasants! No; the great magician who majestically works out the appointed order of the Creator, never reverses his transformations. "If thou be changed into this shape by the will of God," say the seers to the enchanted, in the wise Arabian stories, "then remain so! But, if thou wear this form through mere passing conjuration, then resume thy former aspect!" Changeless and hopeless, the tumbrils roll along.

As the sombre wheels of the six carts go round, they seem to plough up a long crooked furrow among the populace in the streets. Ridges of faces are thrown to this side and to that, and the ploughs go steadily onward. So used are the regular inhabitants of the houses to the spectacle, that in many windows there are no people, and in some the occupation of the hands is not so much as suspended, while the eyes survey the faces in the tumbrils. Here and there, the inmate has visitors to see the sight; then he points his finger, with something of the complacency of a curator or authorized exponent, to this cart and to this, and seems to tell who sat here yesterday, and who there the day before.

Of the riders in the tumbrils, some observe these things, and all things on their last roadside, with an impassive stare; others, with a lingering interest in the ways of life and men. Some, seated with drooping heads, are sunk in silent despair; again, there are some so heedful of their looks that they cast upon the multitude such glances as they have seen in theatres, and in pictures. Several close their eyes, and think, or try to get their straying thoughts together. Only one, and he a miserable creature, of a crazed aspect, is so shattered and made drunk by horror, that he sings, and tries to dance. Not one of the whole number appeals by look or gesture, to the pity of the people.

A Tale of Two Cities

AS he stood by the wall in a dim corner, while some of the fifty-two were brought in after him, one man stopped in passing, to embrace him, as having a knowledge of him. It thrilled him with a great dread of discovery; but the man went on. A very few moments after that, a young woman, with a slight girlish form, a sweet spare face in which there was no vestige of colour, and large widely opened patient eyes, rose from the seat where he had observed her sitting, and came to speak to him.

"Citizen Evremonde," she said, touching him with her cold hand. "I am a poor little seamstress, who was with you in La Force."

He murmured for answer: "True. I forget what you were accused of?"

"Plots. Though the just Heaven knows I am innocent of any. Is it likely? Who would think of plotting with a poor little weak creature like me?"

The forlorn smile with which she said it, so touched him, that tears started from his eyes.

"I am not afraid to die, Citizen Evremonde, but I have done nothing. I am not unwilling to die, if the Republic which is to do so much good to us poor, will profit by my death; but I do not know how that can be, Citizen Evremonde. Such a poor weak little creature!"

As the last thing on earth that his heart was to warm and soften to, it warmed and softened to this pitiable girl.

"I heard you were released, Citizen Evremonde. I hoped it was true?"

"It was. But, I was again taken and condemned."

"If I may ride with you, Citizen Evremonde, will you let me hold your hand? I am not afraid, but I am little and weak, and it will give me more courage."

As the patient eyes were lifted to his face, he saw a sudden doubt in them, and then astonishment. He pressed the work-worn, hunger-worn young fingers, and touched his lips.

"Are you dying for him?" she whispered.

"And his wife and child. Hush! Yes."

"O you will let me hold your brave hand, stranger?"

"Hush! Yes, my poor sister; to the last."

A Tale of Two Cities

THE time wore on: the noises in the streets became less frequent by degrees, until silence was scarcely broken save by the bells in church towers, marking the progress—softer and more stealthy while the city slumbered—of that Great Watcher with the hoary head, who never sleeps or rests. In the brief interval of darkness and repose which feverish towns enjoy, all busy sounds were hushed; and those who awoke from dreams lay listening in their beds, and longed for dawn, and wished the dead of the night were past.

Into the street outside the jail's main wall, workmen came straggling at this solemn hour, in groups of two or three, and meeting in the centre, cast their tools upon the ground and spoke in whispers. Others soon issued from the jail itself, bearing on their shoulders planks and beams: these materials being all brought forth, the rest bestirred themselves, and the dull sound of hammers began to echo through the stillness.

Here and there among this knot of labourers, one, with a lantern or a smoky link, stood by to light his fellows at their work; and by its doubtful aid, some might be dimly seen taking up the pavement of the road, while others held great upright posts, or fixed them in the holes thus made for their reception. Some dragged slowly on, towards the rest, an empty cart, which they brought rumbling from the prison yard; while others erected strong barriers across the street. All were busily engaged. Their dusky figures moving to and fro, at that unusual hour, so active and so silent, might have been taken for those of shadowy creatures toiling at midnight, on some ghostly unsubstantial work, which, like themselves, would vanish with the first gleam of day, and leave but morning mist and vapour.

While it was yet dark, a few lookers-on collected, who had plainly come there for the purpose and intended to remain: even those who had to pass the spot on their way to some other place, lingered, and lingered yet, as though the attraction of that were irresistible. Meanwhile the noise of saw and mallet went on briskly, mingled with the clattering of boards on the stone pavement of the road, and sometimes with the workmen's voices as they called to one another. Whenever the chimes of the neighbouring church were heard—and that was every quarter of an hour—a strange sensation, instantaneous and indescribable, but perfectly obvious, seemed to pervade them all.

Gradually, a faint brightness appeared in the east, and the air, which had been very warm all through the night, felt cool and chilly. Though there was no daylight yet, the darkness was diminished, and the stars looked pale. The prison, which had been a mere black mass with little shape or form, put on its usual aspect; and ever and anon a solitary watchman could be seen upon its roof, stopping to look down upon the preparations in the street. This man, from forming, as it were, a part of the jail, and knowing or being supposed to know all that was passing within, became an object of as much interest, and was as eagerly looked for, and as awfully pointed out, as if he had been a spirit.

By and by, the feeble light grew stronger, and the houses

with their sign-boards and inscriptions stood plainly out, in the dull grey morning. Heavy stage waggons crawled from the Inn-yard opposite; and travellers peeped out; and as they rolled sluggishly away, cast many a backward look towards the jail. And now the sun's first beams came glancing into the street; and the night's work, which, in its various stages and in the varied fancies of the lookers-on had taken a hundred shapes, wore its own proper form—a scaffold, and a gibbet.

As the warmth of the cheerful day began to shed itself upon the scanty crowd, the murmur of tongues was heard, shutters were thrown open, and blinds drawn up, and those who had slept in rooms over against the prison, where places to see the execution were let at high prices, rose hastily from their beds. In some of the houses, people were busy taking out the window sashes for the better accommodation of spectators; in others the spectators were already seated, and beguiling the time with cards, or drink, or jokes among themselves. Some had purchased seats upon the house-tops, and were already crawling to their stations from parapet and garret-window. Some were yet bargaining for good places, and stood in them in a state of indecision: gazing at the slowly-swelling crowd, and at the workmen as they rested listlessly against the scaffold; and affecting to listen with indifference to the proprietor's eulogy of the commanding view his house afforded, and the surpassing cheapness of his terms.

A fairer morning never shone. From the roofs and upper stories of these buildings, the spires of City churches and the great cathedral dome were visible, rising up beyond the prison, into the blue sky: and clad in the colour of light summer clouds, and showing in the clear atmosphere their every scrap of tracery and fretwork, and every niche and loophole. All was brightness and promise, excepting in the street below, into which (for it yet lay in shadow) the eye looked down as into a dark trench, where, in the midst of so much life, and hope, and renewal of existence, stood the terrible instrument of death. It seemed as if the very sun forbore to look upon it.

But it was better, grim and sombre in the shade, than when,

the day being more advanced, it stood confessed in the full glare and glory of the sun, with its black paint blistering, and its nooses dangling in the light like loathsome garlands. It was better in the solitude and gloom of midnight with a few forms clustering about it, than in the freshness and the stir of morning: the centre of an eager crowd. It was better haunting the street like a spectre, when men were in their beds; and influencing perchance the city's dreams; than braving the broad day, and thrusting its obscene presence upon their waking senses.

Five o'clock had struck—six—seven—and eight. Along the two main streets at either end of the crossway, a living stream had now set in: rolling towards the marts of gain and business. Carts, coaches, waggons, trucks, and barrows, forced a passage through the outskirts of the throng, and clattered onward in the same direction. Some of these which were public conveyances and had come from a short distance in the country, stopped; and the driver pointed to the gibbet with his whip, though he might have spared himself the pains, for the heads of all the passengers were turned that way without his help, and the coach-windows were stuck full of staring eyes. In some of the carts and waggons, women might be seen glancing fearfully at the same unsightly thing; and even little children were held up above the people's heads to see what kind of toy a gallows was, and learn how men were hanged.

Barnaby Rudge

THE Maypole was an old building, with more gable ends than a lazy man would care to count on a sunny day; huge zigzag chimneys, out of which it seemed as though even smoke could not choose but come in more than naturally fantastic shapes, imparted to it in its tortuous progress; and vast stables, gloomy, ruinous, and empty. The place was said to have been built in the days of King Henry the Eighth; and there was a legend, not only that Queen Elizabeth had slept there one night while upon a hunting excursion, to wit, in a certain oak-panelled room with a deep bay window, but that next morning, while standing on a mounting-block before the door with one foot in the stirrup, the Virgin Monarch had then and there boxed and cuffed an unlucky page for some neglect of duty. The matter-of-fact and doubtful folks, of whom there were a few among the Maypole customers, as unluckily there always are in every little community, were inclined to look upon this tradition as rather apocryphal; but whenever the landlord of that ancient hostelry appealed to the mounting-block itself as evidence, and triumphantly pointed out that there it stood in the same place to that very day, the doubters never failed to be put down by a large majority, and all true believers exulted as in a victory.

Whether these, and many other stories of the like nature, were true or untrue, the Maypole was really an old house, a very old house, perhaps as old as it claimed to be, and perhaps older, which will sometimes happen with houses of an uncertain, as with ladies of a certain age. Its windows were old diamond-pane lattices, its floors were sunken and uneven, its ceilings blackened by the hand of Time, and heavy with massive beams. Over the doorway was an ancient porch, quaintly and grotesquely carved; and here on summer evenings the more favoured customers smoked and drank—ay, and sang many a good song too, sometimes—reposing on two grim-looking high-backed settles, which, like the twin dragons of some fairy tale, guarded the entrance to the mansion.

In the chimneys of the disused rooms swallows had built their nests for many a long year, and from earliest spring to latest autumn whole colonies of sparrows chirped and twittered in the eaves. There were more pigeons about the dreary stable-yard and outbuildings than anybody but the landlord could reckon up. The wheeling and circling flights of runts, fantails, tumblers, and pouters, were perhaps not quite consistent with the grave and sober character of the building, but the monotonous cooing, which never ceased to be raised by some among them all day long, suited it exactly, and seemed to lull it to rest. With its overhanging stories, drowsy little panes of glass, and front bulging out and projecting over the pathway, the old house looked as if it were nodding in its sleep. Indeed it needed no very great stretch of fancy to detect in it other resemblances to humanity. The bricks of which it was built had originally been a deep dark red, but had grown yellow and discoloured like an old man's skin; the sturdy timbers had decayed like teeth; and here and there the ivy, like a warm garment to comfort it in its age, wrapt its green leaves closely round the time-worn walls.

It was a hale and hearty age though, still: and in the summer or autumn evenings, when the glow of the setting sun fell upon the oak and chestnut trees of the adjacent forest, the old house, partaking of its lustre, seemed their fit companion, and to have many good years of life in him yet.

Barnaby Rudge